WITHDRAWN

Broadway Medieval Library

Edited by

G. G. Coulton and Eileen Power

Sir Lancelot of the Lake

Broadway Medieval Library

Edited by G. G. Coulton and Eileen Power

The Unconquered Knight
By Gutierre Diaz de Gamez

Miracles of the Blessed Virgin Mary
By Johannes Herolt

The Dialogue on Miracles
By Caesarius of Heisterbach

The Goodman of Paris
By a Bourgeois of Paris, *c.* 1393

The Autobiography of Ousâma
By Ousâma Ibn Mounḳidh

Sir Lancelot of the Lake
A Prose Romance of the 13th Century

Little John of Saintré
By Antoine de La Sale

Historical and Other Works
By Liudprand of Cremona

Anecdotes from English MS. Sermons

Anecdotes of Thomas of Chantimpré

Published by
GEORGE ROUTLEDGE & SONS, LTD.

Sir Lancelot of the Lake

A FRENCH PROSE ROMANCE
OF THE THIRTEENTH CENTURY

Translated from MS. in the Bibliothèque Nationale (Fonds
français, 344) with an Introduction and Notes by
LUCY ALLEN PATON, M.A., Ph.D.

Published by
GEORGE ROUTLEDGE & SONS, LTD.
BROADWAY HOUSE · CARTER LANE · LONDON
1929

PRINTED IN GREAT BRITAIN BY HEADLEY BROTHERS,
18, DEVONSHIRE STREET, E.C.2 ; AND ASHFORD, KENT.

CONLEGIO RADCLIVIANO
ALMAE MATRI CARISSIMAE

CUIUS NATALIS
DECEM LUSTRIS FELICITER PERACTIS
HOC ANNO CELEBRATUR

PREFATORY NOTE

THIS book is designed for English-speaking readers, who would like to familiarise themselves with the thirteenth-century French prose romance of *Lancelot del Lac*, but who are not easily able either to read it in the original or to take advantage of the numerous modern discussions of it written by foreign scholars.

The essential parts of the history of Sir Lancelot are contained in the three romances from which selections are translated in this volume, namely, *Le livre de Lancelot del Lac*, *La queste del saint graal*, and *La mort le roi Artus*. They form a huge body of material, a large portion of which has no connection with Lancelot, and in fact no interest save for specialists in medieval literature. Even of the sections that concern Lancelot many are too prolix and have too little significance to be suitable for translation. I have therefore sought to present here only those parts that are fundamental for an understanding of the legend, and have given summaries, printed in small type, of the incidents that connect them in the French text. A few selections from the *Queste* are included because of their importance in the legend, although the entire romance has been translated by President W. W. Comfort of Haverford College. The selected passages, with very occasional exceptions, are trans-

lated in their entirety. The divisions into chapters
with brief titles do not exist in the original text, but
are made here for the sake of convenience. A few
of the headings have been supplied from those that
Caxton inserted in Malory's *Morte Darthur*, when the
episodes in the two sources are substantially the same.

As may be seen from the List of Books below, several
abridged retellings of the *Lancelot* and its two con-
tinuations, as well as a translation of the *Queste*, have
been made in modern French. But we are obliged
to say of Sir Lancelot, as Caxton said of King Arthur,
" Many noble volumes be of him in French, which be
not had in our maternal tongue ". Except for a very
free adaptation into English of a few pages of the
romance made some thirty years ago by the late
Mr. W. W. Newell in his *King Arthur and the Table
Round*, and the recent translation of the *Queste* by
President Comfort, there has been no serious attempt
to produce a modern English rendering of the material
translated below. It is true that our fifteenth-
century literature can boast one of the famous translations of all time in Sir Thomas Malory's *Morte
Darthur*, and that, apart from the original French,
there is no finer medium than this for becoming
acquainted with parts of the Lancelot legend. But
Malory used only a relatively small portion of the
trilogy in his compilation, and left entirely untouched
all the early career and many later valorous exploits

of Lancelot. Nor did he make a complete and exact translation of his sources, but, as Caxton expressly states in his Preface to the *Morte Darthur*, he "reduced" into English certain French books—reduced them, be it said, with singular discernment, and with such an apt and happy rendering of their phrases that no one can translate an Arthurian prose romance to-day without becoming his grateful debtor and acquiring a high regard for his abilities.

Modern editions of our three romances have been published, but only one of them, that of the *Queste* by Professor Albert Pauphilet, presents a critically prepared text, upon which a translator may unhesitatingly rely. From this, of course, I have translated the passages selected from the *Queste*; those from the other two romances, in the lack of a satisfactory edition and in order to secure consistency throughout the work as a whole, I have translated from a manuscript in Paris (Bibliothèque Nationale, fonds français 344), which is identical in text with the Lyons manuscript that M. Pauphilet has used as the basis of his edition. Its obvious errors and defects I have corrected from other manuscipts. Its text is in general very good, and for the purposes of this translation has an advantage over some other excellent manuscripts in being virtually complete in all the portions selected.

The Introduction essays to give the substance of the most illuminating discussions of the legend and its early literary history, and adds little of consequence to them ; the facts and theories that it sets forth are, indeed, in the main derived from them far too often to be acknowledged except by including in the List of Books the titles of the works where they may be found at greater length—an inadequate method of expressing my many obligations to the authors.

The List of Books does not purport to be exhaustive for a study of the legend of Lancelot, but contains merely titles that may be of service to readers who desire to inform themselves more fully upon the subjects treated briefly in the Introduction.

Paris,
   May, 1929.

L.A.P.

CONTENTS

xi

Contents

xii

CONTENTS

xiii

CONTENTS

CONTENTS

BOOK II

THE QUEST OF THE HOLY GRAIL

CONTENTS

LIST OF ILLUSTRATIONS

LIST OF ILLUSTRATIONS

List of Illustrations

xix

List of Illustrations

INTRODUCTION

Ah, Launcelot, thou were head of all Chriſtian knights ; and
thou were never matched of earthly knight's hand ; and thou
were the courtlieſt knight that ever bare shield ; and thou were
the trueſt friend to thy lover that ever beſtrode horse ; and thou
were the trueſt lover of a sinful man that ever loved woman ;
and thou were the kindeſt man that ever ſtrake with sword ;
and thou were the goodlieſt person ever came among press of
knights ; and thou was the meekeſt man and the gentleſt that
ever ate in hall among ladies ; and thou were the ſterneſt knight
to thy mortal foe that ever put spear in the reſt.—
Le Morte Darthur.

I know that he is from the land of France, for right well he
speaketh the language thereof.—*Le livre de Lancelot del Lac.*

I

Sir Lancelot in Legend and in Literature

To many of the personages of Arthurian fi&ion a
twofold intereſt attaches, that of the individual legends
cluſtering about them, and that of the literary pro-
du&ions in which these legends are embodied. Sir
Gawain, for example, appears in numerous episodes the
themes of which are paralleled in early folk tales, and
which consequently lead us at once into the domain of
folklore, but he is also the hero of minor compositions, especially in English verse, that deservedly
rank as admirable members of our poetic literature.
Merlin, as a mythical seer and great enchanter, has

a baffling legendary history, but since he is conspicuous in our first developed Arthurian chronicle, the
Historia Regum Britanniæ of Geoffrey of Monmouth,
and is the subject of one of the earliest known, though
imperfectly preserved members of the so-called
Arthurian cyclic material, a poem by Robert de
Boron, since, moreover, a vast mass of prophecy was for
several centuries promulgated in his name in written
sources on the Continent and in England, he has also an
extensive literary importance.

Mutatis mutandis, the same is true of Sir Lancelot.
His legend, which on the whole is neither complicated
nor obscure, preserves with peculiar completeness, as will
be seen below, in the account of his early years a fairy
theme widely employed in medieval romance, and it
furthermore embodies in a late and distorted form a
myth, that of the rape of Queen Guinevere, which
certainly has its basis in very ancient tradition. No
legend of the Arthurian cycle, on the other hand, with
the possible exception of that of the Holy Grail, has had
greater literary influence or a more appreciable effect
upon the structural development of the great French
Arthurian prose romances.

The larger part of these romances, unlike the
numerous medieval compositions in French verse that
form independent Arthurian narratives, are cyclic in
character and fall definitely into two groups. In one
group the love of Lancelot for Guinevere is the central
theme, prepared for by a series of incidents, emphasised
by countless episodes, and finally branded as the fatal
cause that brings the reign of Arthur to a tragic end.
Because of it arise the wars and series of disasters that

2

culminate with the passing of Arthur and the shattering of the fellowship of the Round Table. " For as well as I have loved thee ", says Guinevere to Lancelot at their final parting, " mine heart will not serve me to see thee ; for through thee and me is the flower of kings and knights destroyed."[1]

The second group of romances, in distinction from those in which the love of Lancelot for the queen is especially prominent, has for its principal theme the quest of the Holy Grail, which many valorous knights undertake but none save he whose life has been lived in perfect chastity may hope to achieve. Lancelot, whose surpassing knightly prowess fits him to win the quest, is rendered unworthy of it solely by his illicit love for Guinevere, the wife of his lord. It is reserved for his son, Galahad, the spotless knight, to perform the high adventure.

Thus the relation of Lancelot to Guinevere not only is a fundamental element in one of the two great divisions of French Arthurian prose literature, but serves also to bind it to its sister group. This, too, is the side of the legend that in all ages has remained the most familiar. None of the exploits of Lancelot recur so frequently in medieval art[2] and letters as those that he performed directly in the service of the queen ; it is as the lover of Guinevere that Dante depicts him in the most famous passage referring to him in literature[3] ; it is his devotion to her that made his name celebrated throughout the Renaissance and that has kept it fresh in modern poetry.

The evolution of the legend in the twelfth and thirteenth centuries, by the end of which it may be said to have received its permanent form, can be traced by means of three sources, each of which marks a development in the ſtory and has a certain importance in medieval literature. These sources are, *Lanzelet*, a Middle High German poem by Ulrich von Zatzikhoven ; *Le conte de la charrette* (*The Story of the Cart*) by Chreſtien de Troyes ; and a trilogy of French prose romances—*Le livre de Lancelot del Lac* (*The Book of Lancelot of the Lake*), *La queſte* (or *Les aventures*) *del saint graal* (*The Quest*, or *The Adventures, of the Holy Grail*), and *La mort le roi Artus* (*The Death of King Arthur*),—portions of which are translated in the present volume. It should not be inferred that there are no later versions of the ſtory of Lancelot before modern times that merit attention. Early redaċtions or translations of the prose romance exiſt in Dutch, German, Italian, Portuguese, and Spanish. In England, in addition to the uses to which it was put by Sir Thomas Malory, it inspired in the fourteenth century a stanzaic poem, not without charm, the *Morte Arthur*, and in the fifteenth, a Scotch romance, with little to recommend it, written in heroic couplets, *Lancelot of the Laik*. In Italy it was especially popular, and from the fourteenth to the sixteenth centuries it appears as the subjeċt of longer or shorter compositions in verse by minſtrels or poets, some of whom gave it an independent development.[1] Many of these later works contain material of intereſt, but a discussion of them lies outside the scope of the present Introduċtion.

II

Lanzelet

Of the three sources that I have mentioned above the first has a somewhat romantic history. In 1194, about a year after Richard Cœur-de-Lion had been taken prisoner by Leopold, Duke of Austria, hostages for his release were sent from England to Vienna. Among them was an Anglo-Norman knight, Hugh de Morville, who, evidently to provide himself with entertainment during his captivity, took with him a French poem on Lancelot. But when, at the death of Duke Leopold later in the same year, the hostages were given permission to return to England, de Morville did not carry his *Lancelot* away from Austria with him, and by channels unknown to us it drifted into the hands of a Swiss priest, Ulrich von Zatzikhoven, who proceeded to translate it into the Middle High German poem that we know as the *Lanzelet*. That de Morville had elected to take the romance to Vienna with him, and that Ulrich desired to translate it into German are indications of the popularity of the story that it contained.

There is no reason to suppose that Ulrich had a more ambitious aim than to produce a faithful rendering of the French poet. The greater part of the German Arthurian romances of about this period are in the main merely translations of French sources. Some of these sources have been lost, but of those that exist the translation is found to follow the original closely and to add little, if any, material of its own. It is a fair inference that the *Lanzelet* was no exception

5

to the rule and that to all intents and purposes it represents accurately the French poem that it purports to reproduce.

The translation is undated, but we may assume it to have been made not long after 1194, when the hostages left Austria. The probable date of composition of the lost French original has been much discussed. Some critics maintain that it was written only very shortly before 1194, and that it owed its inspiration largely to suggestions from the poem of Chrestien de Troyes. Others, whose arguments are more convincing, place the date approximately at 1160, basing their view upon the somewhat archaic character of the material in the poem, and especially upon two passages in works by Chrestien, one in the *Erec*, written about the year 1168, and the other in the *Conte de la charrette*, written about 1172 (according to the usually accepted but by no means certain datings), which show his familiarity with the legend that forms the framework of the *Lanzelet*, the only source known to-day through which he could have learned it.[1] An element of doubt is introduced into this contention merely by the possibility that he may have learned the same story through some other source, of which we have no knowledge. We may be sure, then, that the earliest features of the Lancelot legend had taken shape before the last quarter of the twelfth century, and that the lost French original of the *Lanzelet* is our earliest known source for the history of our hero. Its fundamental theme exists in no more primitive form in our versions of the Lancelot legends than in this poem.

6

Although the *Lanzelet* has thus a special interest, it has never been translated into English. Nor is this extraordinary, for it is full of strange inconsistencies and frequently bears evidence that the manuscript of de Morville was defective and not free from stumbling-blocks for Ulrich. But since at least a slight acquaintance with it is essential for an understanding of the story of Lancelot, a comparatively detailed outline of its contents is given here, together with a translation of the passages relating to the early life of Lancelot in fairyland, the only part of the poem that, strictly speaking, has had a permanent survival.

I. *The Death of King Pant.* The people of the land of Genewis (i.e., Gwynedd, North Wales) rise in rebellion against the stern rule of their lord, King Pant. In a fierce assault that they make upon his castle he is mortally wounded, but makes his escape, taking with him his queen, Clarine, and their only child, Lanzelet, a baby one year old. They succeed in reaching a neighbouring spring, beside which King Pant dies. The queen, carrying the child in her arms, takes shelter behind a tree, hoping to elude the pursuing rebels. Suddenly there arises from the spring before her a fay of the sea, wrapped in a soft cloud of mist, who snatches Lanzelet from his mother and bears him away to her own land, while the rebels overtake Clarine and lead her off to captivity.

II. *Lanzelet in the Domain of the Lady of the Sea.* "A lady bore the child away, a wise fairy of the sea, a queen better than any in all the world to-day. In her realm she had ten thousand maidens, whereof none knew man or man's array. They wore shifts and kirtles of samite and of silk. I will not deny it, but I say not that it is sooth, the Lady's land bloomed throughout the year as it were mid-May, and her domain was fair and broad and long, and full of joy were its borders. The mountain whereon the mighty castle stood was of crystal, round as a ball. No stranger guest and no king's host was feared therein. All round about it lay the sea and a wall so strong that never a man might be bold enough to deem that he could avail aught against it, and albeit there was a gate, it was of hardest adamant. There within they bided, knowing no fear. He that wrought the castle adorned it cunningly. Without and within it

7

was of gold, like a star. Within its moat naught grew old, or even after an hundred years was less fair. None that dwelt therein was churlish from anger or malice, but the maidens that bided there joyously were ever blithe. The stones wherefrom the dwelling was fashioned had such virtue that, as the story saith, he who passed but a single day therein thought no more on sorrow that he had had, and was ever content e'en to the hour when he died.

"Here in this land in all honour grew the child, happy and free from ill. He must be true and courteous and valiant; thus was he taught by the good Lady, who trained him to follow the customs of noble gentlemen; let him never give him over to mockery as do mere knaves. So soon as he had learnt that which was good and seemly, he betook him to the maidens, who made merry cheer with him. There he beheld all manner of noblesse, for all the maidens were fair. They taught him how to bear him, and how to answer ladies; he must ne'er take vengeance on woman for aught that she missaid, for he was born of gentle blood; full oft must he hold his peace. Right well he learned to play on the harp and the viol and all manner of stringed instruments, for such was the custom of the land. The maidens likewise taught him to sing bravely. In all respects he was meek and worshipful. Each of the maidens would fain have had his love, but were he not minded to win her, none held it for churlishness, for he was gentle and discreet. At his entreaty, when that he prayed her eagerly, the Lady to profit him sent for marvellous creatures of the sea, and ordained them to teach him to deal and parry blows. Then would he never give o'er till there was naught for him to learn. And likewise he had to throw the ball, to leap far and high, fight boldly, cast stones, both small and large, and hurl spears. Never did he draw back from aught whereof he heard tell, and he learned to hunt with falcons and with hounds, and to shoot with the bow. They that came from the sea taught him skill. In all respects he was clever and wight, save that of knighthood he knew neither this nor that, for he never mounted horse, and of arms he had no ken.

"In such wise he bided in the land till that he was of the age of fifteen years. Then right heartily he prayed the Lady that he might leave her; he would fain see tourneys and ride and learn to fight. And when he entreated her, he made obeisance in such manner as was seemly when he spake to his Lady the queen.

"'Now an it please your grace,' quoth he, 'grant me the boon that I ask, and tell me of what kin I be born, for I know not who I am. Of the time that I have tarried here I take great shame. I know not my name, and wit ye well this irketh me sore.'

"'It will ne'er be told thee,' answered the Lady.

"'Wherefore not? What letteth you?'

"'My shame and my great need.'

"'Tell them me, however great they be.'

"'Thou art still too young to learn them; thou canst not guard thyself from ill.'

"'Then let me fare forth nameless, and my name will be made known to me.'

"'Thou must first overcome hand to hand the best knight that ever hath lived.'

"'Name him me, and spare not.'

"'He is hight Iweret of the Fair Forest Beforet. His stronghold is called Dodone. This and all its wealth I give thee forever in recompense, and be of this assured that thy name will ever be concealed from thee till that thou hast conquered him. Thou wilt find him, if thou art valiant. God grant that he receive thee well, for his prowess is so great that I know none who is his peer. He is, I ween, above all the best.'

"The youth spake, 'Him will I fight. Make me ready. Now is the time, and tell me what ye may, of your goodness, for I have an appetite to have ado with him.'

"When the queen saw that he would fain leave the land for naught save honour, she gave him a passing good horse that was fleet and strong, whereon he might follow him with whomsoever he had a quarrel. And she gave him armour white as a swan, the best that man ever wore. He was well dight and richly. His coat of mail all hung with little golden bells beseemed a swift rider. He was right worthy of all worship. The Lady likewise gave him a sword that was adorned with gold and cut well iron and steel, for it was forged with evil intent. The shield for him to bear was to his liking. An eagle with outspread wings was wrought in gold on its boss, the ramp was covered with sable from Tyre; it had been wrought with care in the meinie of the Lady. He wore a rich coat of mail, and his gear was good throughout.

"Now fared he forth over the sea, and many maidens bade him God-speed. They watched him so long as they might see him, and could it e'er betide that they might be sad, then never in all the world would a man have been more bewept by so many fair ladies. And the story saith that a maiden of the sea was his pilot. The queen likewise went with him on the way with a goodly following. She counselled and instructed him that he do honour to all the world, and that he be steadfast, and that to whatsoever he applied him therein he do his best. And so in a little while they came to land. The youth took his leave; right courteously he departed."

III. *Lanzelet and Johfrit de Liez*. Lanzelet mounts his horse, but not knowing in the least how to hold his bridle, he grips his saddle-bow, and lets chance guide him. The horse begins to rear when he touches it with his spurs, and the maidens who watch him from the boat fear lest he come to harm. The horse elects to carry him to the castle of Pluris, the gate of which is guarded by a mounted dwarf. With blows from his whip the dwarf drives him away, and Lanzelet rides on still letting his horse go its own gait, until he encounters a young knight, Johfrit de Liez, who, making merry over his inexperience, teaches him how to hold his bridle and takes him as a guest to his own castle, where his mother proclaims a tourney in order that Lanzelet may learn something of knightly prowess.

IV. *Lanzelet at Moreiz*. Three days later Lanzelet again sets forth on his way. He meets two valiant knights, Kuraus and Orphilet, and accompanies them to Moreiz, the castle of Galagandreiz, who has lost his wife, and refuses to give his beautiful daughter in marriage to any man. The maiden proffers her love to the three stranger knights in turn. Orphilet and Kuraus reject it from fear of Galagandreiz, but Lanzelet accepts her advances, and thus incurs the wrath of Galagandreiz, whom in self-defence he is obliged to kill. He marries the maiden and becomes possessed of her lands.

V. *Lanzelet at Limors*. Orphilet and Kuraus, however, endeavour to draw him away from his bride by tales of the court of King Arthur. They beg him to go thither with them, but he refuses to leave his new domains, and Orphilet returns to court, where he sounds the praises of the young lord of Moreiz. Lanzelet, meanwhile, soon wearies of his conjugal happiness, and one day he secretly leaves the castle in search of adventures. His way leads him to the town of Limors, which no stranger bearing arms is allowed to enter. All unaware of this custom Lanzelet rides in at the gates, fully accoutred. At once he is set upon by the people of the place and thrown into prison, but he is rescued by the efforts of Ade, the niece of Linier, the lord of Limors, who has seen him and become enamoured of him. On his exit from prison the custom of the place requires him to do combat in turn with a giant, two lions, and finally with Linier himself. He is victorious in all encounters, marries Ade, and becomes lord of Limors.

VI. *Lanzelet and Walwein*. These exploits have so redounded to the glory of Lanzelet that news of his prowess reaches court at Kardigan, and Walwein (i.e., Gawain) is commissioned to fetch him thither. He goes to Limors, begs Lanzelet to accompany him to Kardigan, and when Lanzelet demurs, lets him understand that no knight who has not seen the court can count himself famous. The conversation ends in a combat between the two knights, in which neither is gaining the upper hand, when they are interrupted by the news that a tourney to which Walwein muſt needs go is to be held. They part, swearing friendship, but Walwein rides away alone in spite of his entreaties that Lanzelet accompany him. Later, however, Lanzelet goes to the tourney. No man knows who he is, but he attraĉts attention by overcoming all knights with whom he juſts. The tourney ended, he decides to betake himself to Pluris with Ade to avenge the insult of the dwarf.

VII. *Lanzelet and Mabuz.* On their way they come to the Caſtle of Death, where Mabuz, the son of the Lady of the Sea, dwells. Before his birth she had learned that he would always be a coward, and fearing that he would fall a viĉtim to the power of Iweret, her great foe, she has placed him in the Caſtle of Death, which she has so enchanted that no man can enter it without becoming a coward. Lanzelet no sooner sets foot in the caſtle than he falls a viĉtim to the spell, and allows himself to be seized and led to prison. Ade, who from without watches the scene, renounces him as an unworthy lover, and takes her departure. But Mabuz, desiring to make use of Lanzelet as a champion againſt Iweret, arms him, though unwilling, by force, and compels him to leave the caſtle in order to attack Iweret. Once outside the caſtle walls, he is freed from the power of the spell and eagerly undertakes to go to the Fair Foreſt where Iweret lives.

VIII. *Lanzelet and Iblis.* Before he goes Mabuz tells him that Iweret has a beautiful daughter, Iblis, and invariably demands combat with any aspirant for her hand. He who would win Iblis muſt go to a certain linden by a spring, where a bell hangs, which muſt be ſtruck three times before Iweret will appear to meet his challenger. His impregnable caſtle, splendid with gold and precious ſtones, ſtands beyond a blooming valley in a wood that is green both summer and winter, and is filled with beaſts for the chase and singing birds. Daily the fair Iblis, in whom is every virtue that can be found in woman, is wont to wander in the valley with her maidens, weaving flowers into garlands. One night she dreams that she finds by the spring a handsome knight, who wins her love. The following day she arrives at the spring at the moment that Lancelot is about to ſtrike the bell. She recognizes him as the hero of her dream, and begs him not to undertake the combat with her father. But in spite of her entreaties he ſtrikes the bell, challenges Iweret as soon as he appears, fights with him and kills him. Iblis readily pardons him, and gives him her hand and her eſtates.

IX. *The Name of Lanzelet.* After the burial of Iweret, as Lanzelet and Iblis sit on the grass beneath a linden tree, a beautiful maiden from the Land of Maidens rides up on a white mule, bringing Lanzelet greetings from the Lady of the Sea, and announcing that she has come to reveal to him his name. " You are Lanzelet by name, gentle and noble by birth. Your father was called Pant. Genewis was his land ; that is your rightful inheritance ; little will it profit them that have taken it from you. This is sooth, I pledge you the word of my Lady." Forthwith she presents Lanzelet with a fairy pavilion, richly wrought and having the power to heal all the ills of him that enters it, and yet so small that a maiden might easily carry it in her hand.

X. *Lanzelet and Valerin.* When the damsel has returned to her land, Lanzelet sets out with Iblis to find Walwein and go to the court of Arthur. On his way he learns that a certain formidable prince, Valerin by name, lord of a grim castle that is surrounded by an impenetrable wall of serpents and monsters, has come to Kardigan to demand possession of Queen Ginovere, who he insists had been promised to him in marriage before she was given to Arthur. The matter is to be settled by single combat within a week. Lanzelet, leaving Iblis at a friendly castle, hastens on his way to Kardigan and arrives in time for Walwein, who has claimed the battle for himself, to relinquish it to him. The fight continues long with varying fortunes, until at length Valerin is so sorely wounded that he must needs declare himself conquered. Lanzelet, however, grants him his life. The gratitude of the king and queen is unbounded, and Walwein is despatched with three hundred knights to escort Iblis to Kardigan.

XI. *Lanzelet and the Queen of Pluris.* But Lanzelet is eager to go to Pluris, where he has heard that the queen of the land dwells in a castle surrounded by one hundred knights, who must be slain by any suitor for her hand. No knight has ever succeeded in this adventure, which Lanzelet, although his marriage with Iblis prevents him from wedding the queen, desires to undertake. He leaves Kardigan secretly, goes to Pluris, and slays the hundred knights. The queen on seeing him after the victory falls in love with him, and refuses to allow him to leave the castle, even depriving him of his armour and keeping him under strict surveillance. Lanzelet is forced to take her for his bride. " I know not if he were loth, for the queen was a fair damsel." He lives a life of pleasure, but is now sad, now happy, and longs for Iblis, however gaily he passes his time.

XII. *The Fidelity Mantle.* Meanwhile at court, as the absence of Lanzelet is prolonged, wonder is turned into anxiety. One day, at an Easter festival, the damsel who had revealed his name to Lanzelet rides into court, and greeting Arthur draws from a small pocket at her girdle a silken mantle of rainbow hues, which she presents to him from

the Lady of the Sea. She bids the king find among the ladies at the
festival one whom it fits. Arthur gives it to the queen, but it proves
too short for her. The maiden explains that the mantle will fit only
the wife who has been true to her lord in both thought and deed, and
that Ginovere, although she is virtuous, has allowed her fancy some-
times to stray to other knights than the king. The mantle is passed
in turn to two hundred ladies of the court, none of whom can wear it.
Then at the bidding of the maiden of the sea Arthur sends for Iblis
the Constant, who in her sorrow for Lanzelet has absented herself
from the feast. Smilingly the maiden bids her don the robe. She
slips it on, and all the company declare that it fits her as it has fitted no
other woman.

XIII. *The Rescue of Ginovere.* The maiden proceeds to reveal
that Lanzelet is an unwilling prisoner in Pluris, and then leaves court.
At once four hundred knights set out to release Lanzelet. From the
battlements of the castle he espies them coming, and by a ruse gaining
permission from the queen to go to meet them, he succeeds in escaping
with them.

On their way to Kardigan they meet a varlet, who tells them that
in the midst of a hunt in the forest, to which Arthur had gone with the
queen, the terrible Valerin had suddenly sprung upon them, stolen the
queen, and wounded the king besides killing many of their attendant
knights, who had attempted to rescue Ginovere. Valerin had carried
her away to his great castle, where in the midst of merrymaking she
alone is sorrowful. The knights hasten to court, where they find
Arthur healed of his wound and eager for their counsel as to how
Ginovere can be rescued. Tristan declares that Malduc, the enchanter
of the Misty Sea, alone can deceive Valerin, and that he must be called
upon for aid. Erec insists that Malduc will refuse this appeal, for
he has reasons for hostility to Arthur and his knights, especially Erec
and Walwein. In spite of these protests, however, the king determines
to seek the enchanter, and takes with him on the expedition Kay,
Tristan, and Lanzelet. Malduc after some persuasion promises to
rescue the queen, provided that Arthur will surrender to him Erec and
Walwein as prisoners. The king agrees and returns with his companions
to court, where they easily obtain the consent of the two knights,
who freely sacrifice themselves to save their lady the queen. Malduc by
laying a spell upon the castle of Valerin succeeds in effecting an entrance.
Valerin is slain, and Ginovere, whom with thirty maidens he has cast
into an enchanted sleep, is unspelled and led back in triumph by
Arthur to Kardigan.

XIV. *The Rescue of Erec and Walwein from Malduc.* Lanzelet
immediately conceives the design of rescuing Erec and Walwein from

their imprisonment, and secretly sets out with some hundred knights, Kay and Triſtan among them, to the caſtle of Malduc. With him he has Esealt, a young giant, by whose aid they ford the sea and scale the walls of the caſtle. They kill Malduc and his followers in their sleep, and return with the rescued knights to court, where they are received with great rejoicings. But no honours are so precious to Lanzelet as the knowledge that the fairy mantle fits Iblis perfectly.

XV. *The Dread Kiss.* Not long after his return Lanzelet hears from Iblis of a horrible serpent, that infeſts a lonely part of the foreſt and has the habit of entreating all passing knights for the love of God to kiss it. All the knights who thus far have encountered it have fled merely on hearing the requeſt. Lanzelet without delay undertakes the adventure, and eagerly makes his way to a point in the foreſt where he comes in sight of the monſter. Immediately it cries out, " Ah, how long shall I tarry for thee ? " and proceeds to announce that it will become as fair as any creature that God has ever made, if only the beſt knight in the world will kiss it on its lips. " That will I, whate'er betide," answers Lanzelet, and kisses the serpent's mouth. It glides swiftly to a neighbouring ſtream, plunges into it, and emerges a beautiful maiden. She is Elidia, the daughter of the King of Thule, who having transgressed the laws of love in her native land, met with her hideous punishment. She goes now to the court of Arthur, and there is made judge in all queſtions concerning love and courtesy.

XVI. *The Return of Lanzelet to Genewis.* This adventure accomplished, Lanzelet's thoughts turn to Genewis and his patrimony there, of which he desires the possession. Arthur supplies him with a mighty following to escort him thither, but he sends messengers before him to learn the will of the people of the land in regard to their lord. The emissaries find that the country is wisely ruled by the uncle of Lanzelet, Aspjol, who has married Queen Clarine, and who on their announcement that Lanzelet is coming to the land with Arthur and a great hoſt, gladly swears fealty to his nephew. Lanzelet after hearing the messengers' report sets out with his following for Genewis, where he is received with honour and rejoicings. " Right gladly his mother saw her son. Each told other much of love and sorrow."

XVII. *The Rule of Lanzelet in Dodone.* Lanzelet leaves his uncle in control of the kingdom and returns to the court of Arthur, where he gathers together a brilliant following, and proceeds to Dodone, the kingdom of Iweret, where he intends to eſtablish himself. Messengers from Dodone come out to meet them laden with gifts, which they lay before Iblis, entreating her to give them no king save Lanzelet. A brilliant entry into Dodone follows, and shortly afterward Lanzelet

and Iblis are crowned with magnificent ceremonies and begin a
rule of peace and happiness. They are blessed with one daughter
and three sons, live to an honoured old age, and both die on the
same day.

From the above summary we see that the *Lanzelet*
is essentially a biographical romance, namely one
which does not deal with an isolated feat of the hero
or a single group of his adventures, but which recounts
his career from infancy to old age and death. It
embodies the so-called Expulsion-and-Return formula,
according to which a king's son is deprived of his
inheritance in his youth, and after living long in ignorance of his name and origin finally learns them in a
romantic manner, and succeeds in eventually regaining
his ancestral estate. The history of Lancelot, however,
as Ulrich relates it, does not run along with even
flow, but is chequered with glaring, not to say, shocking
inconsistencies. Four times the hero is married and
on each occasion to a lady whom he meets under
practically the same conditions. In each instance
he kills her natural protector, who appears in the guise
of her oppressor, or at all events is so little beloved by
her that regard for his memory is no obstacle to her
immediate union with Lancelot, whom in three out
of the four cases she has seen and loved before he
overcomes her kinsman in combat. Each wife, except
Iblis, passes quietly from the story and from Lancelot's
remembrance, unwept, unhonoured, and so far as the
rest of the poem is concerned, unsung. None, except
Iblis, has any influence upon the course of the narrative ; the part of each of the others ends with the
adventure in which she first appears.

Now it should be remembered that in romantic story there are certain conventions demanded by the type to which the individual narrative belongs. When these conventions are not regarded, it is usually because the narrator wants to fit his story into a different framework, with which in their original form they are not consistent. Whether in so doing he adapts them to his whole or stumbles into inconsistencies and kindred pitfalls, depends upon the degree of skill that he has at his disposal. The adventures in the *Lanzelet* of which we have been speaking conform in a general way to a well-known type, in which the hero slays a formidable knight, the guardian of a maiden, whom he afterwards marries; the marriage is the established conclusion of the story. A work, therefore, that, like our poem, presents a series of such narratives told of a single hero and related with no attempt at binding them together is plainly made up of tales already existing as disconnected narratives, that an uninventive author is here stringing heedlessly together. He often betrays his lack of imagination, and without doubt habitually repeats his stories just as he had learned them. They represent, therefore, in general the uncontaminated material of his source. It is not until he is drawing to a close and has decided to include the story of Elidia that he tries to adapt the fate of the serpent-maiden to his main narrative, for, although according to custom he should make the rescuer of the bespelled damsel marry her, he cannot after all that he has said of Iblis dismiss her, like her predecessors, peremptorily from the scene and allow Elidia to usurp her place as the bride of Lancelot.

He therefore disposes of Elidia, ſtiltedly enough, by making her a judge in queſtions of love at court.

There is, however, one principal ſtory prevailing throughout the poem, which in reality centres about the relations of Lancelot to the Fay of the Sea who nurtured him. These relations form an essential part of the framework as, for inſtance, the adventures of Lancelot with Galagandreiz and Linier do not. The fay carries the child away from his mother to the Otherworld not merely to preserve him from the pursuing rebels. She has primarily less disintereſted designs ; she wishes to train him from his infancy especially in all those arts that will enable him to meet in battle the single being whom she fears, Iweret, from dread of whom she is obliged to keep her only son in a bespelled caſtle. As an incentive to this adventure she refuses to tell Lancelot who he is, until he shall have accomplished it. She takes him completely under her proteſtion, provides him with all that he needs, announces to him his name and his high deſtiny, sends a gift to court that shall exalt his wife above all other ladies,[1] reveals the place of his imprisonment, and is thus inſtrumental in effeſting his release. In other words, as a powerful supernatural being she controls his life in its moſt important events.[2]

Lancelot, accordingly, is the hero of a very familiar and widely used fairy ſtory, to which I have referred above, in which a fay takes a child in his infancy to her own land or under her proteſtion, and trains him in all that it behoves him to learn until he reaches the age for knighthood, when she allows him to go to the court of King Arthur and provides that there

2

he shall take part in a valorous adventure of one kind
or another, the object of which shall be to win her own
love and, usually, as a consequence, a life of happiness with her in fairyland.[1] But as a development
from this story and from this conception of the fay,
there came a situation that we find in a large number
of sources, where the fay trains the hero for any great
adventure that she knows is in store for him or that she
wills, for purposes of her own, should be performed
by him. In its entirety the story is not preserved for
us in many romances, but many are based upon its
essential elements, though they have been subjected
to rationalisation and modified to meet outside
conditions that the authors desired to introduce.

In the *Lanzelet* the object of the lady in bringing up
the young hero and guarding him is not to woo him.
She, however, has no less distinctly a personal aim in
training him for the combat with Iweret. Iblis, therefore, whom by slaying Iweret he wins, is naturally his
only permanent wife in the series that he acquires
in the course of the poem. Her hand is the reward
of the exploit for which the lady has previously trained
him, and she therefore belongs inherently in the
story. For the same reason none of the other episodes
are so closely attached to the plot as the adventure
of the fidelity mantle with which the lady designs to
exalt Iblis at the expense even of the queen, and
perhaps the episode at the castle of Pluris, which is
brought to a happy termination by the influence of
the fay. When we recognize the main structure of the
poem, we see that the stories of Galagandreiz, Linier,
Valerin, and Elidia are extraneous to it, and that they,

with their inconsistencies heavy upon them, should be regarded as rather commonplace additions, which may or may not have been previously connected with Lancelot and are certainly made here by the author for the mere sake of extending his narrative. The fairy theme is, indeed, the most fundamental and persistent part of the legend, and we need not hesitate to affirm that it was one of the first stories attached to the name of Lancelot. This is substantially the only part of the *Lanzelet* that has survived in the literary sources for the life of our hero.

Whatever lost material connected with Lancelot existed before the French original of the *Lanzelet* was written, for us he dawns upon romance as a king's son, wrongfully deprived of his inheritance, brought up in ignorance of his origin by a fairy queen, who trains him for an adventure which she desires to see accomplished, and who guards his career till he is reinstated in his paternal domains. He is called Lanzelot du Lac in the German text, showing that in the French version this name had already been given him to denote his upbringing in a land, whose Lady is always called a fay or nymph of the water. This then is our earliest literary and legendary conception of Lancelot, and the feature of the story which gives him his greatest individuality is that he is the fosterling of a fay.

III

Le Conte de la Charrette
(*The Story of the Cart*)

We owe the first mention of Lancelot in extant French literature to Chrestien de Troyes. In the passage from the *Erec* to which I have referred above he asserts that only two knights of Arthur surpassed Lancelot du Lac in valour, Gawain, the acknowledged flower of chivalry, who in romance regularly takes precedence over his companions of the Round Table, and Erec, whom Chrestien, according to the convention of the time which allowed an author to exalt his hero at the expense of any other, however distinguished he might be, naturally places as second in valour to Gawain alone. This statement, therefore is tantamount to a declaration that Lancelot was already elsewhere acknowledged to have no superior save Gawain. In the same vein Chrestien makes a second reference to Lancelot in a scene in the *Cligès*—a poem usually attributed approximately to the year 1170,—where Cligès tilts in succession with Gawain, Lancelot, and two other knights, and overcomes all except Gawain. Unless his four opponents were already renowned for their chivalry, so much the less credit would have redounded to Cligès from his victory. We may therefore gather from both these passages that Chrestien knew Lancelot as a famous knight. That the lost original of the *Lanzelet* may have supplied him with this information is also a fair inference. Certainly the story of Lancelot's earlier years in fairyland with the Lady of the Sea had already been attached to his name by the time that the *Erec* was written, for Chreſtien refers to him there with the surname *dou lac* (*of the Lake*), and again in the *Conte de la charrette* he definitely mentions the fay's foſtering care of him. In any case, it is certain that ſtories about Lancelot du Lac, a knight whose youth had been passed in a fairyland beyond the waves, and who had won a notable place among Arthurian knights exiſted before 1168, namely, before the *Erec* was written.

A few years after Chreſtien had written *Cligès*, but juſt how many we do not know, probably about the year 1172, he composed another poem, entirely devoted to an incident in the career of Lancelot, which he called *Le conte de la charrette* (*The Story of the Cart*). Its subjeᏨ is the rescue of Queen Guinevere by Lancelot du Lac, her lover, from the Land Whence None Returns, or the Otherworld, whither she had been carried by its prince, Meleagant of Gorre. It relates the same ſtory, albeit with many variations, some important and some unimportant, that is translated and summarised from the prose *Lancelot* below in Chapters XLII-LIII, and has been made accessible in an English translation by President W. W. Comfort.

Seldom are two romantic poems treating of the same hero and composed in the same half-century so entirely dissimilar as the *Lanzelet* and the *Charrette*—the former, somewhat rude in quality, devoted to the series of daring feats achieved by the hero from the beginning to the end of his career ; the latter, essentially the production of a court poet, who in facile and polished verse, written under the influence of

courtly conventions, limits his subject to a single
adventure of the hero, and more engrossed with his
emotions than with his achievements, represents him
as entirely actuated, both in undertaking and in
accomplishing his exploit, by love. Moreover the
traditions embodied in the two compositions have
little enough in common. In the *Charrette* there is
not the slightest trace of the adventures that make
up the larger part of the *Lanzelet*. While the central
theme of the *Lanzelet*—the relation of the hero to the
Lady of the Sea—exercises its influence once in the
Charrette, the central theme of the latter, namely, the
relation of Lancelot to Guinevere, is completely
unknown to the *Lanzelet*, where love in any form plays
only a very subordinate part, and Lancelot throughout
is primarily the hardy young knight, absorbed in
proving his valour by means of any adventure that
comes into his path ; with no further incentive than
his own prowess he is the willing champion of Arthur
against Valerin, and in such aid as he gives Arthur in
the rescue of Guinevere he is stirred by no more ardent
love for her than that which was due to their lady the
queen from all the knights of the court. There are
certain obvious points of contact between the abduction
of Guinevere by Valerin in one poem and by Meleagant
in the other, but save for these few details and for the
mere reference to the fay in the *Charrette*, the two
works belong to two different worlds in the Lancelot
tradition.

In their stories of the abduction of Guinevere the
fundamental agreements are that an otherworld
prince carries the queen away to his enchanted domain,

and that Lancelot defeats him in combat. In the poem of Ulrich Lancelot is merely instrumental in retarding the abduction, and Arthur with only inconspicuous aid from him sets the queen free, while according to Chrestien Lancelot alone is her rescuer. The former story has disappeared from Arthurian romance ; the latter has become one of its most famous episodes. That both versions rest upon a common mythological foundation has long been recognised. A very early story, which is preserved in the twelfth century Latin life of a Welsh saint, the *Vita Gildæ* (*Life of Gildas*), attributed to a certain Caradoc of Llancarvan, relates that a wicked king, Melwas of Somerset, abducted Guinevere, the wife of Arthur, and carried her to the abbey of Glastonbury for safe keeping. Arthur after a long search discovered the place of her imprisonment and with a mighty force laid siege to the abbey. Just as he and Melwas were about to engage in battle, the Abbot, St. Gildas and many monks came upon the scene, and counselled Melwas to restore the queen to her rightful lord. With extraordinary submission Melwas obeyed, and peace was made.

It is well known that Melwas was a Celtic infernal deity, who like many other members of the Celtic Pantheon became rationalised in the hands of narrators into a malevolent but powerful human being, who however retained certain supernatural attributes. It is also common knowledge that during the second half of the twelfth century the monks of Glastonbury, who desired to make their abbey as famous as possible, cultivated a false etymology for its name, the Saxon form of which was Glaestingabyrig, namely, " the burg

of the Glaeſtings ", the ruling family of the place, and
insiſted that it had been originally called *Ynys witryn*,
" the Isle of Glass ", one of the names given to Avalon,
the Celtic Island of the Blessed, the fairy Otherworld.
The natural situation of Glaſtonbury in low marshlands, often partly covered by water, encouraged the
acceptance of such a derivation and aided the belief
that it was the supernatural ſtronghold where the
queen had been imprisoned.

Behind this ſtory we can deteét an earlier tradition,
often paralleled in mythological tales, according to
which the love of a fairy prince marries a powerful
mortal king, and is afterwards pursued by her immortal
lover and carried back to the other world, from which
her mortal husband later recovers her. We may be
quite sure that in an early myth Guinevere was a fay,
who was wedded to an otherworld lord, and who
for some reason that we do not know became the wife
of a mortal husband, Arthur ; but he was too powerful
a personality for narrators long to admit any rival in his
claims to his queen, and therefore her original fairy
husband came to be represented as a false claimant
to her hand, or as her abduétor, from whose power
Arthur rescued her.[1] The form in which this
legend appears in the *Lanzelet* retains earlier features
than that of the *Charrette*, for Valerin is said already
to have been the lover of Guinevere, and Arthur
himself is her rescuer, whereas in the *Charrette*
Meleagant has no previous claim upon Guinevere and
Arthur takes no initiative in her release, which is
entirely effeéted by one of his knights. The early ſtory
is disguised and highly rationalised as we know it in

Chreſtien, and its disguise is all the more complete because the queen is saved, not by her husband, but by Lancelot, her lover, who firſt appears in this rôle in the *Charrette*.

Two queſtions naturally present themselves : where did Chreſtien find the tradition that he used, and why did he transmit it in a tone so different to that of his only predecessor in the field ? The answer to the firſt is speculative, that to the second is found in his *milieu*.

When Chreſtien wrote the *Charrette* he was attached to the court of the Countess Marie de Champagne at Troyes, one of the moſt brilliant of the northern French courts at his period. Its lord, Count Henry I, valued learning and gathered about him men of serious and scholaſtic intereſts. He had married in 1164 Marie, the eighteen-year-old daughter of Eléonore de Poitiers and Louis VII of France, who from three generations of anceſtors on her mother's side had inherited social and literary taſtes, to which she gave expression in her court ; her mother, indeed, after her marriage with Louis VII, became perhaps the moſt potent influence of the time in transplanting the ideals of Southern France both in conduÉt and in letters to the north.

For during the eleventh and twelfth centuries the south of France had gradually been finding and express- ing for herself a new ideal of conduÉt. Here, since there were no such powerful centres of intelleÉtual aÉtivity as exiſted in the north, at Paris and Orléans, for example, secular society was less dominated by ecclesiaſtical learning and was able to develop a more individual standard of life. A more genial climate led to the cultivation of greater luxury and ease among the aristocracy, and the castles of the influential nobles of the south became, in the interludes between the sterner duties of war, centres where a taste for refined diversions, such as dancing, music, poetry and games, was cultivated, and social relations, especially those between men and women, assumed great importance.

From the literature of Provence we learn what the fundamentals of right conduct, as it was accepted by this society, were. Since behaviour was acknowledged to be not one of the superficialities of life, but a fine art, the finished expression of inner qualities, he who would worthily fill a place in the court must possess certain virtues of demeanour. Of these the first and all inclusive was courtesy, that is, the bearing and the spirit suited to courts. Close to it in desirability was gentleness, the result of those traits that naturally accompany high birth, in distinction to the *vileinye* that characterised the manner of the feudal villein ; gentleness was such good breeding, for example, as that of Chaucer's Knight :

> He never yet no vileinye ne sayde
> In al his lyf unto no maner wight.
> He was a verray parfit gentil knight.

To courtesy and gentleness it was necessary to add measure, namely, the preservation of the golden mean in all respects, in thought, deed and word ; and these important virtues must be accompanied by courage, liberality, joy (in the sense of glad energy) and youth ; for in spite of its evanescence and its unattainability by effort, youth ranked as a social virtue in the eyes of both young and old. Of all the virtues, however, the chief was love ; this was essential, the centre of the system, and the touchstone for the gentleness of the individual. " Love and the gentle heart are one same thing," Dante[1] sang, repeating the words of Guido Guinicelli, one of his famous predecessors, who, like himself, had come under the influence of the Provençal philosophy of conduct, and had given expression to some of its theories of love. He who was gentle must necessarily love, according to the society of which we are speaking. Love in this sense was less a personal emotion than it was a social convention that affected the relations between men and women. The poems of the troubadours express this conception in wearisome strains, and in highly intricate verses they utter their sentiments towards the ladies of their choice. The poet represents himself as his lady's servant, ready to do her will ; he praises all of her supremely adorable qualities as the cause of his love ; its effect is suffering, sickness, madness, but by it the lover is ennobled and himself becomes possessed of all virtues.

The object of the troubadour's longing is usually a married woman. To understand this situation we must recall that two factors in the life of Provence were acting in combination—the feudal system and the right of women to inherit property, which was recognised in the south as it was not in the north of France. Every vassal, however, must afford his overlord moral and material aid ; consequently, since a woman was physically incapable of rendering him military assist- ance in time of war, he asserted his right to control her

27

marriage in order that he might provide himself with a competent vassal to hold his fief. Inevitably the ideals of marriage deteriorated, and to many women who held, or were to hold, fiefs, it became a necessity, whether agreeable or not, required by the obligations of their feudal position. Since love did not enter into the matter except secondarily, the theory developed that love and marriage are not compatible, and that, inasmuch as gentleness demands that the individual love, " marriage does not excuse from loving."

Naturally, therefore, with this doctrine prevailing, the troubadour's love poems are almost always addressed to a lady who is the wife of another man. It is highly probable that the practices of the time were far less immoral than the theories, and it has been often pointed out that it is as unreasonable to judge of the actual morality of the period by troubadour lyrics as by the stories of saints. The life of the real world was passed on a more level surface between the two heights of emotion. To the troubadour the marriage without love that was necessitated by the system under which he lived was immoral, and it is probable that he may more justly be regarded as the portrayer of an ideal existence, in which personal desire and social exigences were less at variance, than as an advocate of flagrant immorality[1]. But it cannot be denied that, however artificial the conventional love between the troubadour and his lady was, they were playing with fire, and that the theories of the Provençal poets inevitably opened the door to immoral living and to a consequent deterioration of the individual and of society. Their immoral literary convention, be it said, has to the misfortune of France never departed from her romance and drama, leading to the incongruity of the perpetual acceptance of unlawful love as an ever recurrent theme in literature by a people whose family life possesses singular beauty.

With love and conduct occupying so large a place in the thought of the influential classes, and with the prevailing tendency to didactic writing, it was only natural that treatises concerning behaviour should be written, and that even as authorities on moral and ecclesiastical matters prescribed rules to be followed by their disciples, so directions for social conduct should be promulgated. Questions affecting behaviour, especially concerning the theory and practice of love, were discussed in all seriousness at the courts, largely as an intellectual exercise, until in the course of the century definite codes of conduct in such matters were formulated.

Among the ladies whose knowledge of courtly love was authoritative the Countess Marie de Champagne had a high reputation. It is not strange, therefore that the most famous code of love that has come down to us should have been prepared at her court by her chaplain, known as Andreas Capellanus. His treatise, *De arte honeste amandi* (*On the Art of Loving Properly*), is a compendium of information on the ideas that were engrossing her entourage. Andreas begins his code with the dictum quoted above, that marriage does not excuse from loving, and proceeds to set forth the manner of behaviour that must be followed by him who would be a courtly lover. He must grow pale at the sight of his lady; if he meets her unexpectedly, he muſt tremble ; he should always be timid, should eat and sleep but little, and count naught blessed save that which he believes will please his lady. The principal charaĉteriſtics of this *amour courtois*, courtly love, as it was denominated, according to the tenets of Andreas and his contemporaries, have been defined succinĉtly by Gaſton Paris[1] : " (1) It is unlawful and furtive ; the perpetual fear of the lover that he may lose his lady, that he may cease to be worthy of her, that he may displease her in some way, is incompatible with the assured public possession of her. . . . (2) Hence the lover always occupies a position of inferiority before his lady, in a timidity that nothing can reassure, in perpetual tremors, though he is else-where the hardieſt of warriors. She, on the contrary, though loving him sincerely, allows him ever to feel that he may lose her and that at his leaſt transgression againſt the code of love he certainly will do so. (3) To be worthy of the tenderness that he desires or that he has already won he accomplishes every conceivable deed of prowess, and she on her side ever dreams of making him a better and more worthy knight ; her apparent caprices, her passing auſterities have usually this aim, and are but her means of either refining his love or exalting his courage. (4) Finally, and this compre-hends all the reſt, love is an art, a science, a virtue, that has its laws like those of chivalry or courtesy."

It was for a circle fully imbued with these theories that Chreſtien wrote his *Conte de la charrette*. To the Countess Marie, Chreſtien tells us, he owed both the material of his poem and the interpretation of its meaning. It is not clear from this ſtatement whether

she herself recounted to him the story of the *Charrette*
in outline, or whether she merely directed him to use
a story that he already knew; but as the poem is
filled with the spirit of *l'amour courtois*, he certainly
intends to imply that she desired him to interpret
the theme according to her favourite theories of love.
Since in a verse of his dedication to the Countess,
Chrestien in the fashion of a troubadour protests
that he is "wholly hers", in words that he later represents Lancelot as addressing to Guinevere, it has even
been suggested that Marie was the lady of Chrestien
in the Provençal sense, and that, as he did not himself
complete the *Charrette*, but left the last thousand odd
verses to be written by Godefroi de Lagny, he may
either have incurred his lady's displeasure in the course
of his work, or found that the poem too openly betrayed their relations[1]. But this conjecture has only
slender support, for the phrase on which it is based
does not perforce imply more than the conventional
devotion of a vassal to his liege lady, and the reason for
Chrestien's abrupt termination of his work on the
Charrette is purely a matter for surmise. It is known
that later he was at the court of Philippe d'Alsace,
Count of Flanders, but his presence there does not
perforce indicate that he left Troyes because of a dis-
agreement with Marie. Still, it should be said that
as a narrative the *Charrette* is certainly the least successful of the poems of Chrestien, and that he, who was a
gifted *raconteur*, did not take the trouble to improve
the composition is proof that for some reason, which
we can only conjecture, the task was distasteful to
him.

Such pains as he took with it he evidently spent upon the treatment of love that it involved. This was a subject that interested him more deeply from the philosophic than from the sentimental side, and that he had already approached from the scholastic standpoint in his translation of the *Remedia Amoris* and the *Ars Amatoria* of Ovid, whose teachings he again and again reflects in his writings. It is characteristic that in describing the type of love that he depicts in the *Charrette* he should give his best attention to the various mental conditions occasioned by it—melancholy, reveries, exaltation, hope and despair, in short to the analysis of the causes and effects of the passion from which the lovers are suffering. In such analysis he exhibits his delicate skill as an artist and his familiarity as a court poet with the refinements of conception and expression that were habitually used in setting forth the theory of which Lancelot and Guinevere are the exponents.

The principal weakness in the narrative of the *Charrette* is that the individual episodes frequently lack point in themselves and also connection with the rest of the work. We may account for some of these blemishes by remembering that the poem may possibly have been composed primarily for recitation at court in sections day after day, when there would not have been the same necessity for weaving them into a unified whole that exists in a work written in the first instance for reading.[1] Yet even making allowance for the possible purpose of composition, we cannot in reading the *Charrette* fail to observe that Chrestien was writing more negligently than was his wont.

Let us look, for example, at its beginning. Meleagant, whose name we do not learn till later in the poem,
appears one day at the court of Arthur and boasts
that he holds many knights and ladies of Logres in
captivity in his own country, the Land Whence None
Returns. He pledges himself to set them free, if the
king will give Queen Guinevere into the keeping of a
single knight, who shall conduct her into the neighbouring forest and there do combat for her with him. If
Meleagant is defeated, he will release the prisoners ;
if he wins, he will lead the queen away captive. This
opening immediately mystifies us. We have no idea
who Meleagant is, why he should keep a company of
Arthur's subjects captive in his land, nor what motive
induces him to propose a combat which may end in
their release. We are still more puzzled as to how the
captives entered this country, when later we casually
learn that the land of Gorre, where they are imprisoned,
can be entered only by two bridges, impassable
except for the most adventurous knight in the
world, and that the king of the land is the sage and
beneficent Baudemagus, the father of Meleagant, to
whose nature the apparently causeless imprisonment of
the captives from Logres seems to be entirely foreign.

Nor are our perplexities much lessened as we read
further. When Gawain with his attendants, as in the
prose romance, is going on his way through the forest,
hoping to find Kay and to rescue Guinevere, if Kay
is worsted in the combat for her that he has assumed, he
meets the horse of Kay, riderless and blood-besmirched. A little later he sees a knight with his
visor down come riding towards him on a horse that is

spent. He begs of Gawain an extra horse, on which, as soon as he is mounted, he dashes off at full speed. Gawain follows him, and ere long finds the horse lying dead with traces of a struggle all about him. He soon overtakes the knight, who is walking afoot beside a cart, driven by a dwarf, whom he asks if he has seen the queen pass. "At that time", explains Chreſtien in an aside, "the cart was used as the pillory is to-day. . . . He who had been taken in wrong doing was put upon it and led through the ſtreets, and then he was outside the pale of the law, nor might he thereafter be heard in any court nor honoured nor welcomed with glad cheer. Because the cart was so infamous and so cruel folk said, ' When thou shalt see or meet cart, make the sign of the cross and think on God that ill betide thee not ' ". The dwarf replies to the knight that if he will mount into the cart, he shall see the queen on the morrow; otherwise he will have no news of her. The knight takes two ſteps, and then mounts into the cart. " Love willed it, and he sprang in, for little he recked of shame, since Love commanded and willed it." Thus they ride along, Gawain following on his horse, until they arrive at a caſtle, where the dwarf bids the knight alight from the cart. He then drives away and passes out of the ſtory. The knight and Gawain spend the night in the caſtle, and the next morning they see from a window the queen, under guard of Meleagant, going along a road at the foot of the height on which the caſtle ſtands.

All of this arouses many queſtionings in the reader's mind. We take it for granted, of course, that the knight with the visor is Lancelot, but why he is in the

foreſt when Gawain meets him, in what adventure
that has so spent his horse he has been engaged, and
how he chances to appear on the scene juſt at the
moment when the queen is in straits we are left to
wonder. He dashes off on Gawain's horse having
caught sight of Meleagant and Guinevere, and
knowing where he can overtake them ; yet in far
less time than would be required to carry on such
a combat as that of which Gawain sees the traces, and
for Meleagant and the queen to have vanished out of
the sight of the nameless knight, Gawain finds him
walking disconsolately beside the cart. Nor can we
underſtand why the dwarf should be introduced into
the scene across which he merely passes without con-
neċtion with that which precedes and follows his
appearance. It goes without saying that in a
chivalric society a knight always rode on horseback, but
the ſtatements in regard to the disgrace of the cart
are extreme. It seems probable that in the original
story which Chreſtien knew the cart appeared with a
similar mythological significance to that given it in
some folk tales, in which a denizen of the Land of
Youth by mounting on a cart becomes subjeċt to the
Kingdom of Death ; in the original ſtory, therefore,
as Gaſton Paris pointed out,[1] the cart may have been
used as a suitable vehicle in which to approach the
Land Whence None Returns. Chreſtien, feeling
compelled to introduce it into his version, deprives
it of its early meaning, and purposely exaggerates the
ignominy attaching to it.

Lancelot himself is completely shrouded in myſtery
throughout the poem. His name is not mentioned

and he preserves his incognito as the Knight of the Cart until he fights with Meleagant in Gorre, when Guinevere, who recognises him, reveals his identity. Such secrecy in regard to the hero's name is consistent with the furtive character of the love that Lancelot cherishes for the queen, but Chrestien, although maintaining the fiction that the Knight of the Cart is unrecognised even by Gawain, when he sees him without his armour and with his face unshielded by his visor at the castle where the dwarf leads them, forgets himself so far as to make it evident that on the next morning Gawain knows that the knight is Lancelot.

The heaviest demand, however, that Chrestien makes upon our indulgence is in the reason that he gives for the anger of the queen with Lancelot, which in violation of all the ordinary impulses of gratitude leads her without explanation to refuse him her greeting, when he comes before her after having risked and dared the utmost for her release. " What," she says, when she at length is ready to grant him pardon for the offence of which he is unaware, " were ye not ashamed of the cart ? Did ye not hesitate before it ? Loth were ye to mount after that ye had lingered for two steps. For this, in sooth, I would not speak to you nor look upon you." " Another time," Lancelot answers meekly, "may God preserve me from such a misdeed, and may God have mercy on me, if ye were not right." The extraordinary excuse that Guinevere offers for her conduct—that Lancelot had lingered even for an instant before springing into the cart—and his equally extraordinary admission that she is right are entirely in conformity with the code of love, which was intolerant even of the slightest hesitation on the part of a lover in accepting whatever sacrifices the service of his lady demanded. It is this phase of the theory of love that Chrestien seeks primarily to emphasise in his poem. The perfect lover must render implicit obedience to his lady and must hold even his honour and his knighthood subordinate to her slightest wish. It is at once evident that any such social theory as this is subversive of morality, unless it rests upon a just confidence in the nobility and purity of heart of the mistress whose servant the lover is. And it is largely because of the lack of those qualities in the cold and capricious Guinevere, indifferent to her guilt towards Arthur, whom Chrestien depicts, that the implications of the *Charrette* are essentially immoral.

Such are some of the defects and obscurities of this poem that was destined to have a lasting effect upon the Lancelot legend. For the story that it made famous became one of the most important in the later material. Chrestien not only here established Lancelot as the lover of Guinevere, but he also attached the conception of *l'amour courtois* to his name and made him the type of courtly lover, whose every action might truly be said to have been accomplished, in the words of Dante, as " love compelled him ".

IV

The Prose Trilogy

Under the influence of both the *Lanzelet* and the *Conte de la charrette* the prose romance, *Le livre de Lancelot del Lac* (*The Book of Lancelot of the Lake*) was

composed. This romance is undated, but it is gener-
ally believed to have been written in the first quarter of
the thirteenth century. Scholars differ in their interpretation of the indirect and conflicting evidence bearing upon the exact years between which it may have
been produced, some placing them in the first decade
of the century, and others in the second and the early
part of the third.

Like a very large number of important works of
the Middle Ages it should be considered anonymous,
in spite of its own statement to the contrary. It
purports to be a translation into French of a Latin
version of the adventures that it contains, which were
written down by various wise clerks of Arthur's
court as they heard them recounted by the knights
who had performed them. This book is said to have
been discovered in the royal archives after the great
battle on Salisbury Plain, when Arthur received his
final wound, and during the reign of King Henry II of
England it was, according to some of the manuscripts,
translated into French for love of him by Walter Map,
a witty Norman-Welsh clerk in the service of the king.
Inasmuch as it was the practice of medieval writers
in the vernacular to assert, in order to secure greater
authority for their books, that they were translating
from the Latin, Walter Map was for a long time
accepted as the veritable author of his purported
translation of the *Lancelot*. But, in the first place,
nothing that we know of him indicates the cast of mind
or the powers of sustained invention that would have
led him to compose a work like the *Lancelot*; and in the
second place, there are chronological difficulties in the

38

way of accepting his authorship, for by the time that the *Lancelot* was written Map would have been about sixty years of age and hence probably too old to enter upon such a highly elaborate task. He has been dispossessed, therefore, by almoſt unanimous consent from his position as its author, and the ſtatement of the romance is now accepted as either the addition of a scribe to one of the early manuscripts, or a fiction of the unknown author himself, who in pursuance of a not uncommon cuſtom of the time represents his book as issued under the patronage of a potent sovereign; and having suitably selected Henry II, whose regard for the traditions of King Arthur was famous, he further carries on his subterfuge by using the name of Walter Map, already known, albeit not widely, from a Latin work, *De Nugis Curialium* (*Courtiers' Triflings*), that treated of court life.[1] This process is wholly in accord with the literary practice of the period.

The romance that this unknown author produced, as it exiſts to-day in a vaſt number of manuscripts, is extremely long, and the only modern edition of its text —that of Dr. H. O. Sommer—occupies some twelve hundred pages of three large quarto volumes. Immediately connected with the *Livre de Lancelot* in subſtance and ſtructure are the two other shorter romances that with it form a trilogy, *La queſte* (or *Les aventures*) *del saint graal* (*The Queſt*, or *The Adventures, of the Holy Grail*), and *La mort le roi Artus* (*The Death of King Arthur*). So intimately allied are these three works that it is cuſtomary to treat them as a unit so far as the ſtory of Lancelot is concerned, for the two latter complete the account of his life begun in the former.

Owing to their close relation Professor Ferdinand Lot, finding evidences of unity both of structure and of style throughout the three romances collectively, has even advanced the theory that all are the work of a single author, who in the course of their composition turned from them for a time to write also another romance of about the same length as the last two of the trilogy, *L'estoire del saint graal* (*The History of the Holy Grail*), connected with its members, but less closely than they are with each other.[1] This theory has met with no general acceptance, in spite of the learning and acumen with which it is supported by its propounder. The internal evidence of the presence of various hands in the work, differences in style and in point of view that may be detected, point to a composite authorship. Moreover, the belief that a single author could have produced a romance of such formidable proportions in the early years of the thirteenth century, when French prose had but recently developed into a recognised vehicle for literary expression, makes too great a strain upon our credulity.[2]

In its main outline the trilogy forms a biography of Lancelot. The first part, the *Book of Lancelot of the Lake*, narrates his exploits in boyhood and later as a peerless knight, who by moral no less than physical force performs adventures impossible to his fellows, loving none but the peerless lady of the realm, Guinevere, the wife of Arthur, but since he loves her unlawfully, losing the power to win the highest quest open to mortals, that of the Holy Grail, which can be accomplished only by a virgin knight, and which save for his carnal sin with the queen Lancelot could have fulfilled.

This honour, however, God grants to his son, Galahad, born of the daughter of King Pelles out of wedlock, and closely resembling Lancelot, yet sinless. Lancelot's union with the mother of Galahad is brought about by his deception at the hand of a third person, and hence it leaves him guiltless of disloyalty to Guinevere.

The *Quest of the Holy Grail* continues the story with the account of Galahad's achievement of the Grail. Lancelot still lives under the shadow of his sin and recognises its consequences, as he witnesses his own inabilities brought into contrast with the force of purity in his son. By a sudden realisation of his guilt he is led to repentance and the resolution to begin a life in which his former love shall have no part.

But in spite of his vows Lancelot and the queen again fall into sin together. Their punishment is recounted in the *Death of King Arthur*. Justice demands that they shall themselves see and suffer the consequences of their faithlessness, that of Guinevere to her husband, and of Lancelot to his king, and from their guilt a closely linked chain of events leads to the culmination, fraught with bitterness for them, when they are forced to witness, as a final result of the great wrong that they have committed, the fellowship of the Round Table destroyed by internal discord and the king perish at the hands of a traitor. Guinevere enters a cloister, where she dies in repentance. Lancelot in loyalty to Arthur, from which he has never swerved save in submitting to his overmastering passion for the queen, avenges his death, then enters upon a life of religion and ere long dies in the peace of a hermitage.

It must not be supposed that the above brief account of the trilogy by any means comprises all of its material. In the *Lancelot* and the *Quest* the experiences of Lancelot are interrupted by the accounts of adventures of other knights wholly unconnected with his. The *Death of King Arthur* is much more closely welded together, in general one event following upon another as cause and effect, and the unity of the whole being seldom impaired. But a very large portion of the *Lancelot* is entirely extraneous to the story of the hero and is concerned with the doings of knights who have engaged in certain quests that are mentioned in the course of the principal narrative. The experiences of the individual knights are taken up in turn, expanded and followed by others suggested by them, until after prolonged digressions the story again turns to Lancelot. It is largely because of these lengthy and numerous digressions that Professor J. D. Bruce pronounced the *Lancelot* " unquestionably one of the most rambling productions in European literature ".[1] It is also largely because these digressions are often interwoven either by anticipatory reference or by narrative effect with each other and with the main body of the work that Professor Lot has declared that although apparently incoherent, it is in reality as carefully composed as a five-act tragedy, and that the entire trilogy, far from being a mere collection of disconnected bits and fragments is " a vast cathedral constructed from the foundations to the roof by one and the same architect ".[2] The truth lies somewhere between these two opposing and extreme statements. For a large part of the work the manifold incidents are certainly

more or less interwoven, and their sequence is quite
plainly the result of design. But there are a great
number of episodes that merely repeat the same theme
in different settings—the frequent rescues of Guinevere
by Lancelot under very similar circumstances, for
instance,—one of which appears to have been suggested
by the other. Some of these and also numerous weak
and irrelevant episodes we are justified by our acquaintance with the history of other medieval sources in
regarding as interpolations made by redactors of the
original form of the romance, the precise contents
of which cannot be determined until a careful critical
study of the manuscripts of the *Lancelot* has been made
—and perhaps not even then. But from the huge
romance that we have to-day, be it a unit or a composite
whole, we may cull the legend of Lancelot in the
essential form that the world has known and enjoyed
since the thirteenth century.

When we close the prose romance we feel far
removed from the French original of the *Lanzelet*.
Yet it is on the *Book of Lancelot* that this poem has
left its indelible impression. For although the author
of the prose romance had before him few, if any,
models for the literary form in which he elected to
cast his narrative, he made use of the two existing
poems on Lancelot that we have been discussing. The
original of the *Lanzelet* supplied him in the first place
with the bare outline for his biography, and from it
he also drew the account of Lancelot's infancy and
boyhood, his loss of his patrimony, his life with the
Fairy of the Sea, his ignorance of his own name,
which is not revealed to him until after his principal

exploit has been accomplished, and possibly here and there a few unimportant details, of which we seem to hear the echo.

Such features as are utilised are greatly modified. The scene is changed from North Wales to France. The father of Lancelot in the poem is a harsh lord, whose stern rule brings his fate upon him ; in the latter our sympathies are enlisted for the gentle King Ban,[1] who suffers cruel wrongs at the hands of the unscrupulous usurper Claudas, whose treatment not merely of Ban, but of his brother's children, Bors and Lionel, forms an entirely new chapter in the story. The Water Fairy, a true fay in the *Lanzelet*, is given a somewhat equivocal position in the prose romance. Although retaining many of her fairy attributes, such as her supernatural knowledge, her magic possessions, the imperious spirit of a fairy queen, and her other-world control of the career of her fosterling, in several aspects she is euhemerised into simply the powerful lady of a feudal castle, which has been rationalised from the golden dwelling on a crystal mountain into an earthly domain. But since the story requires that the fay spring with the baby into a lake when she carries him away from his mother, and since, moreover, the very name of the hero demands his connection with a lake, the dwelling of the Lady is placed beneath a lake that, merely to conceal the abode from mortal view, has been cast by enchantment over the plain where the Lady's territories stretch. The most important difference, however, in the relation of the fay to Lancelot is that whereas in the poem she trains him for the conquest of her enemy, Iweret, in the

44

Book of Lancelot she has apparently no motive for her devoted interest in him and his two cousins, Bors and Lionel, upon whom she lavishes scarcely less care. It may be that from the deep-seated hostility to Claudas that she manifests we are meant to infer that her enmity against him as an evil knight already existed when he was warring against King Ban, and that it impelled her to rescue the sons of his enemies in order that they might eventually regain their patrimony from him ; but this is nowhere stated, and her feelings towards Claudas are apparently the result of his treatment of King Ban and the children of King Bors, which arouses her sympathies.

On the other hand our author directly implanted the *Conte de la charrette* in his book, giving it a central place, and also developing throughout the work the conception of Lancelot as the lover of Guinevere and as the embodiment of courtly love and courtly virtues that Chrestien had initiated. Many of the incoherencies of the *Charrette* are made clear and many of its defects remedied in the *Lancelot*. It is, for example, narrated how the knights and ladies of Britain happen to be imprisoned in Gorre, and why the mysterious bridges leading to it were constructed ; the motive in Meleagant's demand for the queen is explained ; the incidents accounting for the presence of Lancelot in the forest are related ; the rôle of the dwarf is more closely knit with the rest of the story ; the queen's anger against Lancelot has a reasonable, though mistaken, cause, and we hear nothing of the trifling, arbitrary excuse that she makes in the *Charrette* ; the story of the cart is given a sequel that lifts from

Lancelot the ignominy of his ride in it. Altogether
we see from some of the differences that the author
of the prose romance knew details of the episode that
Chreſtien had not chosen to give, and also that he had
sufficient ability to improve upon Chreſtien where he
saw fit, though following him on the whole closely in
the outline of his narrative.

The subjeċt matter that is of ſtruċtural importance
groups itself about the relations of Lancelot to three
personages, the Lady of the Lake, Galehot, lord of
the Far Away Isles, and Queen Guinevere. These
are all beings of supernatural origin, which in the case
of Guinevere had been long forgotten, and in the case
of the Lady of the Lake and Galehot faded under the
touch of our author.

The *enfances*, namely, the youthful aċtivities, of
Lancelot under the tutelage of the Lady of the Lake
form the introduċtion to the ſtory, throughout which
her guardianship follows him, manifeſting itself chiefly
in the encouragement that it supplies him in his love
for the queen. This encouragement does not appear
consiſtent with her ſternly moral discourse on knighthood to Lancelot,[1] but it muſt be remembered that
she is *au fond* supernatural and hence is not limited
by mortal ſtandards. Otherwise she is the beneficent
otherworld influence of the romance, even as Morgain
la Fée, the malicious fairy siſter of Arthur, is the
contraſting malign and siniſter being, who seeks to
bring trouble upon Lancelot, and who finally succeeds
in awakening the king's suspicions againſt him, and
so in leading to his undoing.

Galehot, the High Prince, the son of the Fair

Giantess, lord of the Far Away Isles, is a conspicuous figure in a large section of the *Lancelot*. Professor Ferdinand Lot[1] suggests that he appears in the *Lanzelet* as a young giant Esealt, the form of whose name is due to a misreading of *Galehalt* or *Galeholt* (common spellings for *Galehot*) by Ulrich when he was translating the French poem, but whose part there has nothing to do with that of Galehot in the *Lancelot*. Here he stands as the type of devoted friend, who from the love and admiration that the prowess of Lancelot excites in him renounces his ambitious projects of conquest, and demands for his future contentment nothing except the companionship of Lancelot. Although he knows that he cannot live apart from Lancelot, he still gladly for love of him acts as intermediary between him and the queen, whose power over Lancelot he is confident will in time supplant his own and deprive him of the presence that is indispensable to his welfare. It is to be noted that Lancelot, closely bound to Galehot in friendship though he is, falls short of him in unselfish devotion, as indeed is to be expected, inasmuch as he is completely under the sway of his love for Guinevere and can know no other great affection. Even the news of the death of Galehot fails to move him, so absorbed with Guinevere is he at the moment; " he would have grieved thereat, but this was neither the place nor the time ".[2] Lancelot and Galehot, accordingly, cannot be put on a par with some of the other pairs of friends made famous in story, such, for example, as Achilles and Patroclus, Orestes and Pylades, Amis and Amile. Upon none of these great friendships

47

is the author specifically basing that of Lancelot and
Galehot, although it is perhaps worth noticing as one
of the rare cases in Arthurian prose romance where
classical legend may possibly be conceived to have
exercised a constructive influence—and extremely
weak at that—in an episode, that the fight of Lancelot
for the body of Galehot, to which he is incited by the
damsel sent him by the Lady of the Lake, faintly
recalls the part of Achilles in the fight for the body of
Patroclus, to which he went, gloriously equipped by
Athena, at the bidding of Hera's messenger, Iris.[1]

The rôle of Galehot is created by the exigencies
of the story.   He is an essential intermediary between
the queen and Lancelot, for the latter would never
have dared approach her alone.   This is a question-
able part for any good knight to play, and it is therefore
fitting that it should be filled by a being of supernatural origin, who, like the Lady of the Lake, is not
actuated by human scruples ;[2] moreover Galehot is
almost as completely dominated by his love for Lancelot
as Lancelot is by his love for Guinevere, and having
no responsibilities toward Arthur, his only desire is to
gratify his friend.   His service is ended when the love
of Lancelot and Guinevere is consummated, and
Lancelot has definitely become a member of the
household of Arthur.   His death follows, therefore,
as a natural dramatic conclusion.

Guinevere in the romance is nobler in character
than she is in Chrestien's poem and more worthy of
the devotion of Lancelot.   In spite of her love for
him, and in spite of the deceptions that it leads her,
as well as Lancelot, continually to practise upon

Arthur, she is in all other respects the loyal wife of
the king, who, be it said, is himself by no means
blameless. She pardons him his treatment of her
when he forsakes her for the False Guinevere and she
visits her wrath upon Gawain when he hesitates to
accord to Arthur the meed of knightly excellence.[1]
Of Lancelot she demands his highest endeavour in
her service, and incites him to the utmost proofs of
his courage ; the condition that she sets to her love
is his unceasing pursuit of valour, and her grief is
poignant when she first learns that it is his passion
for her that debars him from attaining the Grail.
Not free from coquetry and quite capable of casuistry,
she still is altogether above the cold capriciousness that
Chrestien attributes to her in the *Charrette*. One of
her most characteristic speeches is her impassioned
outburst when the maiden of Morgain repeats before
the assembled court the false story of Lancelot's
confession of their relations.[2] Although she believes
that he has been untrue to her, she impetuously
delivers a eulogy of him that in its frankness completely
disarms all suspicion of her love for him, and which
her pride would have otherwise forbidden her to utter
even to herself. But the most important difference
between the Guinevere of the two works is that,
whereas in the poem she is heedless of the guilt
attaching to her love, in the prose trilogy she becomes
acutely aware of her shame, although not until after the
tragic experience related in the *Death of King Arthur*
is she brought to profound contrition. "Never lady of
high degree made a better end or a more full repentance,
or more sweetly cried mercy of our Lord than she."[3]

4

The centre and the controlling motive of the work
is the love between Lancelot and the queen. The
narrative tells in sequence of his preparation for it,
his awakening to it, his exploits that prove him a
worthy lover, and finally his consciousness of guilt,
repentance, and expiation of his sin. From his first
meeting with Guinevere he obeys the rules of *l'amour
courtois ;* timidity before his lady, concealment of his
love, reveries unfitting him for action, sense of inferiority in her presence, instant acquiescence to every
demand made in the name of the being that he " loves
best of all earthly things ", implicit obedience to the
dictates of his lady, all these requirements of the
service of love he perfectly fulfills. But, originally the
formal expression of a social relation, they are here
employed to depict a passion. To the author of the
Lancelot love does not present the curious meta-
physical problem that it does to Chrestien, but is a
full tide of emotion sweeping the lover on to continual
action. The Lancelot of the romance is far too deeply
engrossed by the active service of his mistress to give
place to a psychological analysis of his sentiments,
and even in the *Quest* at the moment of confession he
accepts the reproofs of the hermit very simply and
with no elaborate probing of his inner self.[1]

In the *Quest* we find ourselves in an atmosphere
wholly different to that both of the *Lancelot* and of the
Death of King Arthur. It is as if we had passed from the
brilliant glamour of the court into the more tranquil,
clearer light of day before the heavy clouds of
passion darken the sky. There is ample evidence that
the author of the *Quest* was a Cistercian monk,[2] and

the sin of the lovers, which more than once, in contraſt
with the *Charrette*, is emphasised in the *Lancelot*,
he uncompromisingly condemns. With the ſternness
of an ascetic he portrays Guinevere as the temptress,
who is the guilty cause of Lancelot's fall, unrepentant,
and meriting the coldness with which, in addition to
his own shame, Galahad, in his absolute purity meets
her queſtionings as to his father.[1] The climax of
Lancelot's praise of her is that she has been to him
the source of " all earthly good " ; what is this in
comparison with the eternal life that will be his, if
he renounce her ?[2] She passes from the ſtory when
Lancelot has parted from her to join in the queſt of
the Grail. From this exploit let all daughters of Eve
be banished. " Let no man lead in this queſt lady
or maiden, leſt he fall into sin thereby," is the warning
pronounced by an aged man in religious garb before
the knights depart. For the queſt is no exploit of
worldly chivalry. The aim of the author, perhaps in
disapproval of the secular ambitions treated in the
romances that he knew, was to represent the Chriſtian
life under the form of a romance of knightly adventure,
and cherishing the sacred associations of the Grail,
which had already almoſt loſt its original secular
charaƈter as a magic talisman, he clothes it with an
allegorical and myſtical significance, and identifies it
with the grace of the Holy Spirit. The queſt of the
Grail, then, for him is the queſt of the soul after the
hidden treasures of God, revealed by His grace.
Galahad he regards as the symbol of Jesus Chriſt
Himself, filled with the grace of the Holy Spirit and
diffusing it among mankind.[3] Lancelot becomes in

his hands the type of repentant sinner, who is aroused
to a sense of his sin, and profoundly penitent craves
and in a measure receives the healing and illuminating
grace of God. Ever quickly influenced through his
affections, he is first moved to confess his sin by the
sight of the Cross and by the hermit's reminder of
Divine Love,[1] but, as it has been happily said, he is
" as easy to seduce as to convert, as impossible to
pervert as wholly to sanctify ".[2] Deeply stained by
his long years passed in secret sin, still so far the
servant of love that he is not strong enough completely
to root out of his heart his worldly affections, he cannot
attain to the full radiance of Divine grace or the full
knowledge of its hidden mysteries. The good that
he would he does not, and the evil that he would not
that he does. When he is again under the influence
of the queen, his penitance is speedily forgotten, and
it is only after her death that he utterly forsakes his
love and lives a life of holiness.

Thus the trilogy as a whole presents in the story of
Lancelot and Guinevere the contradiction that existed
between the medieval social conception of love as a
virtue that ennobled and that permitted, nay, demanded
the adoration and idealisation of his mistress by the
lover consecrated to her service, and the opposing
ascetic estimate of woman as the " confusion of man ",
the accursed temptress, who has ever, since the days
of Eve, offered him the forbidden fruit. It is perhaps
a strange coincidence that the love of Lancelot and
Guinevere has been made famous by the pen of
Dante, for it is primarily through the conception of
love depicted in each of these two important medieval

52

works, one of France and one of Italy, the *Lancelot* and the *Divina Commedia*, immeasurably far apart in their qualities as literature, that they still must always come into comparison. The *Lancelot* exhibits courtly love raised to a high degree of excellence, but banished from the heart by the ascetic ideal; in other words, it shows the earthly supplanted by the spiritual desire. The *Commedia* purges the mundane elements from the troubadour love under the influence of which Dante first wrote of Beatrice, and transforms it by exalting its object into the Heavenly Grace that leads man to Divine Love. And even as Dante declared that allegorically the subject of his poem is man, " according as by his good or ill deserts he renders himself liable to the reward or punishment of Justice,"[1] so the underlying theme of our trilogy, though only in part set forth in allegory, is sin and its consequences to man, his punishment and repentance, followed by Divine forgiveness—the course by which a soul, tempted but endowed with high capabilities, drifts from the tempest of passion into the peaceful haven of God's mercy.

There is a general truth that the part of the Lancelot story of which we are speaking especially illustrates. Legend and literature alike are plastic material on which the touch of successive epochs leaves its imprint and its evidence of the development of human thought. They have as clearly defined a place in the study of mental and moral evolution as botanical or geological specimens have in that of the natural and physical worlds. Thanks to the fortune that has preserved to us the *Lanzelet*, the *Charrette*, and the prose trilogy,

we can watch the effects of the influences that one
after another moulded the legend into its final shape.
We can follow the relations of Lancelot and Guinevere
from their innocent entrance into Arthurian story
through the formal conventions of courtly love to the
laying bare of their sin under the searching light of
asceticism. There are three passages that clearly
illustrate the steps in the evolution :—the eager,
" Can I be there in time ? " with which, in the
Lanzelet,[1] his heart filled only with the desire for
adventure, Lancelot greets the news of the proposed
single combat with Valerin for Guinevere ; the scene
at the window of Guinevere, in the *Charrette*,[2] where
by a furtive glance and seductive, coquettish words she
conveys to Lancelot the assurance that he would be
welcome, if he could enter her chamber ; and the
prayer with which in the *Chantari di Lancellotto
(Songs of Lancelot)*,[3] a fourteenth-century Italian
rhymed version of the story of the *Death of King
Arthur*, Lancelot receives the tidings of the death of
Guinevere, and which, though not contained in the
French romance, embodies the spirit that had entered
into it :—" And Lancelot fell on his knees, saying,
' Lord God, Thou who didst deliver mankind from
the pains of Hell, and on the Holy Cross didst pardon
the unhappy thief, and by Thy Holy Spirit didst
inflame Thy apostles on the day of Thy Ascension,
of Thy love pardon the queen ' ".

As a literary production the *Book of Lancelot* has
more conspicuous defects than the two later members
of the trilogy. The most glaring of these defects
cannot fail to be evident to the modern reader, to

whom the prolixity of style, the triviality of some of the incidents, and the semi-rationalisation of the supernatural are not congenial. To read the book sympathetically we must remember that the public for which it was intended demanded from its story-tellers first of all entertainment, and preferred that their stories should present an improbable world. Moreover, notwithstanding the prodigious length of the prose romances, they are always made up of short narratives, each usually broken off in its midst, while "the story begins speaking" of another hero, whose exploits are soon interrupted to resume a previously suspended episode, itself shortly abandoned for the sake of taking up a new or an already interrupted narrative. This method was probably adopted for the purpose of stimulating the curiosity of the reader, and perhaps, too, because the tolerably rapid change of story made a less exacting demand upon his mentality than the steady recounting of the deeds of a single hero, where the connection of events must be more closely followed; just as the shifting scenes of the cinema are less trying to the mental capabilities of the public of to-day than the sustained interest of the spoken drama.

In spite of the evident weaknesses there is much in the romance that has distinct literary merit. The life of the young Lancelot to the time of his knighting presents a series of delightful pictures of the interests and pursuits of boyhood in the Middle Ages, and the eagerness with which as a young squire and maiden knight he undertakes daring adventures (even though the first, the release of the knight with the truncheons,

is preposterous) is recounted with spirit and vigour.
His meeting with Guinevere, the story of the first kiss
that she vouchsafes him, the characterisations of
Lancelot himself, of the queen, and the Lady of
Malohaut, the visit of Sir Bors at Corbenic when he
first sees the infant Galahad, the scene between
Lancelot and Guinevere when she reproaches herself
as the cause that prevents him from winning the Grail,
their parting when the knights are setting forth in
search of it, Lancelot's farewell to Logres when
Arthur has banished him from the kingdom—these
are some of the passages that have incontestable
excellence and make a universal appeal.

The Nuns' Priest spoke more wisely than he was
aware when he pronounced the book of Launcelot de
Lake to be "trewe", for in spite of the enchantment
and marvellous exploits and unrealities with which it
regales us, it shows us in its personages men and
women of seven centuries ago as they were, prompted in
their actions by the same instincts, experiencing
essentially the same feelings, ambitions, struggles,
successes, and failures as ourselves ; they are "but
prophecies of this our time, all *us* prefiguring". Behind
their surroundings, their manners, conventions, habits,
their very fashion of speech, all of their own period,
they themselves stand vividly and perennially human,
even as their costumes and bearing in the miniatures
that depict them belong to a vanished past, but the
emotions that they express, like the gold that embellishes
the page, have a freshness of to-day. Many medieval
modes of thought that seem remote from the present
are so only on the surface, for they are simply a by-gone

expression of our abiding human nature. The story of Lancelot, for instance, exemplifies admirably the medieval belief that the most heroic among mortals are favoured by fairy protection, and that the man most truly blessed is he who is worthy to attain the highest spiritual goal. For to the apprehension of the twelfth and thirteenth centuries the supernatural world was very close to this and very real, whether it were conceived in mundane terms as the " happy land of Faëry ", or in exalted faith as the heavenly city, the New Jerusalem. Both visions were evoked and cherished by the craving of men for a better world than that in which they found themselves. And what is this desire but the impulse that in modern life expresses itself in schemes for social betterment, the fundamental difference being that, whereas the present age in its ideals aims at material ease rather than at spiritual welfare, the thirteenth century was in general disposed to recognise the immaterial as the real, and valued, at all events theoretically, spiritual more highly than material interests.

It is a mistake to regard medieval Arthurian literature solely through the glamour of romance. We may turn to it more profitably, and with no fear of spoiling its charms, for a record of the kind of beings who in varied classes constituted the actual society of the period, and just for the reason that they were different from ourselves, yet the same, we find them, with all their foibles, permanently stimulating and enlightening. Because the *Lancelot* emanates from an epoch when spiritual perception was keener than our own, it brings us a clearer vision of what constitutes right living. It warns againſt social immorality and the desecration of the marriage tie, and emphasises the value of spiritual aims in exiſtence. That the world of to-day, in its present moral depression, ſtands in need of both lessons the commoneſt observation tells us. Caxton's admonition to readers of the *Morte Darthur* is no less timely to us, who nearly four centuries and a half later read the *Lancelot* : " Herein may be seen noble chivalry, courtesy, humanity, friendliness, hardiness, love, friendship, cowardice, murder, hate, virtue, and sin. . . . All is written for our doctrine and for to beware that we fall not to vice nor sin, but to exercise and follow virtue, by the which we may come and attain to good fame and renown in this life, and after this short and transitory life to come unto everlaſting bliss in heaven ".

The Damsel carrying Lancelot into the lake

BOOK I

THE BOOK OF LANCELOT OF THE LAKE

CHAPTER I

How Claudas of the Desert Land made war on King Ban
of Benoich

I<small>N</small> the march of Gaul and of Little Britain there were
of old two kings that had two sisters to wife, and they
themselves were brothers. One of the two kings hight
King Ban of Benoich and the other King Bors of
Gannes. King Ban was an old man and his wife was
young, and she was a fair and passing good lady, and
beloved of all folk. And never a child had the king
by her save one alone, the which was a boy. And
his surname was Lancelot, but his name at christening
was Galahad, and wherefore he was cleped Lancelot
the story will show plainly hereafter,[1] for this is neither
the place nor the time.

But now the story goeth on its own way and saith
that the king had a neighbour whose lands marched
with his by Berry, that then was called the Desert
Land.[2] This neighbour hight Claudas, and he was
lord of Bourges and of all the country round. This
Claudas was king, and he was a good knight at arms
and wight, but he was passing traitorous, and he was
liegeman to the king of Gaul, that is now called
France. The land of Claudas was called Desert for
that it had been made desert by Uterpandragon and
by Aramont, who at that time was lord of Lesser

Britain and had been given the surname Hoel by the
people. This Aramont had under his obeisance Gaul
and Benoich and all the land so far as the march of
Auvergne and of Gascony, and he should likewise have
had Bourges and all the country round about. But
Claudas would not acknowledge him or do him
hommage, but he made the king of Gaul his lord.
And at that time Gaul was subject to Rome and paid it
truage, and all the kings were chosen by election.

When Aramont saw that Claudas refused his signory
with the support of the Romans, he summoned him
to war, and Claudas had the king of Gaul to aid him.
And Aramont lost much in the war, that lasted over
long. Then he betook him to Uterpandragon, that
was king of Britain, and he became his man, and they
made a covenant that Uterpandragon should bring the
war to an end for him. So Uterpandragon passed
the sea with all his host, and they heard tidings how
that the lords of Gaul had joined Claudas to go against
Aramont, that drew nigh, he and Uterpandragon with
him. Then together they set upon Claudas, and they
discomfited him, and they took from him all his land
and they drave him forth therefrom. And the land
was left without a lord, and it was utterly laid waste,
so that never a fortress was there whereof one stone
remained upon another, save in the city of Bourges,
that by commandment of Uterpandragon was spared
from fire and water and destruction, for he was
mindful that he had been born therein.

And thereafter Uterpandragon went to Little
Britain, and when he had tarried there so long as it
pleased him, he passed over to Great Britain. And

henceforth Lesser Britain was subject to the kingdom
of Logres. When that king Aramont was dead and
likewise Uterpandragon, and King Arthur held sway
in the land of Logres, then wars arose in many places
in Great Britain, and the most part of the barons
fought against King Arthur. And it was at the
beginning of his reign, and he had been but short
while wedded to Guinevere, and he had much to do in
all parts.

Then King Claudas took up the war that he had
left for so long, but he began it again because he had
recovered all his land so soon as King Aramont was
dead. Then he made war again upon King Ban of
Benoich, for that his domains marched with his own,
and for that he had been the liegeman of Aramont,
who for long time had deprived him of his lands, and
while he had the upper hand had done Claudas great
wrong. At that time there was come from Rome a
consul that hight Pontus Antonius, and he aided
Claudas and gave him sway over all Gaul and the lands
that belonged thereto. And they wrought so for
King Ban that they took from him his city of Benoich
and all his other lands save one castle, that was called
Trebe, and it was the chief castle in his domains, and
it was so strong that until that day it had feared nought
save famine or treason. And Claudas came with
his host before Trebe. And King Ban had sent oft
to King Arthur for succour, but King Arthur had
had so much to do in many parts that he might not
lightly concern him with the affairs of another. And
King Bors, the brother of King Ban, that oft-times
aided him, lay sick unto death.

CHAPTER II

*How King Ban set out to beg succour from King Arthur
against Claudas*

Claudas perceives that he will not easily be able to take Trebe.
He accordingly offers, if Ban will surrender it to him and acknowledge him as overlord, to reinvest him with the castle.   Ban
at once rejects this proposal on the ground that he is the liegeman
of Arthur.   Claudas then suggests that Ban seek aid from Arthur
with the understanding that, if he does not receive it within
forty days, he will yield up the castle on the stipulated terms.
Ban promises to consider the matter and to give Claudas his
reply on the following day.

Claudas proceeds by secret bribery to win the seneschal of
Trebe to his side.   On his disloyal advice Ban decides to go
in person to Arthur, without the knowledge of Claudas, and seek
his aid.   In order the more surely to enlist the compassion of
Arthur, he resolves to take the queen and Lancelot with him.
On the eve of his departure he sends the seneschal to Claudas
with his plighted word that he will surrender the castle in forty
days, provided that Arthur in the meantime fails to send him
help.

THAT night King Ban went early to rest, for the
nights were short, and it was, as the story saith, the
night of mid-August, on a Friday in the evening.   The
king was disquieted for the journey that he needs must
make, and he was heavy thereat, and he rose full
three hours before dawn.   And when the saddles were
put upon the horses and all was ready, he commended
his seneschal and his other folk unto God, and then
he issued forth by a secret drawbridge over the little
stream that flowed below the castle.   For the castle
was besieged only on one side, and the besiegers were
more than three bowshots distant at the point where
they were the nearest; for before the hill were

mountain and valley and many a misadventure, and on the other side by the river no host might find a place, for the marsh there was broad and deep, and there was but one little, narrow causeway, that was more than two good leagues in length. By this causeway the king went forth, and he took with him his wife, mounted on a strong palfrey, that was fair and ambled softly, and also a good and faithful squire that had the child in a cradle before him on his great horse, that was strong and good, and he bare the shield of the king. And this same squire that was mounted on the horse drave before him a sumpter beast, and he carried the spear of the king withal. The sumpter beast was well laden with jewels and with plate and with coin. King Ban rode in his greaves of iron and his hauberk, with his sword girt to his side, and his mantle against the rain wrapped about him, and he was the last of all in the company. And he rode so far that he passed beyond the marsh and entered a forest, and when he had ridden about half a league through the forest, he came to a fair lawn where he had been many a time afore. He rode on with his company till that they came to a lake at the end of the lawn at the foot of a high hill, wherefrom all the country round might be seen. And it drew toward day.

The king said that he would not go thence till that the day was come. And he alighted down from his horse, for he was minded to go up to the top of the hill to see his castle that he loved beyond all castles in the world. He waited until the dawn, and then he mounted his horse, and he left the queen and his company below on the shore of the lake, that was wide.

The lake had been named from the days of the pagans the Lake of Diana. Now Diana was queen of Sicily, and she reigned in the time of Virgil, the great author, and the foolish heathen folk of that day held her for a goddess. And there was no lady in the world that more loved woodland pleasures, and every day she went to the chase, and the foolish heathen folk called her the goddess of the woods. This foreſt wherein the lake lay surpassed all others of Gaul and of Little Britain as a little foreſt, for it was but ten English leagues in length and six or seven in breadth. And it was called the Wood in the Vale.

CHAPTER III

How King Ban saw his caſtle burn, and how he died

After King Ban has departed from Trebe, his seneschal betrays to Claudas all that has taken place, and on condition that Claudas shall inveſt him with the caſtle, he opens its gates to him. The retainers of King Ban make a bold resiſtance, but Claudas speedily takes possession of the place. To his wrath one of his followers sets fire to the town, and many dwellings are deſtroyed. The seneschal, according to the pledge, is inveſted with the domain, but is speedily killed in single combat by Banin, the godson of King Ban, who has challenged him on the charge of treason to his lord. Banin then leaves the land.

Now the ſtory saith that King Ban ascended up into the hill to see the caſtle that he held so dear. And the day began to break. And he looked and he beheld the walls grow white and all the bailey round about. But he had scarce looked upon it ere he was ware of a great

The death of King Ban

[*face p.* C

smoke in the castle, and a little after he saw huge flames dart forth, and anon he saw the halls thrown to the ground, and the churches and abbeys fall, and the fire leap from one part to another.

King Ban beheld his castle burn that he loved more than aught other that he had had, for therein was all his hope and all his comfort. Now he had naught in the world whereto he looked for aid, for he was old and broken, and his son was not of age to help or to succour him, and his wife was young, and she had been nurtured in ease, and she was a lady of high estate in the sight of God and of the world, for she was descended from the royal line of David. And Ban was sore grieved that his son must pass from riches to poverty and want, and that his wife should be in the power of another, she that full oft had had many folk in her own power. And he himself must needs be poor in his old age and pass the rest of his life in penury, he that had been so rich and so honoured and so bounteous of his gifts, and had led so joyous a life with fair company.

Of all these things King Ban bethought him. And he covered his eyes with his hands, and for his great sorrow of heart his ears were stopped, and his heart nigh burst in his breast, and he swooned. And he fell so heavily from his palfrey to the ground that but a little and he had broken his neck, and the blood gushed out at his nose and his mouth. Long time King Ban lay in such plight, and when that he had come out of his swoon, he spake as best he might, and he looked up toward heaven and he said :—

" Ah, Lord God, I thank Thee, sweet Father, for that it pleaseth Thee that I should end my days in want, for Thou camest poor and needy to suffer death for us. Sire, since that I may not abide longer on earth without sin, I cry Thee mercy, for I see and know full well that I am come to mine end. And, fair Father, Thou that camest to purchase me with Thine own blood, suffer not my spirit, that Thou hast put within me, to be lost, but in this last day, when mine end is come and awaiteth me, receive me as him that confesseth to Thee the burden of his sins, so many and so grievous that I may not tell the sum thereof. And if my body hath done ill on earth, where none may be without sin, grant, Sire, that my unhappy soul may do penance therefor in such wise that it may at some time be seated in everlasting bliss. Father, fair and pitiful, have mercy upon me and upon my spouse, Elaine, that is descended from the noble lineage[1] that Thou didst establish in the Adventurous Kingdom to exalt Thy name and the greatness of Thy faith, and to behold Thy great mysteries. Lord, console her that is disconsolate, and that is descended from this high lineage and hath loved Thy faith. And be mindful, Lord, of my unhappy son, that is left fatherless in his youth. For all power lieth in Thy hands."

When that the king had said these words, he looked up to heaven, and he beat his breast and bewailed his sins with a true heart. And then he plucked three blades of grass in the name of the Holy Trinity and in the name of Holy Faith.[2] And his heart swelled within him, and for the great grief that he had for his wife and his son he lost all power to speak, and his eyes rolled, and so grievously he gasped for breath that his veins burſt and his heart broke within him, and he lay dead on the ground with his hands crossed on his breaſt and his head toward the eaſt.

His horse was affrighted at the fall that King Ban made, and he turned and fled down the hill ſtraight to the other horses. And when the queen saw him, she cried out to the squire to take the horse. And the squire took the horse, and he set the child down upon the ground, and he rode up the hill, and he found his lord dead.

The squire alighted down from the horse, and he gave a cry so loud that the queen heard it, and she was so dismayed that she left her child at the hoofs of the horses, and she gathered up her robe about her, and she sped afoot up the slope, and she found the squire lying on the body of the king, and he made the greateſt sorrow that he might. And when she espied her lord, she fell in a swoon, and when she awoke from her swoon she cried out, " Woe is me ! " And she rent her garments, and she tore her hair, that was long and golden, and she wailed so loud that the hill and all the foreſt round and even the lake re-echoed with her cries.

CHAPTER IV

How the Damsel carried Lancelot into the Lake

When that the queen had lamented the valour of her lord and had bemoaned his losses and his sorrows, she cursed Death that he tarried. And when that she had made dole on this wise for long, she bethought her of her son, and she said that by naught else would she e'er be comforted. And in her dread leſt the horses near the which she had left him might have killed him, she sprang to her feet as if she were mad, and ſtraightway she sped down the mountain-side to the child at a great pace with her locks dishevelled, and she was all diſtraught. And when she drew nigh to the horses on the lake shore, she saw her son unswaddled out of his cradle, and she espied a damsel that held him in her lap, and she pressed him gently to her bosom, and she kissed him again and again, for he was the faireſt babe in all the world.

The morning was bright and cold, for the day had come. And the queen said to the damsel, " Fair, sweet friend in God's name, let the child be, for enough trouble and sorrow will he have from this day forth. For in his orphanage to-day he is like unto him that is bereft of all joy, for his father hath even now died, and he hath loſt all his lands, that would ne'er have been small, if he had kept them even as he should have had them ".

The damsel answered never a word to aught that the lady said. And when she saw the queen draw nearer, she rose with the child in her arms, and she went speedily down to the lake, and she put her feet together, and she sprang thereinto. When that the queen saw her son in the water, she swooned, and when she came out of her swoon, she saw naught of the damsel. And then she began to make dole such that no lady might make greater, and she would have leaped into the lake had she not been withheld by the squire, that had left the king on the mountain-side and had

followed her, if haply he might comfort her, for he
feared that she would go out of her wits from the
great sorrow that he saw her make.

It chances that an abbess with two nuns, a chaplain, a monk,
and other attendants passes by, and recognises that the lady,
whose sobs attract her attention, is the queen. "In sooth,"
Elaine replies in answer to her questions, "I am the Queen of
many Sorrows." Hence this part of the romance is said to be
called *The Tale of the Queen of Many Sorrows*. The queen
recounts the story of her misfortunes to the abbess, and entreats
to be made a nun and to be allowed to build with the treasure
that she has with her a chapel where masses shall ever be said
for the soul of King Ban. The abbess consents, and Queen
Elaine immediately takes the veil. The squire forthwith
becomes a monk and enters a convent. After the chapel is built,
the body of King Ban is interred in it, and the place is henceforth
known as the Royal Minster.

Two days after the death of King Ban his brother, King Bors
of Gannes, dies, leaving two sons, Lionel, who is not yet two
years old, and Bors, who is younger. Claudas at once attacks
Gannes and succeeds in gaining possession of the entire country.
The queen, Evaine, however, with Lionel and Bors, makes her
escape into the neighbouring forest. Here she is waylaid by
Pharien, a knight of Gannes, who has allied himself with Claudas,
but who promises to lead her to safety, provided she give into
his keeping her two sons, whom he will rear as befits their station.
This he desires to do, believing that the children, when they
are grown, will regain their inheritance, and that it will be to
his advantage to have their favour. For their sake the queen
yields, and by order of Pharien she is conducted to the convent
of the Royal Minster, where Queen Elaine is cloistered, and
where the two sisters now remain together, mourning for their
husbands and for their sons, who are lost to them.

CHAPTER V

Of the Lady that carried Lancelot into the Lake

Now the story saith that the Damsel that carried Lancelot into the lake was a fay. In those days all maidens that knew enchantments or charms were called fays, and there were many of them at this time, and more in Great Britain than in other lands. They knew, as the ſtory saith, the virtue of herbs and of ſtones and of charms, whereby they might be kept in plenty and in the great wealth that they possessed. And after the Damsel had borne Lancelot away to the lake, there is no need to ask if she held him dear, for not even a woman that had carried him in her womb might have brought him up more tenderly. She dwelt not alone, but she had ladies and maidens with her. And she sought a nurse for the child that cherished him, and when that he was able to do without her, he had his maſter that taught him how he should demean him. And none of the meinie of the Damsel knew his name, but they called him after divers manners. Some called him Fair Foundling, and others Son of a King, and she herself often called him thus, and times there were when she called him Rich Orphan. Thus was Lancelot in the keeping of the Damsel for three years at full great ease, and he thought in truth that she was his mother. And he grew in those three years more than another child would have grown in five, and in all respeɑts he was so fair a child that none might find a fairer.

The Lady that nourished him abided only in woods

and in forests that were vast and dense, and the lake whereinto she sprang with the child was naught but enchantment, and it was in the plain at the foot of a hill that was lower than that whereon King Ban had died. In the part where the lake seemed widest and deepest the Lady had many fair and noble dwellings, and in the plain below there flowed a little stream, that abounded in fish. And her abode was so hidden that none might find it, for the semblance of the lake covered it so that it might not be seen. Thus bided Lancelot in the keeping of the Damsel, so as ye shall hear. But the story speaketh no more of him now, but returneth to speak of Lionel and of Bors, his brother, the sons of the King of Gannes.

> For a time Pharien successfully conceals Lionel and Bors, but at length Claudas learns that they are in his keeping, and by promising to render them their inheritance when they are of the age for knighthood, he induces Pharien to confide them to his care. He at once lodges them with Pharien and his nephew, Lambegues, in a tower in Gannes, where they remain virtually his prisoners.

CHAPTER VI

How Lancelot bided in the keeping of the Lady of the Lake

Now the story saith that when Lancelot had been for three years in the keeping of the Damsel of the Lake, so as ye have heard, he was so fair that there was none that saw him but thought him to be of more than thrice so great an age as he was. And he was not only

large, but he was good and underftanding and nimble
and wight, and more so than a child of his age can
be. The Damsel gave him a mafter that taught him
how he should bear him after the manner of a gentleman ; howbeit, of all them that were there none
knew who he was save only the Damsel and one of
her maidens, and they called the child even as the
ftory hath said tofore.

So soon as he could do for himself, his mafter made
him a bow befitting his ftature, and light arrows, and
he let him shoot at a target, and when that he had
grown skilled therein, he taught him to draw his bow
at the little birds in the foreft. And even so, as he
grew in might and in ftrength of body and limb, his
mafter made his bow and arrows ftronger, and he began
to shoot at hares and at small beafts and at large birds,
wheresoever he might find them. And so soon as
he could mount a horse, one that was good and ftrong
and seemly was made ready for him, and it was well
caparisoned with bridle and saddle and other gear,
and he rode up and down about the lake, and never
far away. He was not alone, but with him he had a
right fair company of young squires, large and small,
of gentle birth. And he knew well how to bear him in
their midft, so that they that saw him thought that
he was a gentleman passing all others in the world.
And so in truth he was.

Chess and draughts and all manner of games that
he saw he learned so well that when he came to the
age of a bachelor none might teach him aught. And
he was, as the ftory saith, the faireft child in the world
and the beft fashioned in form and limb. And the

Lancelot learning to shoot

The brother of Aiglin des Vaux

[face p. 74

Story doth not forget his aspect but portrayeth it for all folk that would hear tell of the beauty of a child. His skin was passing beautiful, neither fair nor dark, but intermingled of one and the other, and it might be said to be of a clear brown. His visage was ruddy with its natural colour, but so reasonably measured that God of His skill had put there white and brown and red in such wise that neither the white was obscured or spoiled by the brown, nor the brown by the white, but one was tempered by the other. And the rosy hue that was beneath lighted both itself and the two other colours at the same time, so that there was not overmuch white nor brown nor red, but a mingling of all three. His mouth was small and seemly, and his lips were rosy and somewhat full, and his teeth were small and close and white. And his chin was shapely with a little dimple therein. His nose was long and somewhat high in the middle. His eyes were gray and laughing and full of joy so long as he was happy, but when he was wroth, of a surety he was like unto a living coal, and to all them that beheld him it seemed that drops of red blood started from his eyeballs, and he wrinkled his nose in his wrath even as a horse, and he ground his teeth together so that they gnashed, and the breath that issued from his mouth seemed all red, and then he lifted up his voice so that it was like a trumpet, and whatever he held in his hands or between his teeth he rent in pieces. In short in his rage he was mindful of naught save that whereat he was wroth, as was well proved full oft.

His forehead was high and shapely, and his eyebrows were dark and arched, and his hair was fine and blond

by nature, and as shining as if he were a child, and a
fairer colour no locks might be. But when he came
of age to bear arms, even as ye shall hear, they changed
from their natural gold and became tawny, and they
were always light in hue and somewhat curly, and
they were goodly to look upon.

Of his neck there is no need to ask, for if it had been
that of a fair lady, it would have been seemly enough,
and it was well fashioned according to the size of his
body and shoulders, neither too thick nor too thin,
neither long nor short beyond measure. And his
shoulders were broad and conformably high, and never
was there a chest that was so broad or so full or so deep.
And none found in him aught to blame save this,
but all they that regarded him said that were he not
so full chested, he had been more to be desired and
more pleasing. But she that chose him before all
others, the noble Queen Guinevere, said that God had
not given him a chest beyond measure broad or full
or deep, for even so great and full was the heart
within, and needs must be that it would burst by
reason of its narrow limits, had it not a place wherein
to rest according to its measure. "Not if I were
God," said she, "would I have put in Lancelot either
more or less."

Such were his shoulders and his chest. And his
arms were long and straight, and they were well
supplied by the body beneath, and they were well
garnished with bones and with sinews, but they were
poor in flesh, though in measure. His hands had been
those of a lady, had the fingers been somewhat more
delicate. And for his loins and his hips, they might

not be called better fashioned in any knight. His thighs
and his legs were ſtraight, and his feet were arched,
and no man ever ſtood more erect. And he sang marvellously well when he would, but that was not often,
for none ever so seldom made joy without good reason.
But when he had reason to make joy none might be
so gay or merry that Lancelot was not more so, and
oft when he was joyous he said that whate'er his
heart dared undertake his body might bring it to an
end, so sure was his truſt in the joy that in many a
great emprise gave him the upper hand. And because
he said this so boldly, it was accounted unto him for
ill by many folk who thought that he spake in mockery
or in boaſting. But he did not, for he said it because
of the firm truſt that he had in that wherefrom all
his joy came.

Such were the members of Lancelot and such was
his aspect. And if he were well made of his body and
his form and his limbs, neither had the qualities of
the heart been forgotten in him, for he was the
gentleſt man on earth and the moſt debonair of all
the debonair, but againſt felony he showed him
felonious. And never was there seen a man of such
largesse, for he gave gifts to his comrades as gladly as
they received them. He did honour to the gentle
with so whole a heart that he never turned his thoughts
elsewhere. And never was there beheld so mannerly
a man, for none e'er knew him to show ill semblance,
if he had not good reason and such that he might not
juſtly be blamed therefor. But when he was angered
for that ill had been done him, he might not lightly
be appeased. And he was of such clear wit and such

77

good intent that after he had passed ten years of age he did scarce aught that was not befitting a good child. And if he had the desire to do a deed that seemed to him in his heart to be right, he was not easily to be moved therefrom. And he feared his maſter in naught nor trembled before him.

CHAPTER VII

How Lancelot gave his horse to a fair youth

It befell on a day that Lancelot hunted a roe, and his maſter and his companions with him. And they had ridden so hard that they all began to give over the chase, and Lancelot and his maſter were the better horsed, and they left all the others behind them. And within a while the maſter fell to the ground, horse and man, and the horse brake its neck in twain. The lad regarded him no whit, but he spurred after his prey till that he slew it with a dart on a great highway. And then he alighted down to truss up the roe behind him and the brachet in front, that had followed him all day.

Now while he was on his way back to his comrades, that were sore disquieted for him, he met in his path a man that led a horse weary and spent. And he was a passing fair youth with the firſt down on his cheek. He wore his tunic girt up short about him, a mantle on his shoulder, and his spurs were all red with the blood of the horse that he had sped so faſt that it

could go no further. And he was abashed, and he
held his head bowed down, and he began to weep
right piteously. And the lad waited for him a little
out of the path, and he asked him who he was and
whither he fared in such wise.

And the youth thought within him that this was
a man of great worth, and he said, " Fair sir, God
bless you, but it concerneth you not who I am, for
certes I am poor enough, and still less shall I have
within three days, if God grant me not other counsel
than He hath granted me hitherto. And I have full
oft been more at ease than I am now; and whatever
my chance, either good or ill, hath been, I am of
gentle stock of father's side and of mother's side,
and therefore I grieve the more in my heart for the
mischances that o'ertake me. For if I were a villein,
the more willingly would my heart endure my ills ".

And the lad felt great pity for him, and he said,
" How is it ", said he, " that ye are of gentle birth
and yet weep for any mischance that befalleth you,
save for a friend that ye have lost or for dishonour that
ye may not avenge ? No heart of worship should be
dismayed at aught that may be amended or repaired ".

Now the man wondered within him who this lad
was, that had spoken such noble words and was so
young withal. And he replied, " In sooth, sir,"
said he, " I weep not for the loss of a friend or of land
that I have yielded. But I am summoned on the
morrow to the court of King Claudas to answer a
traitor that short time since killed a valiant knight,
a kinsman of mine, for the sake of his wife. And
when I came on my way, he let lie in wait for me at

a cross roads in a forest, and I was set upon as I passed,
and my horse beneath me was wounded to death.
But even so he bare me to safety. And a good man—
may God bless him!—gave me this horse, but so
hard have I pressed him to escape from death that
scant need now hath he of me or of any other man.[1]
And I make dole for my friends that I have lost there
where I was assailed, that were slain or wounded.
And on the other hand I am passing heavy for that
I shall not be in time on my day, for if I might be
there, I should solace my heart by maintaining the
cause wherefrom a part of my grief justly ariseth.
And now I shall remain dishonoured by reason of
my tarrying".

"Now tell me," said the boy, " if ye had a good
horse, might ye be there in time ? "

"Certes, sir," said he, " yea, very well, even if I
should go the third part of the way afoot."

"Then, before God," said the lad, " ye shall not
be dishonoured, neither ye nor any other gentleman,
for lack of a horse that I may give you, so long as I
have one."

Then he alighted down, and he gave the other his
horse, and he mounted upon the horse that the other
had led, and he trussed up his venison behind him,
and he went to the brachet and put it in the saddle
and took it away with him. And when he had gone
a little way, he must needs alight, for the horse was
in too great pain to go farther. And he alighted
down, and he drave it before him.

CHAPTER VIII

How Lancelot gave his venison to an aged vavasour

Now ere Lancelot had gone far he met a vavasour mounted on a fair palfrey, with a ſtaff in his hand, and he had with him two hounds and a brachet. The vavasour was a man of years, and the lad so soon as he saw him gave him greeting, and he answered, " God reward you ". And then he asked the lad whence he was, and he said that he was from the other country yonder.

" Certes," said the vavasour, " whoe'er ye be, ye are fair and well mannered. And whence have ye come, my child ? "

" Sir," said he, " from the chase, as ye may see here, and I have taken this venison, and ye shall have it, if ye will deign take it, for methinketh that with you it would be well employed."

" Gramercy, dear child," said the vavasour, " I will not refuse it, for I ween that ye have offered it to me from a good heart that is kind and debonair, and me seemeth that ye are of as good and gentle lineage as ye are of gentle heart. And I ſtand in need of the venison, for today I have given my daughter in marriage, and I have even now been on hunting to take something wherewith to make good cheer for them that are at the wedding. But I have failed to take aught."

The vavasour alighted down, and he took the venison, and he asked the lad what part thereof he should carry away. " Sir," said the lad, " are ye a

81

knight ? " And he said that he was. " Then shall
ye carry away all, for never might I better employ it
than for the wedding of the daughter of a knight."

When that the vavasour heard him, he was right
glad, and he took the roe, and he trussed it up behind
him. And heartily he begged the boy to lodge with
him that he might give him of his venison and other
gear. But the lad said that he would not lodge with
him. " For my fellowship is not far from here," said
he. " And I commend you to God's keeping."

Forthright the vavasour parted from him, and he
fell to thinking on the child, who he might be, and
to whom he was like, but he knew not, and as he rode
he pondered thereon. And he said that him seemed
that he was more like to King Ban of Benoich than to
any other man. Then he struck the horse with his
spurs, and he rode back at a great pace after the boy
till that he overtook him, for he rode slowly, and he had
but even now mounted on his horse, that was lightened
of the roe that had been taken from him.

And the vavasour said to him, " Fair, sweet lad,
would ye tell me who ye are ? "

And he replied that he would by no means. " And
what have ye to do with that ? "

" In sooth," said he, " ye seem to me an ancient
lord of mine, that was a man of great worship. And if
ye had need of me, I would put in jeopardy my land
and my life, both I and at least fifty other knights
that are two leagues hence."

" Who was the man of worship that I am like unto ? "
said the lad.

And the vavasour answered, " Certes," said he,

" he was King Ban of Benoich, and all this land was his. And he was wrongfully deprived of his inheritance, and his son, that was the fairest child in the world, was lost ".

" And who deprived him of his land, fair friend ? " said the lad.

" Certes, sir," said he, " a mighty and puissant king, that was named King Claudas of the Desert Land, that marched with this realm. And if ye are his son, in God's name tell me, for I should have great joy thereat."

"Never the son of a king was I," said the lad, " albeit folk have said many a time that I was. And for all that ye tell me I love you the more, for ye speak as a loyal liegeman."

Then the vavasour saw that he could draw no more forth from him, yet he could not leave thinking on the matter in his heart, and he believed in truth that the child was the son of his lord, and he said to him, " Fair, sweet sir, whoever ye are, both by your form and by your face ye seem indeed to be of high lineage. And see here are two of the best hounds in the world. I prithee take one of them, and may God speed you and grant you increase, and may He guard our young lord, if so be that he is alive, and may He have mercy on the soul of his father that begat him ".

When the lad heard him speak of the excellence of the hounds, he made great joy thereat, and he said that he would not refuse the dog, for he would fain reward him well therefor, if so be that in time he might. " But give me the better of the two," said he. And the vavasour gave it to him by the chain, that was full slender. And he looked at it, and forthright they commended each the other to God, and one went in one way and the other in another. And ever the vavasour thought on the child.

CHAPTER IX

How Lancelot was angered against his master, and how the Lady of the Lake pardoned him his wrath

Now within a while the lad met his master and some of his companions, that went seeking him, and there were four of them. And they marvelled greatly when they saw him on his lean horse with the two dogs on the leash, his bow on his shoulder, and his quiver at his belt. And he had pricked the horse with his spurs so that the blood ran down its haunches. Then his master asked him what he had done with his horse. And he said that he had lost it.

" And this one," said he, " where came ye by it ? "

" It was given me," said he.

But his master believed him not, but conjured him by the faith that he owed his lady to say what he had done with the other. And the lad, who would not perjure him, told the truth about the horse and about the roe that he had given to the vavasour.

" What," said his master, that would show his rule over him, " then for your own pleasure without my leave ye have given away your horse, and there was

Lancelot striking his master

none other such under heaven, and the venison that was my lady's."

And the master sprang forward and threatened him. And the lad said, " Master, be not angered, for this hound that I have won is worth two such horses as he was ".

" By the Holy Rood," said the master, " 't was in an evil hour that ye thought on doing it. Never again will ye commit such folly, when ye have escaped from this."

Right so he raised his hand, and he smote him such a buffet that he felled him from the horse to the ground. And the lad neither wept nor cried out for the blow that he had had, and ever he said that the hound pleased him more than two such horses. When the master heard him speak again contrary to his will, he raised a slender stick, and he struck the hound on the flank, and the stick was slender and cutting, and the tender hound cried out piteously.

Then was the lad passing wroth, and he left both the dogs, and he snatched his bow from his shoulders, and he grasped it in both hands, and he came toward his master in wrath. And when his master saw him come, he thought to throw his arms about him and to hold him. And the lad was swift and nimble, and he sprang to the other side and struck the master with the sharp edge of his bow on his uncovered head so hard that it cut through the hair and the skin and the flesh withal even to the bone, and he gave him such a stroke that he felled him down to the earth. And his bow was all shivered. And when he saw that his bow was broken, he was wroth beyond measure,

and he swore that ill should betide the mafter for
that he had broken his bow for him. Then he returned
and smote him again on the head and the arms and
the body so that naught remained of the bow wherewith he might deal a stroke, for it was all shivered to
bits. Then the three other lads ran to take him, and
when he had naught wherewith he might defend him,
he drew his arrows from out his quiver, and he hurled
them, and he sought to slay all the others. And they
piked them away as beft they might. And the mafter
fled, and he hied him afoot to that part of the
foreft where he saw that it was the thickeft.

And the lad took from his attendant the horse
wherefrom he had smitten down his mafter, and he
mounted thereon, and thus he rode away with his
dogs, trussed up, one before, the other behind, till
that he came to a deep valley, and there he espied
a great herd of does feeding. And he raised his
hands and thought to take his bow, for him seemed
that it ftill hung on his shoulder. When he remembered that he had broken it in ftriking his mafter, he
was so wroth that he was well nigh out of his wits.
And he swore within him that an he could find
his master, he should pay dear for it, for by him
he had loft one of the does. " For I could not have
failed to take one," said he, " for I had the beft hound
in the world and the beft brachet."

Thus he went on his way in great wrath till that
he came to the lake, and he entered through the gate
into the court. Then he alighted down from his
horse, and he took his hound to the Lady to show it
to her, for it was fair. And when he came before

86

her, he found his master there all blood-besmirched, and he had already made his plaint. And the lad greeted his Lady, and she gave him greeting as she that loved him even as no heart of woman may more love a child that is of its own flesh. But she made semblance that she was passing wroth, and she said, " Fair Son of a King, why have ye wrought such outrage, ye that have smitten and wounded him that I had given you to instruct you and to be your master ? "

" In sooth, Lady," said he, " he was neither my master nor my instructor when he smote me for that I had done naught save good, and I care not for the buffet that he dealt me. But for that I loved my hound here, that is one of the best on earth, he gave him such a blow that but a little and he had killed him before my eyes. And he hath done me another greater wrong, for he hath not suffered me to slay one of the fairest does that I have e'er seen or hope to see on earth."

Then he told her how he had given away his horse for the hound, and how he had found the does, and how he would have slain them, if he had had his bow. " And wit ye well, Lady," said he, " that never shall I come to a place where he is that he will molest me." When the Lady heard him speak so proudly, she was right glad thereat, for well she saw that he could not fail to become a man of worship with the help of God and with her own, which she deemed of great avail. And none the less she made semblance that she was angered. And when he saw her thus, he left her in wrath, and he uttered great threats upon him that had made her so wroth with him.

And she called him back, and she said, "How is this ? " said she, " are ye so bold that ye give away your horse and that which belongeth to me, and ſtrike your maſter that I have placed over you to keep you from folly and to teach you to do well ? Neither of these two deeds would I have you do".

"Lady," said he, " I muſt needs reſtrain me so long as I would remain in your power and under the tutelage befitting a child. And when I would no longer abide thus, I shall go there where I would be, and I shall purvey me of that whereof I have need. But before I go, I would have you know that the heart of a man that bideth over long under maſter may never attain greatness, for it muſt needs often tremble. And as for me, I care no more to have a maſter ; I speak not of lord or lady. But evil be found the son of a king, if he dare not give freely of that which belongeth to another, when he giveth boldly of his own."

" What," said the Lady, " think ye then that ye are the son of a king, for that I call you thus ? "

" Lady," said he, " son of a king am I called, and for the son of a king have I been held."

" Now, wit ye well," said she, " that he knew you ill who held you for the son of a king, for that ye are not."

" Lady," said he sighing, " that irketh me, for my heart would dare be it."

And forthright he turned him away, so sore vexed that he could neither speak nor utter a single word.

Then the Lady sprang up, and she took him by the hand and led him back, and she began to kiss him on the eyes and the mouth right gently in such wise that whoe'er saw her would have deemed that he was her child. And then she said, "Fair son, be not disquieted. For, so help me God, I will that ye give horses and other gear, and that ye shall still have enough to boot. And were ye at the age of forty years, ye would have done well in that ye gave away the horse and the venison. And from henceforth I will that ye be your own lord and master, since that ye know well of your own knowledge that which it is seemly and fitting for a good lad to do. And whosoever ye are, ye have not lacked the heart of the son of a king and of such a one as from prowess of heart and body would dare assail the most mighty king in the world".

Thus the Lady of the Lake comforted Lancelot and reassured him, even as the story recounteth the adventure, only for the sake of the noble words that he had spoken.

CHAPTER X

How Lancelot desired to be made knight of King Arthur, and how the Lady of the Lake devised to him the emprise of knighthood

The Lady of the Lake is troubled at the fate of Lionel and Bors, and resolves to take them out of the hands of Claudas. She accordingly sends one of her most trusted maidens, Saraide by name, to Gannes, charging her to bring the children back to the lake with her.

On the anniversary of his coronation Claudas is sitting at dinner with his barons and his son, Dorin, when Saraide appears before him, and greeting him from her Lady, pleads so convincingly for better treatment of the sons of King Bors that Claudas gives orders to his seneschal that the children be brought to court from the tower where he has kept them in confinement. They in the meantime have learned their own history, and Lionel has vowed vengeance upon Claudas. When they come before the king, Saraide crowns them with enchanted wreaths and hangs enchanted chains about their necks, which fill them with frenzy and also make them invulnerable. Lionel at once strikes Claudas, and in the fray that immediately follows, he and Bors kill Dorin. Saraide instantly further protects them by changing them to greyhounds, and when Claudas still tries to kill them, she saves them by flinging herself between them and the sword of the king, from which she receives a wound in her cheek. She succeeds, however, in effecting the escape of the children in the semblance of hounds. When they have reached a place of safety, Saraide breaks the spell that she has cast and restores them to their proper form.

They ride on to the lake, where the Lady joyously awaits them. She gives Lancelot to understand that Lionel and Bors are her nephews. "Right well Lancelot loved the company of the two children, and whether it were by nature, or by the grace that God had given them, or for that he believed them to be the nephews of the Lady, his heart drew him more to them than to any of the others. And he held all the others for his servitors, but these twain for his boon companions. And from the first day they ate but from one bowl, and they all three lay on one couch. Thus bided the three cousins germain in the keeping of the Lady of the Lake."

IN this place the story saith that Lancelot was in the keeping of the Lady of the Lake till that he reached the age of eighteen years. And he was so fair a youth that none might seek a fairer in all the world, and he was so discreet that none might rightly blame or reproach him for aught in whatever he did. When he was of the age of eighteen years he was marvellously big and strong. And the Lady that nurtured him

Lionel and Bors as fairy hounds

Lancelot and his cousins

[*face p.* 90

was ware that it was full time and season that he should
receive the order of knighthood, and that if she should
longer delay, it would be a sin and a shame. For well
she knew by his fate, the which she had many a time
caſt, that he would yet come to great worship. And
if she might ſtill have hindered him that he should
not take the order of knighthood, she had done it
right willingly, for with full great grief would she
part from him. For all the love that springeth from
pity and from foſtering care she had set upon him.
But if she kept him from knighthood after the proper
age, she would commit a mortal sin as great as treason,
for she would deprive him of that which he could
not lightly recover.

Now a little after Pentecoſt, when he came to the
age of eighteen years, he went into the foreſt, and he
came upon a ſtag so large that never in his life had
he seen a larger, and that he might show the marvel he
drew his bow and killed it. When he had slain it,
he found that it was as fat as if the month were Auguſt,
and all his companions held it for a great wonder.
He sent the ſtag to his Lady by two varlets, and she
marvelled how it might be so fat in that season, and
at its size she wondered greatly.[1]

The ſtag was held for a great marvel, and the Lady
took pleasure therein. And Lancelot went back to
the foreſt with his companions, and he lay long beneath
an oak tree in the green grass, for the weather was
exceeding hot. And when that the heat grew less,
he mounted on his horse, and he rode back to the lake.
And well he seemed a foreſter and a man that came
from without, for he wore a foreſt coat that was over

short and green in colour, a chaplet of leaves was on
his head for the heat, and his quiver hung at his belt,
for he was never without it, wheresoever he might
go. But one of the varlets carried his bow for him.
And he drew nigh to the hostel, and he rode on his
horse straight and well set in his stirrups.

He came to the court of the Lady, who awaited
him. And when she saw him, the tears mounted to
her eyes from her heart. She arose from her place,
for she bided not for him, and she entered into the
great hall, and she leaned against the wall at the end
thereof and stood long in thought. And Lancelot
followed her, and so soon as she saw him, she betook
her to a chamber. And he saw her go and he marvelled
what might ail her, and he went after her, and he
found her in her largest chamber lying prone on a
great couch. In haste he went to her, and he saw
that she groaned and wept heavily. He greeted her,
but she said not a word nor looked at him, and he
marvelled greatly, for he had learned that she hasted to
meet him and to kiss and embrace him from wheresoever he came.

Then he said, " Ah, Lady, tell me what aileth you,
and if any man hath vexed you, conceal it not from
me. For I would not believe that any man would
dare vex you while I am alive ".

When that she heard him, she wept and wailed
aloud, and was in such sorrow that not a word could
she utter with her lips, for her sobs broke her speech.
But within a while she said so that he heard her
plainly, " Ah, Son of a King, begone from here, or
my heart will break in my breast ".

"Lady," said he, "liefer would I go ; ill ſtaying have I here, since I have vexed you sore."

Forthwith he turned him away, and he came to his bow, and he took it and hung it on his shoulder, and he girt his quiver on again, and he went to his horse, and he put the bridle on him and led him into the court. But she that loved him above all else thought that she had spoken overmuch, and that he went away in wrath. And she knew him for so proud and so orgulous that he valued naught in comparison with his heart.

The Lady sprang up, and she dried her face and her eyes, that were red and swollen, and she went speedily into the court, and she saw the lad, that would mount on his horse, and well it seemed that he was wroth. She sprang before him, and she ſtood at his bridle, and she said, "How is this, sir vassal, where would ye go ? "

"Lady," said he, "I would go into the foreſt."

"Alight down speedily," said she, "for now ye shall not go."

And he alighted down, and she took his horse, and she let ſtable it, and then she led Lancelot by the hand to her chamber, and she seated her again on her couch, and she bade him sit beside her. And she conjured him by the great faith that he owed her forthright to tell her without falsehood whither he would go.

"Lady," said he, "methought that ye were angered with me, when ye would not speak to me, and since I ſtood ill with you, I had no wish to bide here."

"What then would ye do, fair Son of a King ? "

"What, Lady?" said he. "In faith, I would have gone thither where I might purvey for myself."

"Now by the faith that ye owe me, to what place would ye have gone?"

"Where, Lady?" said he. "I would have gone to the household of King Arthur, and there would I have served some man of worship till that he made me knight. For folk say that all the men of worship are in the household of King Arthur."

"How is this, fair Son of a King?" said she. "Then would ye be dubbed knight? Tell me."

"Certes, Lady," said he, "there is naught in the world that I more long for than the order of knighthood."

"That I understand," said she, "if ye should dare take it upon you. Me seemeth that, an ye knew how great is the emprise of knighthood, never would ye desire to charge you therewith."

"Why, Lady?" said he. "Are all knights of greater strength of body and of limb than other men?"

"Nay, Son of a King," said she, "but a knight must needs have that within him that other men need not have. And if ye should but hear it described, your heart, be it never so bold, would in sooth tremble thereat."

"Lady," said he, "are those qualities that beseem a knight to be found in either the heart or the body of any man?"

"Yea," said the Lady, "right well. For the Lord God hath made some men more valiant than others and more full of worship and more gracious."

"Lady," said he, "then he must in truth be a

caitiff and devoid of all good taches who through fear
withholdeth him from the order of knighthood. For
every man should seek each day to grow ſtronger and
better in good taches, and much should he hate
himself who through indolence loseth that which
every man might have, to wit, the virtues of the heart,
that are an hundred fold more lightly to be had
than those of the body."

"What difference", said the Lady, "is there
between the virtues of the heart and those of the
body ? "

"Lady," said he, "I will tell you what I think
thereon. Me seemeth that a man may have the
virtues of the heart who may not have those of the
body, for he may be courteous and discreet and
debonair and loyal, valiant and bounteous and bold—
and all these are virtues of the heart,—who may not
be big and ſtrong and wight and fair and well beseen.
And all these qualities, methinketh, are virtues of
the body, and I ween that a man bringeth them with
him from his mother's womb in the hour when he
is born. But the qualities of the heart, methinketh,
each man may have, if so be that indolence deprive
him not of them. For every man may have courtesy
and graciousness and the other excellencies that come,
me seemeth, from the heart, and therefore I think
that a man faileth to win worship only through indolence. For oft-times I have heard you say that naught
maketh a man of worship save the heart only. Yet
if ye set forth to me how great a charge is chivalry
so that none may be so hardy as to become a knight,
I will hearken gladly."

"I will set forth to you the duties of a knight,"¹ said the Lady, "so far as I know them, but not all, for I have not wit enough. And none the less hearken well when ye listen to them, and give your heart and reason thereto with loyalty, for since that ye have the desire to be a knight, ye should not so urge on your desire that ye first regard not reason. For reason and understanding were given to man that he might regard that which is right before he undertake to do aught. And wit ye well that knights were not made and created for a jest, or because at the beginning one man was more gentle or of higher lineage than another, for all men are descended from one father and one mother. But at the time when envy and covetousness began to increase in the world and might began to conquer right, one man and another were equal in lineage and in gentleness. And when the weak might no longer suffer the strong or endure against them, then were there established over them guardians and defenders to protect the weak and the peaceable, and to maintain justice, and to thrust back the strong from the wrongs and outrages that they committed.

"And to take upon them this defence there were appointed those that were the most worthy in the eyes of the assembly of the people, and these were the big and the strong and the fair and the nimble and the loyal and the valiant and the hardy, they that were full of the virtues of the heart and of the body. But knighthood was not given them as a jest or for naught, but many great charges were laid upon them. Now wit ye well what these were. At the beginning when the order of knighthood was first established, it was ordained that he that would be made knight and that had been rightfully chosen thereto, should be courteous without villeiny, debonair without felony, pitiful toward the suffering, and bountiful of his gifts, prepared to confound robbers and murderers, a just judge without love and without hate, and without desire to favour injustice at the expense of righteousness. A knight from fear of death should do naught wherein dishonour may be seen or perceived, but he should fear dishonour more than the pains of death. Moreover the knight was created to protect Holy Church, for she may not further her by means of arms, or render evil for evil. And therefore was the knight created that he might protect her that turneth the left cheek, when she hath been smitten on the right. And wit ye well that at the beginning, even as it is written, none was so hardy that he mounted on a horse, if he were not already a knight. And for this reason were knights called horsemen, or *cheval-iers*.[1]

"But the arms that he beareth and that none save he who is knight may bear were not given him without reason, but they have good reason and great significance. The shield that hangeth from his shoulder and wherewith he is covered in front signifieth that even as he placeth it between him and buffetings, so should the knight put him between Holy Church and all evil doers, be they robbers or miscreants. And if Holy Church is assailed or in peril of receiving blows or strokes, the knight should place him before her to endure the stroke even as her son. For she should be

97

defended and protected by her son. For if the mother is buffeted and outraged in the presence of her son, and he avenge her not, his bread should be refused him and his door should be closed.

" And the hauberk wherewith the knight is clothed and protected in all parts signifieth that even so should Holy Church be covered and surrounded by the defence of the knight. For so great should be her defence and so wise her provision that the evil doer may never henceforth come to the door, whereby to enter into or issue forth from Holy Church, that he find not the knight ready and awake to defend her.

" The helmet that the knight hath on his head, that is seen above all his arms, signifieth that even so should the knight be seen before all other folk that go against them that would injure Holy Church or work her ill. And he should be like unto a watchtower, the which is the house of the sentinel, that may be descried from all parts above other houses, for to bring dismay to evil-doers and thieves.

" The lance that the knight carrieth, that is so long that it pricketh an adversary ere he may have at the knight, signifieth that even as dread of the lance, whereof the shaft is strong and the head sharp, leadeth them that are unarmed to spring back for fear of death, so should the knight be so dread and so hardy and so strong that fear of him should speed afar in such wise that no thief and no ill-doer should dare approach Holy Church, but should flee away from fear of him, against whom he may have no more power than he that is unarmed hath against the lance, whereof the head is sharp.

"And the sword that the knight hath girded on is sharp at both edges, but this is not without reason. The sword is of all arms the moſt honoured and the moſt worthy and that which hath the moſt dignity, for therewith may one do threefold harm. He may drive back and kill with the point by ſtabbing, and likewise he may deal a blow with both edges, at the right and at the left. The two edges signify that the knight should be the servant of our Lord and of His people. Therefore one of the edges should smite them that are the enemies of our Lord and that do despite to His faith, and the other should take vengeance on them that do despite to the fellowship of mankind, that is, on them that rob and kill one another. Such power the two blades have, but the point in yet another wise. The point signifieth obedience, for all folk should obey the knight. The point signifieth obedience right well, for it pricketh, and naught, neither loss of lands nor of goods, pricketh the heart so sore as to obey from force and againſt its will. Such is the significance of the sword.

"But the horse, whereon the knight sitteth and that beareth him wheresoever he muſt go, signifieth the people. For even so should they bear the knight in all his needs, and upon them should he be mounted. The people should bear the knight in this wise, for they should seek and purvey for him all whereof he hath need for honourable living, that he may guard and proteċt them both night and day. And upon the people should he be mounted, for even as he who sitteth upon the horse spurreth it and driveth it where he would be, so should the knight drive the

people according to his will and in subjection, for
that he is and should be above them. Thus ye may
see that the knight should be lord of his people and
servant to the Lord God. And he should be lord
of the people in all respects. And he should be the
servant of God, for he should protect and defend
and maintain Holy Church. It is the clergy whereby
Holy Church is served, and by widows and orphans
and by tithes and by alms that are established in Holy
Church. And even as the people maintain the
knight on the earth and purvey to him that whereof
he hath need, so should Holy Church maintain him
spiritually and procure for him the life that will never
end, that is, by orisons and by prayers and by alms,
that God may be his saviour forevermore, even as he
is the protector and the defender of Holy Church
on the earth. Thus all the need that he hath for
worldly goods should fall upon the people, and all
the needs that pertain to the soul should belong to
Holy Church.

"The knight should have two hearts, one hard and
firm as a diamond, the other soft and yielding as
heated wax. That which is hard as diamond he
should turn against the disloyal and the felonious, for
even as the diamond yieldeth to no polishing, so should
the knight be stern and cruel towards felons, that sin
against the right and abuse it as much as in them lieth.
And even as wax that is soft and warm may be moulded
and turned wheresoever one would, so should good
men and compassionate turn the knight towards all
those things that pertain to graciousness and sweetness.
But let him take heed that the heart of wax be not

abandoned to the felonious or the disloyal. For he
would have loſt utterly whatever good he had done
them. And the Scripture telleth us that the judge
condemneth himself when he delivereth from death
and releaseth him that is guilty. And if he showeth
a hard heart of diamond towards the good that need
naught save mercy and pity, then he hath loſt his
own soul. For the Scripture saith that he who loveth
disloyalty and felony hateth his own soul, and God
Himself saith in the Gospel that whatsoever a man hath
done to the needy he hath done it unto Him.

"All these things should he have that dareth become
a knight, and let him that willeth not to do thus,
even as I have devised to you, beware of knighthood.
For when he leaveth the right path, he will forthright
be disgraced firſt in this world and afterwards before
God. He that would be a knight should with his
whole heart be passing pure and discreet, and he that
would not be so, let him keep him from so high a matter
and have naught to do therewith, for better it availeth
a young squire to live without knighthood all his life
than to be dishonoured in this world and loſt to God.
For passing great is the charge of knighthood. Now,
Son of a King," said the Lady, "I have set forth to
you a part of the toils that belong to a loyal knight,
but all I have not told you, for I know them not.
Now, tell me which pleaseth you, the taking or the
leaving of them."

"Lady," said the lad, "since knighthood began
was there ever knight that had all these virtues within
him ? "

"Yea," said she, "many an one, whereof Holy

Scripture beareth witness to us, even before Jesus Christ suffered death."

"Lady," said the youth, "since that there have been so many that were full of all the prowess that ye have set forth to me, then he would be full of villeiny indeed that should refuse and dread to undertake knighthood lest he might not attain to all its virtues. None the less I blame neither these, if they dare not be knights, nor the others, if they dare, for each me seemeth should act according to that which he findeth within his heart, be it villeiny or prowess. But as for me, I know in sooth that if on a day I find him that would fain make me knight, I shall not leave it be through fear that in me knighthood may be misplaced, for God may well have put more goodness in me than I know, and He is powerful enough withal to put within me yet more discretion and valour, if there be need thereof. And howsoever it may befall that I receive the high order of knighthood, I shall by no means leave it be, if I find him that may give me the honour thereof. And if God will put within me the noble taches, it will be a passing great joy to me, but I shall dare give heart and body and toil and labour thereto."

"Then, Son of a King," said the Lady, "is your heart in accord with your will that ye be made a knight ?"

"Lady," said he, "there is naught wherefor I have so great desire, if I find him that will accomplish my will for me."

"Certes," said the Lady, "ye shall be made knight with no long delay. And wit ye well that for this

I wept even now when ye came before me, when I said to you that ye might go even if my heart broke in my breaſt, for I have set on you all the love that a mother may set upon her child.   And I know not how I may e'er endure to be without you, for I shall be heavy at heart.   But I would liefer suffer my great misease than that through me ye should lose the high order of knighthood, and I ween that in you it would be well employed.   And if ye knew who your father was, and from what lineage ye come by your mother, ye would not fear to undertake to become a man of worship, as I think.   For none that was of such lineage would have a heart of villeiny.   But now ye shall hear no more thereof from me until it be my will, nor ask me no more about it, for this is my will.   And ye shall soon be made knight, and at the hand of the moſt worshipful man in the world today, to wit, at the hand of King Arthur.   And we will set out within this week that hath now begun, so that we shall come to him the Friday before the Feaſt of St. John at the lateſt, for the Feaſt of St. John will be on the Sunday thereafter.   And that is but eight days from this Sunday, and I will that ye be made knight on the day of the Feaſt of St. John, and that ye delay no longer. And may God, Who was born of the Virgin to redeem His people, grant you as a gift that even as Messire St. John was in recompense and in desert the greateſt man that was e'er conceived by woman in carnal union, so likewise ye may surpass in excellence and in chivalry all knights that are alive to-day.   And I wit well in great measure how this shall befall you."

CHAPTER XI

*How Lancelot rode with the Lady of the Lake to the
court of King Arthur*

Thus the Lady of the Lake promised the lad that he
should soon be knighted. And he made so great joy
thereat that he could not make greater. "Now,"
said she, "look well that none know aught thereof.
And I will prepare all that ye need so that it shall not
be noted." Right well the Lady made ready for the
lad all that it behoved him to have, for long time
afore she had set apart for him all those things that
were requisite to a knight,—a hauberk, white and
light and strong, a helmet of polished silver, that was
rich and beauteous, and a shield white as a nut with
a right fair buckle of silver. And since she would
that he had naught save that which was white, she
had made ready for him a sword that was well tested
many a time after that he had it and before. And it
was somewhat large, and it was marvellously sharp
and weighed little. And a lance was prepared for
him with a white shaft that was short and thick, and
the blade was white and sharp and keen. And likewise
the Lady had for him a horse that was big and strong
and swift, and well proved in speed and hardihood,
and it was as white as the fresh fallen snow. And she
had made ready for his knighting robes of white
samite, tunic and mantle, and the mantle was lined
with ermine, that he might have naught that was not
white, and the tunic was lined with white sendal.

In such wise the Lady provided for the young squire

all whereof he had need for his knighting. And then she set out on the third day early in the morning, and it was a Tuesday, and from the Sunday thereafter there were eight days to the Feast of St. John. The Lady rode on her way, and she went full well beseen to the court of King Arthur, for she had in her following forty horses, nor was there one that was not white, and they that were mounted upon them were also clad in white. In her retinue there were five knights, and her fair and valiant lover withal. And with the Lady there were three damsels, she that had been wounded for the sake of the children,[1] and two others. And the three were there that it was seemly to take, to wit, Lionel and Bors and Lambegues,[2] and of other young men there were not a few.

They rode until they came to the sea, and they arrived in Great Britain on a Sunday in the evening at the port of Floudehuec. And thence they rode on in accordance with the tidings of King Arthur. And it was told them that the king would be at Camelot for the Feast. And they followed the road till that they came on Thursday in the evening to a castle that was called Lawenor, and it is twenty-two English miles from Camelot. And on the morrow the Lady rose betimes to go on her way in the morning, since the heat was great, and she rode through the forest, that stretched to within two English miles from Camelot. And she was wonderly sad and downcast, for heavily it weighed on her that the young squire would leave her, and she sighed from her heart and wept tenderly. But now the story leaveth speaking of her for a little and speaketh of King Arthur.

CHAPTER XII

*How the Lady of the Lake brought Lancelot to King
Arthur that he should be made knight*

On the Friday morning before the Feast of St. John, King
Arthur, who intends to hold a large court at Camelot for the
festival, goes out to the forest with a few knights to hunt. On his
way he meets coming towards him two palfreys bearing on a litter
a wounded knight, in whose side the truncheons of two lances
remain, while half a sword projects from a wound in his head.
He begs Arthur to draw the weapons from his wounds, but he
adds that, although he has killed the knight who wounded him,
he can be freed of the weapons only by him who will swear to
avenge him on all them who say that they love his assailant
better than they love him. Arthur declares that the condition
is unreasonable, for nobody knows how numerous the friends
of the dead knight are ; but since the knight refuses to believe
that, considering the reputed prowess of Arthur's court, he will
be refused all succour, Arthur grants him permission to remain
in the palace as long as he chooses, and has a couch laid for him
in the upper hall. But the companions of the Round Table
agree that it would be folly for any knight to undertake the
adventure.

THE king was in the forest all day, and he hunted until it
drew toward evensong, and then he turned homeward.
And when he came to the road without the forest,
he looked to the right, and he was ware of the route
of the Lady of the Lake that came toward him. And
he saw at the head thereof a boy afoot that led two
sumpter-beasts all white. On one of the two sumpter-
beasts there was trussed up a little light pavilion,
one of the goodliest and the richest that hath e'er
been seen, and upon the other was the robe for the
young squire, wherein he should be made knight, and
another robe wherewith to adorn him, and another

wherein to ride, and they were in two coffers, and on the two coffers there was a white hauberk and greaves of iron. After the sumpter-beasts came two squires on two horses all white, and one bore a shield as white as any nut, and the other bore a helmet that was seemly and well fashioned. After these two there came other two, whereof one carried a lance all white, and the girdles of the sword that was hung from his shoulder were all white, and the scabbard thereof was all white ; and the other led by his right hand a horse that was of great beauty and as white as a nut. After them came servitors and squires in great numbers, and the three maidens thereafter, and the knights beside them, the which all rode white horses, and all that were in the calvacade rode two by two along the road. But the Lady came last, she and her young squire, and she taught and instructed him how he should bear him at the court of King Arthur and at the other courts whither he should go. And she commanded him that, as he held her love dear, he should be made knight without fail on the Sunday, for thus she willed it, and if he were not, great ill would betide him therefor. And he replied that never would he delay, for he would even now be a knight, if he had his will.

So talking they rode on till that the cavalcade drew nigh that of the king. And the king and all his following marvelled as they looked upon them, for that they were all clothed in white and rode white horses. And the king showed them to Sir Gawain, and he said that never had he beheld a route of folk that were so well beseen. The word came to the

Lady that this was King Arthur, and she haſtened her pace, and she passed before all the company with the young squire, and thus she came before the king who awaited her ; for so soon as he saw her haſten, he came to meet her, for well he thought within him that she would fain speak with him.

The Lady was richly dight, for she wore a marvellous tunic of pure white samite and a mantle lined with ermine, and she was mounted on a shapely palfrey that was more beauteous than tongue can tell. The palfrey was good and fair, and the bridle was of silver, fine and pure, and so also was the breaſtplate and the ſtirrups, and the saddle was of ivory, wherein figures of ladies and knights were wrought. And the housings were all white, and they hung in folds to the ground, and they were made of the samite wherewith the Lady was clad. Such was the array of the Lady and of her palfrey, and in such wise she came before the king. And the young squire wore a Breton mantle that was rich and became him well, and he was mounted on a big and fleet courser, that bore him swiftly. The Lady lowered her wimple from before her face, when she came before the king, but not so soon that he had not firſt greeted her, and she him.

" Sire," said she, " God bless you, as the beſt of all earthly kings. King Arthur," said she, " I have come to you from afar, and I have come to require of you a gift, the which ye shall not refuse me, for ye may not have hurt or shame or ill therefrom, nor shall it coſt you aught of your subſtance."

" Damsel," said the king, " though it coſt me much, if it brought neither shame to me nor hurt to my friends, ye should surely have it. But ask me it boldly, for the gift would be passing great that I would refuse you."

"Gramercy, Sire," said she. "Now I ask you that ye make this my young squire here knight with such arms as he may have at such time as he would be knighted."

"Damsel," said the king, "ye are right welcome here. Gramercy for that ye have brought him to me, for he is a passing fair young man, and I will gladly make him knight at whatsoever time he may wish. But ye pledged me that ye would ask no gift wherefrom I should have shame, yet if I did this that ye ask of me, I should have shame. For it is not my custom to make any man knight if he wear not my arms. But leave the young man with me, for I will gladly make him knight, for I will give him that which it is mine to give, to wit, the arms and the accolade, and God will give the remainder, that is, the prowess and the noble taches that a knight should have."

"Sire," said she, "it may well be that ye have not been wont to dub knight any save those of your own court, for haply none hath asked it of you, but if it be asked of you and ye do it, ye are not shamed thereby, me seemeth. But know that this young squire may not be made knight in other arms or other robes than those that are here. And if ye will, do ye make him knight, and if ye will not, I shall seek elsewhere. And I had liefer dub him myself than that he should not be made knight."

"Sire," said Sir Gawain, "refuse not to make him knight, even as the Lady asketh. And even if in so

doing ye do ill, ye muſt not let go so fair a young
squire. For never, as I remember, have I seen one
so fair."

Thereupon the king granted the Lady her will,
and she thanked him right heartily. And she gave
the young squire the two sumpters and two of the
goodlieſt palfreys in the world, that were all white.
And likewise she gave him four worthy and valiant
squires to serve him withal.

Forthright the Lady took leave of the king, but
he prayed her to abide ; but she said that might in
no wise be.

"Lady," said the king, "it irketh me sore that ye
will not remain. But, an it pleaseth you, tell me
who ye are, for I would fain know."

"Sire," said she, "from a man of worship, even
as ye are, I may not conceal my name. I tell you that
folk call me the Lady of the Lake."

At this name the king marvelled greatly, for he had
never heard thereof. Right so the Lady departed
from him, and the young squire went with her for
half a bowshot. And she said to him :—

"Fair Son of a King, ye will go your way, but I will
that ye know that ye are not my son, but ye were the
son of one of the moſt worshipful men in the world
and peerless among knights, and of one of the beſt
ladies and the gentleſt that I have ever seen. But
ye may not learn yet the truth about your father or
your mother ; howbeit ye shall know it ere long. And
give heed that ye are as fair of heart as ye are of form
and limb. For of beauty have ye as much as God may
beſtow upon a child, and 't will be great shame if

prowess doth not ally itself to beauty. And see that
on the morrow in the evening ye require of the king
that he make you knight, and when that ye have been
knighted, rest not thereafter in his household a single
night, but go throughout the land seeking adventures
and marvels, for thus may ye win good fame and
renomee. And abide in no place beyond the least
time that ye may, but see that ye do so much that
none may assay feats of chivalry where ye have left
them undone. And if the king ask you who ye are and
how ye are called, and who I am, tell him once for
all that ye know naught save that I am a lady that
hath fostered you. And I have likewise forbidden
your squires to tell aught. But before I leave you
I will tell you this much, that I would fain have you
know that these two sons of a king that have been with
you are no less gentle than ye, and they twain are your
cousins germain. And for that I have set upon you
all the love that may come in nurturing a child, I
shall keep them with me so long as I may in remembrance of you. And when it is fitting that Lionel
shall be made knight, then Bors will be left me."

When Lancelot heard that the two children were
his cousins, he made marvellous great joy, and he
said to the Lady, "Ah, Lady, how well have ye done
in that ye have told me this! For now am I more at
ease both for your comfort and from my joy".

Then the Lady drew from her finger a ring, and
she put it upon the finger of the young squire, and
she told him that it had virtue to undo all enchantments. Thereupon she commended him to God, and
she said, " Fair Son of a King, this much I will teach

III

you ere I part from you, that when ye shall have
accomplished perilous adventures, the more lightly
will ye be able to accomplish others. For where ye
fail to achieve adventures by the prowess that God
hath put within you, he is not yet born that will
bring them to an end. Much would I tell you, but
I may not, for my heart is too heavy within me, and
words fail me. But now go from me, fair Son of a
King, and God grant you grace that ye be beloved of
all folk and that ye be a good knight. And such, I
wit well, ye will be ".

Thereupon she kissed his mouth and his eyes, and
she turned away making more sorrow than may be
told. And the young squire was moved to great
pity, and the tears came to his eyes, and he ran to his
two cousins, and he kissed first Lionel and then Bors.
And he said to Lionel, " Be not dismayed if Claudas
hath your land in his power, for ye shall have more
friends to recover it withal than ye think ". Thereafter he kissed all the others, each in turn, and then
he rode back at a great gallop, and he joined again
the king and his fellowship, that were awaiting him
to see him. And the king took him by the chin, and
he saw that he was so fair and so well made in all
points that there was naught to amend. And Sir
Ewaine said, " Sire, look at him well, for ye have
never seen so well visaged a man or young squire.
God hath not been unkind to him, if He hath given
him noble taches in as full measure as He hath given
him beauty ".

CHAPTER XIII

How Lancelot saw the Queen, and how she spake with him

Now both Sir Gawain and the others said so much that the young squire stood all abashed thereat, and the king regarded him well, but he would ask naught of him till another time. Thereupon he said to Sir Ewaine, "I commit the young squire to you to keep and to teach the best that ye can, and ye will know how he should demean him". Then he gave him the young man by the hand, and Sir Ewaine thanked him. Right so they came to Camelot, and the press was so great about the young squire for to see him that one could scarce step for the throng. And he alighted down from his horse at the lodging of Sir Ewaine, and all his following with him. And all they that saw him said that never had they seen so fair a youth.

When the Saturday came, in the evening the young squire went to Sir Ewaine, and he said to him, "Sir, say to my lord the king that he make me knight on the morrow, even as he promised my Lady, for I would be a knight".

"Fair, sweet friend," said Sir Ewaine, "would ye be knight so soon?"

And he said, "Yea".

"How now," said Sir Ewaine, "would ye not do better to wait till ye have learned more of arms?"

"Sir," said the young man, "I would be a squire no longer, but I pray you to say to my lord the king that he make me knight on the morrow without fail."

8

" Certes," said Sir Ewaine, " I will do it with a good will."

Right so he went to the king, and he said to him, " Sire, your young squire requireth you that ye make him knight on the morrow ".

" Which young squire ? " said the king.

" Sire, the squire that was brought to you yester-evening, that ye committed to my keeping."

As they spake thus, the queen passed through the hall, and beside her was Sir Gawain. And the king looked upon Sir Ewaine, and he said to him, " Ye speak of the young squire that the Lady of the Lake brought to me, that wore the white robe ? "

" Yea, sire, in sooth, I speak of him."

" What," said the king, "would he so soon be made knight ? "

" In sooth, on the morrow."

" Hear ye, Gawain," said the king " of your squire of yestere'en, that would already be made knight ? "

" Certes," said Sir Gawain, " he is right, and I trow that in him knighthood would be well employed, for he is gentle, and he seemeth, in sooth, to be of gentle blood and of high lineage."

" Who is this young man ? " said the queen.

" Lady," said Sir Ewaine, " he is the fairest young squire that ye have ever beheld."

Then he told her how the squire had been led to the king on the day before, and how the lady that had led him had come richly dight.

" What," said the queen, " came he to court but yesterday, and would he be made knight on the morrow ? "

" Even so, lady," said the king.

" He hath overmuch desire thereto," said she, " and I would fain see him."

" I' faith," said the king, " ye will see in him the fairest squire that ye have ever beheld."

Then he bade Sir Ewaine fetch the young man. " And let array him so richly as ye know how, and I trow that he hath gear enough." Thereupon the king told him how the Lady of the Lake had required of him that the youth should not be made knight save in his own arms and his own robes. And the queen marvelled greatly thereat, and she was passing desirous to see him. Sir Ewaine went to the young man, and he let adorn him as best he might, and he led him to court on his own horse, that was good. But he led him privily, for there were so many folk about him that the road was full. And the news was brought to the hall that the fair young squire had come to court, and that he would be made knight on the morrow. Forthwith the people of the town ran to the windows, and when they saw him, they said that they had never seen so goodly a young squire. He came to the court, and he alighted down from his horse, and the news of him spread throughout the hall and the chambers, and knights and ladies and maidens hastened forth, and the king and the queen came to the windows.

When that the young squire was alighted down, then Sir Ewaine took him by the hand and led him into the hall above. The king and the queen came to meet him, and they took him each by the hand, and they went to seat them on a couch, and the young bachelor sat before them on the green rushes wherewith the hall was beſtrewn. And the king looked gladly upon him, and if he had seemed fair to him when he came, it was naught in comparison with the beauty that he now had, and it seemed to the king that he had waxed bigger and ſtronger. And the queen said, " God make him a man of worship, for He hath given him plenteously of beauty ". And right fixedly she looked upon the young squire, and he upon her, whensoever he might turn his eyes toward her covertly. And he marvelled greatly whence so great beauty might come as he saw in her, for not the beauty of his Lady of the Lake or that of any other lady that he had ever seen had aught of value for him beside hers. And he was not wrong if he prized her highly, for she was the lady of ladies and the fountain of all beauty. But had he known the great noblesse that was in her, he would have eſteemed her yet more, for none, neither poor nor rich, was of her noblesse.

The queen asked Sir Ewaine what this young squire was called, and he answered that he knew not.

" And know ye ", said she, " of whom he was born ? "

" Lady, nay," said he, " I know only that he is from the land of France, for he speaketh the language thereof."

Then the queen took him by the hand, and she asked him whence he was. And when he felt her touch him, he trembled even as if he awoke from sleep, and he so set his thought upon her that he knew not what she had said to him. And she saw that he was abashed, and she asked him a second time, " Tell me," said she, " whence ye are." And he made answer, sighing, that he knew not.

And then the queen perceived that he was abashed and full of thought, but she ne'er believed that it was for her sake, and none the less she suspected it somewhat, and she left him be. And for that she would not put him to greater thought, she rose from her place, for she would not that any should think evil or perceive that which she suspected. And she said that this young squire seemed to her little discreet. "And whether he be wise or foolish, he hath not been well bred."

"Lady," said Sir Ewaine, "we know not, you and I, how it is with him ; perchance he is forbidden to tell his name."

And she said that it might well be. And this was said so softly that the young squire heard it not.

When it drew to evensong Sir Ewaine led his young squire forth. And the king and the queen and the knights and sergeants went behind the hall to a fair garden that adjoined the dwelling of the king. And Sir Ewaine led his squire here also, and after them came a great company of squires that would be made knights on the morrow.

CHAPTER XIV

How Lancelot was knighted, and how he freed a wounded knight from the weapons in his wounds

On their way back from the garden to the palace for supper Lancelot and Sir Ewaine pass through the hall where the knight who has the weapons in his wounds is lying. Lancelot immediately inquires who he is, and on hearing his story, at once goes to him and offers to free him from the weapons. Sir Ewaine

interferes, telling him of the conditions of the adventure, and
reminding him that he is not yet a knight hurries him away.
Lancelot in spite of his eagerness dares say no more.

FORTHRIGHT Sir Ewaine led the young squire into
the hall where the tables were ready, and they sat at
meat. After that they had eaten, Sir Ewaine took
the young squire to his lodging, and at nightfall he
led him to a minster, where he watched all night.
And Sir Ewaine ne'er left him. In the morning he
led the young squire to his lodgings, and he took care
that he slept until the high mass, and then he led him
to the minster with the king. For it was the custom
of the king to hear mass on high festivals at the greatest
minster of the town where he was. When it was time
to go to the church, their arms were brought to all
those that were to be made knights, and they armed
them, as was the custom in those days, and then the
king gave them the accolade, but he girded not the
swords upon them till that they should have come
from the minster and had heard mass all armed, even
as was the custom at that time.

And so soon as mass was said and they came out of
the minster, the young squire left Sir Ewaine, and he
went to the upper hall to the wounded knight, and
he said to him that now, an it liked him, he might
set him free of the weapons. "Certes," said the
knight, "that liketh me well, but on the conditions
that are set." And he told them to him again, and
he said that he was ready to swear thereto. Then he
turned him to a window, and he stretched out his
hand toward a church that he saw, and he swore
in the presence of the squires of the knight that he

would do all in his power to avenge him on all them
that should say that they loved better him that had
wrought thus for the knight than they loved the
knight himself. Then was the knight passing glad,
and he said to the young man, " Fair sir, now ye may
set me free, if ye will, for ye are the desired knight ".
And the young man put his hands upon the sword
that was thru∫t into the head of the knight, and so
softly he drew it out that the other felt it but a little,
and afterwards he drew out the truncheons of the
lance.

While that he set the knight free of the weapons
in this wise, it chanced that a squire espied him, and
he sped down into the court before the hall, and he
went thither where the king girded the new knights
with their swords, and he told Sir Ewaine how the
young man had set free the knight. Sir Ewaine came
running into the hall where the knight was, and saw
that he was set free, and he said to the youth, " Ah,
fair knight, may God make thee a man of worship,
and thou wilt be, if thou live∫t long enough ".

And the wounded knight said, " Now I should be
all whole, an I had a leech that would give heed
unto me ".

When the young squire espied Sir Ewaine, he said
to him, " Ah, fair sir, seek a leech for him ".

" What," said Sir Ewaine, " then have ye set him
free ? "

" Yea, sir," said he, " as ye may see. For I felt
such pity for him that I might no longer endure it."

" Unwisely have ye done," said Sir Ewaine, " and
this will be accounted unto you for folly. For there

are here some of the best knights in the world, yet they would not undertake this adventure, for none might lead it to an end. And ye, that know not how great an adventure it is, have undertaken it. Now before God, this that ye have done irketh me sore, and I had liefer that the knight had departed hence, however great shame the king and his household might have had, if he went away without help. For an ye should live long, ye might yet come to great worship."

"Ah, sir," said he, "it is better that I should die in this adventure, if die I should, than this knight, who is perchance full of great prowess ; for the king and all his household would be blamed therefor, and none knoweth yet what my worth is. But since the matter hath gone thus far, for the love of God let seek a leech for the knight to heal him."

And Sir Ewaine in sore distress replied that the knight should never lose aught by him. He sent to fetch a leech, and he led the young squire up into the hall whither the king was gone, and he had even now heard the tidings how that the young man had set free the knight.

"How is this, Ewaine ? " said the king. "Hath your young squire set the knight free ? "

"Yea, sire," said Sir Ewaine.

"Certes," said the king, "it should weigh heavy upon you, and I am sore displeased with you therefor, since ye have suffered the fairest young squire in the world to take upon him an adventure that no man may undertake save to die."

"Sire," said Sir Ewaine, "by the faith that I owe you who are my lord, I was not there when he set him free. And liefer would I have broken one of my arms than that he had done this."

"Certes," said the king, "ye would not have been wrong. For never have I seen a man of whom it were so great a pity as of him."

"Ah, Sire, save your grace," said the young squire, "it is better that I should die than one of the moſt honoured men of your household, for I cannot yet avail much."

And the king bowed his head, and he was so heavy thereat that the great tears came to his eyes. The tidings spread abroad till that the queen heard them, and she was sore grieved, for she feared that the young squire loved her with so great a love that he had undertaken to set free the knight, and she said that it was great pity for him. And now one and now another bemoaned him, and for the dole that all made the king forgot to gird the sword on the young squire. And anon the cloths were laid, and the new knights were unarmed, and all went to meat.

CHAPTER XV

How the Lady of Nohaut sent to King Arthur to demand
succour

Now after that the king had sat at meat for a time there entered a knight armed at all points save for his helmet, and he had lowered his ventail on his shoulder. He came before the king and saluted him. "King Arthur," said he, "God save thee and all thy house. The Lady of Nohaut, whose I am, greeteth thee. My lady sendeth me to thee, and she biddeth thee know that the King of Northumberland warreth upon her, and he hath laid seige to one of her castles. He hath harassed her sore and slain many of her following, and he accuseth her that she hath broken a covenant with him, whereof my lady knoweth naught. And the matter hath gone so far that the king saith that he is ready to appeal my lady for the covenant even as judgment shall decree. And it is adjudged that if the king desireth to defend him, my lady must prove the matter as liketh her best, either by one knight against another, or by two knights against two, or three against three, or by as many as she may have, if she will. Wherefore my lady sendeth to thee as her liege lord and as thy liegewoman to ask thee that thou wilt succour her in her need, and that thou wilt send her a knight who may defend her right against another. For she will accept the battle, if for the proof she may purvey her of a single knight."

" Fair friend," said the king to the knight, " I will succour her right gladly, and I know well that, since she is my liegewoman, I ought to do so, for she holdeth all her lands of me. And even if she held naught of me, yet is she so gentle a lady that I ought to succour her."

Thereupon they that gave the places at table led to meat the knight that had brought the message, and they ceased speaking of the succour. And so soon as they removed the cloths, the young squire sprang up, and he came before the king and he kneeled before him, and he said right simply, " Sire, ye have made me knight, save your grace, and I require of you as a gift that ye grant me to bear the succour that this knight hath asked of you ".

" Fair friend," said the king, " ye know not what ye ask, for ye are still so young that ye know not how high an emprise is a deed of knighthood. And the King of Northumberland hath many good knights, and I wit well that he will give the battle to the best of them according to his judgment. And ye are yet of such an age that ye have no need to undertake an act of chivalry in such a cause or in such wise, or to take so great a charge upon you, and 't were overmuch pity, if ye were thus o'ercome. And ye have already undertaken a hard adventure, and God grant that ye bring it to a good end, for the peril is passing great therein."

" Sire," said the young squire, " this is the first petition that I have asked of you since that ye made me knight. Look well to my honour and refuse me not that which I ask of you with good reason. And I require of you again as a boon that ye send me to the lady to succour her ; and if ye refuse it me, I shall be put to despite, and I myself will esteem myself the less."

Then Sir Gawain sprang forward, and he said to the king, " Ah, Sire, for the love of God, grant it him. For, certes, we believe that he will lead it to a good end, and ye cannot with reason refuse it him ".

" Well, my friend," said the king, " I grant you to succour the Lady of Nohaut. God send that ye win worship and renown therefrom."

" Gramercy, Sire," said the young squire.

Forthright he took leave of the king and of Sir Gawain and of the other knights, and Sir Ewaine led him to his lodging to arm him. And the knight that had asked for the succour came to the king, and he said, " Sire, ye have given the battle to your new knight. Look well that he be one that is fitting for such a charge ".

" Certes," said the king, " he asked it of me as a boon, or else I had sent thither one of the best knights of my household. And none the less me seemeth that the boon is well employed in him."

" Sire," said he, " by your leave, I will go my way."

" God speed you," said the king.

CHAPTER XVI

How Lancelot took leave of the Queen

RIGHT so the knight departed, and he went to the lodging of Sir Ewaine, where the young squire armed him. And when that he was all armed save his head and his hands, he said, " Ah, Sir Ewaine, I have been over forgetful ".

" Whereof ? " said Sir Ewaine.

" I have not taken leave of my lady the queen."

" Ye are right," said Sir Ewaine.

" Now go before me," said the young squire to the knight, " and I will spur on after you so soon as I have spoken to my lady the queen. And ye," said he to his squires, " do ye go after him, and take all my gear."

Then he bade one of his squires take his sword also, for he desired to be made knight by the hand of another than the king. Then the knight and the squires went their way, and the young squire and Sir Ewaine went to the court of the king, and they passed through the hall where the king and many other good knights ſtill sat. The young squire had lowered his ventail, and they went on until they came to the chamber of the queen. And the young squire kneeled before her, and he looked at her so long as he durſt, but when shame o'ercame him, he fixed his eyes on the ground. And Sir Ewaine said, " Lady here is the young squire of yeſtere'en that the king made knight, and he hath come to take leave of you ".

" What," said the queen, " would he go away so soon ? "

" Yea, lady," said Sir Ewaine, " he will bear succour from the king to the Lady of Nohaut."

" But, in God's name, why doth my lord truſt him so far ? He already had overmuch to do elsewhere."

" In sooth, my lady," said Sir Ewaine, " it grieveth me and also my lord. But the squire asked it of him as a boon."

And then everybody said, " This is the young squire that set free the knight. God, how great is his hardihood ! " Then the queen took him by the hand, and she said to him, " Rise, fair sir. I know not who ye are. Perchance ye are of more gentle blood than I, and I will not, nor do I, suffer you to remain on your knees before me ".

" Ah, lady," said he, " first pardon me for the misdeed that I have done, in that I went from hence and took not leave of you."

" Certes," said she, " I pardon you right willingly."

" Gramercy, lady," said he. " Lady," said he, " an it pleaseth you, I would henceforth hold me for your knight wheresoever I might be."

" Certes," said she, " that pleaseth me well."

" Lady," said he, " with your leave I will go."

" God be with you, fair, sweet friend," said she.

" Gramercy, lady," said he, " since it pleaseth you that I be so." But this he murmured between his teeth.

Therewith the queen raised him by the hand, and he was passing happy when he felt her hand touch his own. He took leave of the ladies and of the damsels, and Sir Ewaine laced his helmet and his gauntlets for him, and then he bethought him that the king had never girt on the sword, and he said, " Now by my head, ye are not knight at all ".

" Wherefore ? " said the young squire.

" For that the king hath not girt on your sword," said he. " Let us go to him forthright, and he will gird it on."

" Then wait, sir," said he, " and I will run after my sword that the squire carrieth for me, for I would not that the king should gird me with other sword than that."

Right so the young squire went away, but he was not minded to return, for he had the intent to be made knight not by the hand of the king, but by that of another wherefrom he thought to profit more.

Long time Sir Ewaine waited for him, and when he perceived that he came not, he betook him to the king, and he said, " Sir, we are sore grieved, for we have been ill deceived in our young squire, that went to Nohaut ".

" How is that ? " said the king.

" Sire," said he, " ye have not girded on his sword."

And then he told the king how he intended to return, when he went to seek his sword, and the king marvelled greatly.

" Certes," said Sir Gawain, " I wend that he is of very high lineage, and perchance he held it for despite that the king girded not on his sword before those of the others."

And the queen said that it might well be. But now the ſtory telleth no more about the king and his fellowship, but it returneth to the young squire that went to do battle for the Lady of Nohaut.

CHAPTER XVII

How Lancelot sought the big knight and the damsel of the pavilion

Now the ſtory saith that the young squire rode after the knight that came to seek succour, and after his gear that went before him, and he overtook them in the foreſt. And they rode together in the foreſt till noon, and the heat was great. And the young squire took off his helmet and gave it to one of his squires, and he fell into a study. And the knight that rode before him left the high road.

" How is this ? " asked the young squire of the knight. " Is not the straight road good ? "

" Yea," said the knight, "but it is not so safe as this."

" Wherefore ? " said the young squire.

" That I shall never tell you," replied the knight.

" I' faith, ye shall tell me," said he, " for ye have done me more harm than ye think in this way."

" What harm, my friend ? " said the knight.

" Such harm ", said the young squire, " that ye may never make it good to me. But now, tell me, wherefore is the way yonder not safe ? "

" I will never tell you ", said the knight.

" Ha ! " said the young squire. Then he took the sword that one of the squires carried, and he came back to the knight, and he said, " Now shall ye tell me forthwith, or ye are dead ".

And the other began to laugh, and he said, " Do ye think to slay me so lightly ? "

" Yea, certes," said the young squire, " an ye tell me not forthright."

" I am not so lightly to be slain as ye suppose," said he, " but I will tell you sooner than that ye should have ado with me. For I should ill perform the errand of my lady, if I let you have ado with me. Now come on," said he, " and you shall see wherefore I turned you aside from the high road, and I will show you."

Then they turned them back, and they had not ridden far ere they found a stone nigh to a fair fountain, and they looked afore them and they saw a passing rich pavilion.

" Sir," said the knight, " yonder is a beautiful maiden, but she is kept there by a knight that is taller than other knights by half a foot, and ftronger. And he is passing cruel to all them that he overcometh, to wit, all them that have ado with him, and therefore I turned aside from the road, for I would not that ye should go there to see her, for 't will irk me sore, if ye go."

" In sooth I will go," said the young squire.

" Then God keep you," said the knight, " for I will not lead you further than this ftone."

Now from the ftone to the pavilion it was a good bowshot, and the pavilion was enclosed round about by a thick, leafy hedge, and it was on the border of the foreft in a fair lawn. And at another bowshot from the pavilion there was a Welsh lodge. The young squire took his sword in his hand, and he left his horse and his squires at the ftone, and he went as far as the pavilion with his sword in his hand. And when he saw the door open, he espied the big knight sitting in a chair, and he said, "Sir, tell me who ye are".

" Fair sir," said the knight, " that is no concern of yours."

" No concern of mine ? " said the young squire. " Before God, it is, for I would see the damsel that is therein."

" She is asleep," said the knight. " Now leave her to awake, and then I will show her to you."

" Do ye promise it me ? " said the other.

" Yea," said the knight.

9

And the young squire left the pavilion and turned him to the lodge that he had seen. And he was ware of two damsels, that stood before it. He went toward them at a great pace, his helmet in his left hand and his sword in his right, and when he drew nigh with intent to greet them, one of them said, " Lord, how fair a knight is this ! "

" In sooth," said the other, " he is the fairest knight in the world. Fie on him that he is such a coward."

" Certes," said the first, " a coward he is, nor can he be accounted a knight, if he durst not see my lady, that is the mirror of all ladies."

The young squire heard right well all that they said. " Certes," said he, " ye have spoken sooth." Right so he turned him to the pavilion, and he put his helmet on his head, but when he came to the chair, he found the big knight there no longer. He went throughout the pavilion, but he discovered therein neither the maiden nor any other being. Thereupon he returned to the lodge where he had left the two damsels, but he found neither of them. Then he was grievously cast down, and he went back to the stone where he had left the knight and his two squires, and the knight asked him what he had done. " Naught," said he. Then he told him how he had lost the sight of the maiden. " But, certes," said he, " I shall never leave this adventure till that I have seen her." And right so he mounted on his horse.

" How now," said the knight, " ye should bring succour to my lady."

" Dismay you not," said he. " I shall come there in good time."

"Then I shall go my way," said the knight, "to bid my lady await you so long as she may, for she hath respite but for eight days."

"Go," said the young squire, "for I shall be there between now and then."

Thereupon the knight turned him toward Nohaut by the ſtraight road, and the young squire fared forth and his companions with him.

CHAPTER XVIII

How Lancelot rescued the maiden of the pavilion, and how he was girt with his sword by the Queen

Ere long Lancelot meets a knight, who on hearing that he is seeking the maiden of the pavilion, promises to lead him to her in return for his aid in doing combat on the way with two knights for a maiden whom they have imprisoned on an island in the midſt of a lake, and whom Lancelot willingly agrees that the knight who is his guide shall keep, if they win the battle. He and his companion meet and overcome the oppressors of the maiden, although Lancelot, absorbed in thinking of the queen's farewell to him, "God be with you, fair, sweet friend", forgets to carry his shield or sword into the fight, and accordingly is wounded in the shoulder. They take the maiden under their protection, and pass the night in a tent that the guide of Lancelot spreads.

When they arose, the young squire said to the knight, "Fair sir, lead me thither where ye have agreed to lead me".

"Gladly," said the knight, "on condition that if ye win the maiden, she shall be mine." And he granted it him. They mounted and the maiden with them, and they rode till they came to the pavilion.

" Sir," said the knight to the young squire, " ye must needs do one thing that this damsel and I require of you."

" What is that ? " said the young squire.

" That ye gird on your sword," said the other, " and hang your shield at your neck. And ye have a good lance that this maiden hath given to your squire."

" The shield and the lance I will take right gladly," said he, " but the sword I may not nor should I gird on, till that I am bidden."

" Then suffer me to hang it to your saddle bow," said the knight, " and ye will find it ready, if ye have need thereof. For ye will have ado with a passing cruel man."

So much the knight and the maiden entreated him that he hung it to his saddle bow. Then he took his shield and his lance, and he came to the pavilion, and he found the big knight even as he had found him the other time. " I am come," said he, " to ask that ye show me the damsel, even as ye promised me yesterday." And he made answer that he should not see her without a combat. " If fight I must," said the young squire, " I will do so sooner than that I should not see her. And arm you speedily, for I have elsewhere to go."

Then the big knight turned and began to laugh for that the young squire said that he should arm him. " I' faith," said he, " should I arm me for you ? " He leaped upon a horse that stood nigh, and he took a shield and a lance, and he drew back and so likewise did the young squire. Then they came together

speedily, for their horses ran swiftly, and each gave
other great strokes and mighty on their shields, and the
big knight brake his lance so that the splinters thereof
flew. And the young squire smote him such a buffet
that he felled him to the ground so fiercely that he was
stunned, and in his fall his lance brake. The knight
swooned, for he was wounded, and the young squire
thought that he was dead. And when he came out
of his swoon, he sat up, and the young squire said to
him, "Now will I see the damsel". "In sooth, fair
sir," said he, "I yield her to you. Cursed be the hour
wherein I saw her, for I am dead thereof." Thus he
gave the damsel over to him. But the young squire
would not let him go till that he had made him promise
that never would he fight with a knight save in his own
defence. Whereupon the knight that had led the
young squire thither came forward, and they all
marvelled greatly at the wonders that he had wrought.
Then the young squire entered into the pavilion, and
he took by the hand the damsel that was then first
arisen, and he gave her to the knight. "Take her, sir
knight," said he.

"These maidens never shall be mine," said the other,
"for they are passing fair, and not I, but ye have won
them, and they should be yours."

"Mine shall they never be," said the squire, "for
we made a covenant that ye should have both."

"Sir," said the knight, "since it is your pleasure
that I keep them, tell me what I shall do with them,
for it shall be done even as ye wish."

"Take them then," said the young squire, "to the
court of King Arthur, and say to my lady the queen

that the young squire that went to succour the Lady of Nohaut sendeth them to her. And say to her that, an she would keep me ever in her service, she send me a sword and make me knight as him that will ever be her knight, for my lord the king girt no sword upon me the day before yesterday when that he knighted me."

When the knight heard that he was so new a knight, he was astonied. "Sir," said he, "where shall I find you on my return?"

"Come straight to Nohaut," said the young squire.

Right so the knight went to the queen, and he gave her tidings of the exploits of the young squire that he had witnessed. And she made great joy thereat, and she sent him a right good sword with a richly wrought scabbard and girdle. The knight took the sword and rode to Nohaut, for well he knew the way. And when he drew nigh to the town, he found the young squire, that was not yet arrived there, and he gave him the sword from the queen. "And she biddeth you gird it on," said he. And he girt it on right gladly, and he gave to the knight that which hung at his saddle bow, and he said that now, thanks to God and his lady, he was knight.

The knight that had gone to seek succour for the Lady of Nohaut was already come on the third day before. And he had so praised the new knight to his lady that she awaited him with great desire, nor would she that another should take the combat upon him. When that the young squire came, there were many that made him good cheer, for the knight that came with him had gone before to give tidings of him to the lady. And she and many of her following mounted, and they rode out to meet him, and they made so great joy of him that greater might not be made of any man.

CHAPTER XIX

How Sir Lancelot did battle for the Lady of Nohaut

WHEN that the young knight saw the lady he neither marvelled at her comeliness nor gave great heed thereto, albeit she was one of the fairest of ladies. Nevertheless he took none of her beauties to heart, but he said, " Lady, my lord King Arthur hath sent me to you to do battle for you, and I am ready to do it now or whensoever it pleaseth you ".

"Sir," said she, "blessed be my lord King Arthur, and ye, ye are right welcome, for gladly I receive you." Then she looked upon him, and she was ware that his hauberk was rent on the shoulder, where he was wounded when that he had won the damsel in the lake. And he had given no heed to his wound, and it was worse. " Ye are wounded, sir," said she.

"Lady," said he, " I have no wound that will hinder me from doing my service when it pleaseth you, and I offer it to you herewith."

The lady let unarm him, and she found that the wound was wide and deep. " In sooth, ye have no need to do combat while that ye are in this plight.

Now wait till that ye are healed ; and I shall have respite from the battle."

" Lady," said he, " I have much to do elsewhere, and I muſt needs make haſte both for your sake and for mine."

And she said that in no wise would she suffer him to do combat while that he was in such case ; but she let send for a leech, and she put the young knight to reſt in a chamber, and she kept him thus fifteen days till that he was all healed and reſtored.

Within the fifteen days the tidings came to the court of King Arthur that the Lady of Nohaut was not yet succoured, and Kay the seneschal said to the king, " Sire, think ye that so young a man as he is may perform so great an adventure. Certes, he cannot. Send me, for it behoveth you to send a man of valour on such an errand ". And the king granted it him. Sir Kay rode on his way till that he came to Nohaut. And he sent a squire before him, and the lady and her following mounted on their horses, and they rode out to meet the seneschal of the king, and they received him with great joy. And the new knight was now all healed.

" Lady," said Sir Kay, " my lord the king hath sent me to you to do battle for you, and he had sent me or another man of worship erewhile, but a new knight asked the boon of him, and he granted it him. But when the king heard it said that your affair was not yet brought to an end, he sent me to undertake your battle for you."

" Sir," said the lady, "I am much beholden to you and to my lord the king, and to the knight that he sent, but the knight hath not refused the combat, for from the first day he would have undertaken it, but I had no desire therefor, seeing that he was wounded. And now he is healed, and he will take it."

"Lady," said Kay, "that may not be. Since I have been sent here, I shall take it, or I should be put to shame, and my lord the king would win no honour thereby."

When the lady heard this, she was sore perplexed, and she knew not what to do, for greatly she desired the new knight to do battle for her, and in respect to the seneschal she knew not what to do, for that he was a man of valour and a lord in the service of the king, whose liegewoman she was, and he might work her good and ill.

Thereupon the new knight came forward, and he said, "In truth, Sir Kay, since the first day I would have done combat, if the lady had willed it, and still I am ready therefor. And I demand that no other do it, for I should do it that came first."

"Fair friend," said the seneschal, "the lady would be wronged, if she suffered not the better to do it."

"Ye are right," said the new knight. "Now let us two make essay together, and let him that winneth undertake the combat."

And the seneschal granted it him.

"That shall never be, so help me God," said the lady, "but I will make peace to the honour of my lord the king, that hath sent you hither, and to the honour of you both. For I may do battle by one knight or by two or by three or by as many as I would. And I will ordain that my battle be done by two knights."

Thus she appeased him even as a discreet lady.

137

CHAPTER XX

How the Lady of Nohaut had tested Lancelot to prove him

In the morning the new knight and Kay meet two knights
of Northumberland, and after terrific combats overcome them,
Lancelot winning his victory more easily than Kay. The king
of Northumberland sees that he is powerless against the cham-
pions of the Lady of Nohaut, and promises her under oath to
depart and never again to work her ill. Thus peace is made.
Kay returns to court, bearing the thanks of the Lady of Nohaut
to Arthur.

AND the new knight abided at Nohaut, for the lady
kept him so long as she might, and when she might no
longer keep him, she was heavy thereat. And he
parted from her on a Monday morning, and the lady
herself attended him with a great number of knights,
and often she offered herself and her service and her
land to him. When that she had accompanied him a
space, the knight forced her to return. And after that
they were all gone back, the knight that had brought
the sword of the queen returned not but accompanied
him for a long way, for he loved the new knight from
his heart, and he said to him, " Sir, I am at your
pleasure, and I pray you for the love of God that ye
be not displeased at that which I have done unto
you ".

" At what ? " said the new knight.

" At this," said he, " that I led you to fight the
two knights for the maiden that dwelt on the lake,
for I did it not save for your honour, and I will tell
you how it befell. My lady said that she would fain

prove the knight that the king sent her, before he should do her battle, and she sent me and these twain wherewith ye fought, to juſt againſt you. And they thought that ye were more wounded than ye were."

"And the big knight," said he, "who was he?"

"Sir, he is a knight of passing great prowess, that is named Agrais, and he had made proffer to my lady to do battle for her, if so be that she would give him her love. And she said that, if he were a better knight than he whom the king sent her, she would give him her love and he should do her battle. Now I have told you wherefore these plots were prepared againſt you, and I pray you in God's name that ye pardon me my misdeed."

"Certes," said the new knight, "I see no misdeed, and if there were a misdeed, I pardon it."

"Gramercy, sir," said the knight, "and wit ye well that I am your knight in all places."

And he thanked him heartily, and either commended other to God, and then they parted each from other. The new knight rode on his way with his squires, and he bethought him that he would go secretly, as one that desireth naught save to win honour and renomee. Then he entered into a foreſt, and he rode all day without finding adventure to speak of, and that night he lay in the foreſt in a house of religion, where great honour was done him.

CHAPTER XXI

How Sir Lancelot went to the Dolorous Gard

For the two following days Lancelot rides through the forest, but save for a victorious encounter at the so-called Ford of the Queen with a knight, who afterward carries to court a report of the valorous young knight who has overcome him, he finds no adventure.

AND the white knight passed that night with a forester, that gave him good lodging. And on the morrow he rose early, and he rode all the morning till terce. And anon he met a damsel mounted on a palfrey, and she made great dole, and he asked her what ailed her. And she said that she had greater sorrow than she had ever had. And he asked her wherefore.

"I have great sorrow," she made answer. "The lord of that castle yonder hath put my lover to death, and he was one of the best knights in the world."

"Damsel," said he, "wherefore is he dead?"

"Sir," she made answer, "by reason of the evil customs there. Cursed be the soul of him that established them, for never knight hath entered there that hath not died for that he was knight errant."

"And will a knight e'er enter there," said he, "that will not die?"

"Yea," said she, "if he be such an one as the adventure requireth. But he must needs be better than any knight that now liveth."

"Damsel," said he, "what requireth the adventure? Tell me."

"An ye would learn it," said she, "then go thither, for this is the path."

Forthwithal the damsel rode away, and ever she made the dole that she had begun. And he rode a great gallop till that he came before the gate. And then he looked at the castle, and he saw that it sate orgulously and that it was passing fair, for all the fortress was placed on a high natural rock, and it was in no wise small, for the distance all around it was more than a crossbow might shoot. At the foot of the rock on one side ran the Humber, and on the other flowed a great stream that came from more than sixty springs, that all rose at less than a bowshot from the rock.

The knight rode straight to the castle, and when he came before the gate, he found it closed and well locked, for this gate was never open. And the castle hight the Dolorous Gard, for that no knight errant came there but either he was slain or he was at least imprisoned so soon as he was vanquished. And thus it was with all that came hither, for none might endure the toil at arms that he must needs suffer. For there were two pair of walls, and at each wall there was a gate, and at each gate the knight errant must needs fight with ten knights. But this was in a passing strange fashion. For so soon as the knight that came from the castle was weary and would fight no more, another was ready in his place, and when he was awearied, yet another came, and in this wise no single knight might enter, if he were not of such prowess and had such good fortune that he might vanquish them all one after the other.

Above the other wall on high above the gate there was a knight wrought in copper, and he was tall and armed at all points. And he held in his two hands a

great axe, and he was placed there by enchantment.
And so long as he stood there, the castle had no fear
lest it should be conquered by any man. But so soon
as he that was to conquer the castle entered within
the first gate and could espy the copper knight, he
would fall forthright to the ground and be broken to
pieces, and then all the enchantments wherewith the
castle was full would depart in such wise that it might
be seen openly. But ever there would remain a part
thereof till he that conquered the castle had bided there
forty days without e'er issuing forth. Such was the
power of the enchantments of the castle. And it was
well supplied within, where might be found all that
of which a knight errant might have need. And it
was set on high above the bank of the Humber.

When the knight with the white armour came before
the castle gate and saw it closed, he was sore distressed.
And then there came to meet him a fair damsel, and
she greeted him and he her. "Damsel," said he, "can
ye tell me aught about the customs yonder?" The
maiden was veiled, for if she had unwimpled her to
him, he would have known her well. And she told
him all the custom of the castle, and how he must fight
and at what risk, if he would enter therein. "But an
ye believe me," said she, "ye should ne'er think on
entering there."

"Damsel," said he, "thus I shall never let the matter
be. Either I shall fulfil the custom of the castle, or I
shall be placed with the other men of worship that have
been taken there. For I might well miss having a more
honourable life."

Then the damsel departed, and it was late, and it

Lancelot attacking Dolorous Gard

drew toward evensong. And right so the knight heard a man above the gate, that asked him, " Sir knight, what seek ye ? "

" I would enter therein," said he.

" Certes," said he that was the guardian, " when ye have entered, mayhap it will disquiet you."

" I know not," said he. " But, in God's name, fair friend, make haste to further me in mine errand, for it will soon be night."

Then the porter sounded a horn, and in a little there issued forth by the wicket gate a knight armed body and limbs, and his horse was led after him, and he said to him that was without, " Sir knight, ye must needs repair down yonder, for here there is no open place where we may fight at ease ".

And he made answer that thus it pleased him.

CHAPTER XXII

How Sir Lancelot destroyed the evil customs of the Dolorous Gard

The two knights go down to the open place and begin to fight. Lancelot slays his opponent and compels the surrender of four other knights, who come in turn against him. When the last of the number has yielded himself, the veiled damsel appears and bids Lancelot cease fighting for the night, but warns him that on the morrow he must win other victories, if he would enter the castle.

Now the damsel led the knight down within the city to a fair and good lodging, and he had great need thereof. When he was lodged, she led him to a chamber to unarm him, and ever she was veiled. And he looked and he espied in a chamber three shields hang on high, and they were all within their covers. He asked the damsel whose these shields were. And she said that they belonged to a single knight. " Damsel," said he, " I would fain see them uncovered, an ye list." And then she let uncover them. And he saw that the three shields were of silver, and one had a red bend across it, and another two bends, and the other had three. And he looked long at them. While that he looked at the shields, a damsel came from another chamber, and she was richly beseen, and her face was uncovered, and there were many lights there.

" Sir knight," said she, " what think ye of the shields ? "

" Lady," said he, " they are seemly."

And then he looked well at her, and when he saw her unveiled, he knew her well, and he sprang toward her with his arms outstretched, and he said, " Ah, fair, sweet damsel, ye are more welcome than all other damsels. Now tell me, for the love of God, how fareth my good Lady ? " " Right well," said she. Then she drew him apart, for her Lady of the Lake had sent her to him.

" And on the morrow," she said, " ye shall learn your name and the name of your father, and 't will be up yonder in this castle, whereof ye shall be lord e'er it ringeth to evensong. For I know soothly by the mouth of my Lady herself that the three shields that we have seen are yours, and wit ye well that they are

marvellous, for so soon as ye shall have at your neck
that whereon there is but one bend, ye shall have gained
the ſtrength and prowess of a knight along with your
own, and if ye hang on your neck that with two bends,
ye shall gain the prowess of two knights, and from that
with three bends ye shall receive the prowess of three
knights.   And I will let carry them to the field on the
morrow, and look well that ye truſt not overmuch in
your youth, and that so soon as ye feel your ſtrength
wane, ye take the shield with the single bend, and then
that with two bends, if ye needs muſt, and when ye
would turn all to ill and cause all the world to marvel
at you, then take that with the three bends.   And then
shall ye see openly the greateſt wonders that ye ever
saw or heard, and such as ye may not conceive.   But
look well that ye abide not at the court of King
Arthur nor of any other lord till that ye shall be
known by your feats of prowess in many lands.
For thus my Lady willeth in order to exalt and
amend you."

Long time the damsel talked with him, and they sat
at meat when it was made ready.   And that night they
from above and they from below were desirous to see
the knight, and they prayed our Lord that He would
grant him ſtrength and valour to overcome all the
knights, even as he had conquered the other five, for
greatly they longed that the enchantments and the evil
cuſtoms of the caſtle should be brought to an end
forever.

CHAPTER XXIII

How Sir Lancelot learned how he was named and whose
son he was

On the following day by the aid of the shields with one and
with two bends Lancelot overcomes the ten defenders of the firſt
gate of the Dolorous Gard ; the gate springs open with a mighty
noise, and Lancelot sees the ten defenders of the second gate
awaiting him. The damsel, who has attended him, gives him
the third shield. At this moment the copper image over the
second gate falls to the ground, killing one of the defenders,
and Lancelot passes on to his conteſt with the nine other
knights, whom he forces either to surrender or flee. The lord
of the caſtle, with whom the cuſtom requires that he fight, has
already made his escape. A damsel opens the gate, and Lancelot
enters amid the rejoicings of the people.

AND anon the people of the caſtle led the white knight
to a marvellous cemetery that was between the two
walls, and he was aſtonied thereat, when he saw it, for
it was closed all about with high walls, close embattled,
and on the crenels were the heads of knights wearing
their helmets, and hard by each crenel there was a tomb,
whereon there were letters that said, " Here lieth such
an one, and yonder ye behold his head ". But by the
crenels where there was no head, the writing was not
in this wise, but the letters said, " Here will lie such
an one ". And there were written there the names of
many a good knight of the land of King Arthur and
from elsewhere, in sooth the names of all the beſt
knights that were known. And in the midſt of the
cemetery there was a great slab of metal marvellously
wrought of gold and enamel and ſtones, and there were
letters written that said, " This slab will ne'er be raised
by hand or ſtrength of man, save only by him that will

Lancelot learning his name

[*face p.* 142

conquer this dolorous castle, and his name is written beneath ". Many folk had assayed to raise the lid of this tomb by might and by craft for to learn the name of the good knight. And even the lord of the castle had oft-times assayed to discover the knight, for an he knew him, he would let slay him, if he might.

Then they led the knight to the tomb, armed as he was at all points, and they showed him the letters, for he knew well how to read, for he had learned long time afore. And when he had read them, he looked at the slab up and down, and he was ware that if it were set free for half its length, four of the strongest knights in the world would have enough to do to lift it, if they raised it even by the smaller of the two ends. Forthright he seized it with both hands by the larger end, and he raised it till that it was higher than his head by a foot, and then he saw the letters that said, " HERE WILL LIE LANCELOT OF THE LAKE, THE SON OF KING BAN OF BENOICH ". And then he put the slab down, and full well he knew that it was his own name that he had read. Then he looked at the damsel, that was come from his Lady, that had likewise seen the name even as he had.

" What have ye seen ? " she asked.

" Naught," said he.

" Yea, ye have seen somewhat," said she. " Tell it me."

" Ah, nay," said he, " in God's name, spare me."

" ' In God's name, spare me ! ' " said she. " I have seen it as plainly as ye have."

Then she whispered it in his ear, and he was wroth thereat, and he prayed and he conjured her so earnestly as he might that she speak thereof to no man. "I will not," said she. " Have no fear."

Right so the people of the castle led him into one of the most beautiful palaces in the world, although it was small, and they unarmed him and made great joy of him. This palace belonged to the lord of the castle, and it was rich in all those riches that pertain to the court of a man of high estate. Thus the white knight conquered the Dolorous Gard, and the damsel was with him, and she bade him sojourn there that he might be healed of his hurts and his wounds, whereof he had a plenty.

A valorous squire, the brother of Aiglin des Vaux, a knight of the Dolorous Gard, speeds on a swift horse to court with the news that the white knight has broken the spells of the castle. Later Gawain, who learns the name of the white knight through the damsel of the Lady of the Lake, announces that he is none other than Lancelot of the Lake, the son of King Ban of Benoich. Lancelot in the meantime does not remain at the Dolorous Gard for the forty days requisite to terminate the enchantments of the castle. After he has achieved sundry exploits, he is led back to the castle by a ruse of the inhabitants, and rather than abide there for forty consecutive days, he performs a series of perilous adventures, the accomplishment of which completely destroys the evil customs of the castle. It is from that time forth known as the Joyous Gard.

CHAPTER XXIV

How Galehot, the son of the Fair Giantess, summoned King Arthur to yield the kingdom of Logres unto him, and of the reply of King Arthur

Now the story saith that King Arthur returned from the forest at high noon, and in the evening while that he sat at meat, there came before him an aged knight, that seemed a man of worship. He was armed save for his hands and his head, and he came before the king with his sword girt on his side. He gave the king no greeting, but he ſtood before the board and said to him, " King, the moſt valiant man that now is living, to wit, Galehot, the son of the Fair Giantess, sendeth me to thee. And he biddeth thee yield up all thy land to him, for he hath conquered thirty kingdoms, but he would not be crowned till that he shall have conquered the realm of Logres. Wherefore he demandeth that thou give thy land up to him, or that thou hold it of him. And if thou wilt be his man, he will cherish thee beyond all the kings that he hath conquered ".

" Fair sir," said the king, " I hold land of none save God. Never shall I hold aught of Galehot."

" Certes," said the knight, " that irketh me, for thou shalt lose honour and land thereby."

" I care not for aught that ye say," said the king, " for never, please God, shall he have the power whereof thou speakeſt."

" King Arthur," said the knight, " now know that my lord defieth thee, and I tell thee from him that within a month he will enter into thy land, and when he shall have come he will not depart hence till that he hath conquered it. And he will take from thee Guinevere, thy wife, whom he hath heard extolled for her beauty and her nobleness beyond all ladies on the earth."

And the king made answer, " Sir knight, I have heard well that which ye have said, and not even for your mighty threats have I the greater fear. But let each man do the best that he may. When that your lord hath taken from me my land, I shall be passing heavy. But never will he have the power to do so ".

Therewithal the knight departed, and when he came to the entrance of the hall, he turned him towards the king, and he said, " Ah, God, what sorrow and what misadventure is here ! " Then he mounted on his horse and went on his way, he and two other knights, that awaited him without the gate. And the king asked Sir Gawain, his nephew, if he had ever seen Galehot, and he said that he had not, and so said also many of the knights that were there. But Galegentis the Welshman, that had made quests in many lands, came forward, and he said to the king, " Sire, I have seen Galehot. He is full taller by half a foot than any other knight that is known, and he is more beloved by his folk and hath won more lands than any man of his years on earth. For he is a young knight, and they that have seen him and are acquaint with him say that he is the most gentle knight and the most debonair that is known, and the most bounteous of his gifts withal. But none the less I say not ", said he, " that I believe that he or any other may have power over you. For an I thought thus, so help me God, I had liefer be dead than alive ". And then the king left speaking thereon, and he said that in the morning he would go to the forest.

CHAPTER XXV

How King Arthur went to war with Galehot, the son of the Fair Giantess

In the meantime Lancelot, riding on his way, one day approaches a town, called the Height of Malohaut. Outside its walls, guarding the road that leads to it, he encounters a knight, who proves to be the nephew of the knight slain by the knight of the truncheons, whom he consequently loves less than he loved the dead knight. Lancelot, therefore, by his promise to the wounded knight is obliged to fight with him. In the combat Lancelot kills his opponent. He rides on to Malohaut, but when he enters he is set upon by the people of the place, and is defending himself against them, when the Lady of Malohaut appears and charges him with having slain the son of her seneschal. Lancelot declares that he could not avoid the combat, and without hesitation he yields himself to the Lady as her prisoner.

It befell on a day when King Arthur sojourned at Camelot that the Damsel of the Marches sent a messenger to him. And she made known to him that Galehot, the son of the Giantess, had entered into her land and had taken it all from her save two castles that she held at the further border of her domain.

"King Arthur," said the messenger, "for this cause my lady beggeth you that ye succour her and your own land, for she can no longer hold it, if ye succour her not."

"I will go with all speed," said the king. "How great a following hath he?"

"Sire, he hath full an hundred thousand horsemen," said the messenger.

" Fair friend," said the king, " go and say to your
lady that I will set out on the morrow for to go againſt
Galehot."

" Nay, Sire," said his men, " await rather your
following, for he hath led a passing great hoſt with
him, and ye are here with only your household, and
ye should ne'er put you in peril."

" Now never may God help me," said the king,
" if e'er a man enter into my realm to work ill,
and I abide in any town before I am there where
he is."

On the morn the king departed, and he rode till
that he came to the caſtle of the Damsel of the Marches,
and he lodged in tents, for he had full seven thousand
men and no more, but he sent a summons far and near
that from all parts all should come to him, both horse
and foot, and let them bring with them so large a
following as they might.

Galehot lay before the caſtle that he had besieged,
and he had led with him a great company that bare
arrows dipped in poison, and they were well armed as
footsoldiers. And they had brought nets of iron in
wains and carts, and there were so many of these nets
that they had enclosed therewith all the hoſt of
Galehot in such wise that they had no fear of an
attack at the rear. Galehot heard it said that King
Arthur had come, but that he had not yet all his
hoſt with him. Thereupon he summoned of his men
the thirty kings that he had conquered and of the
others as many as it liked him, and then he said,
" My lords, King Arthur is here, but he hath a scanty
following, as men tell me. And it would not be to

my honour, if I met him while that he hath so few people with him. But I would that some of my knights meet with some of his".

"Sire," said the King of the Hundred Knights, "in the morning send me."

"Good," said Galehot.

On the morrow in the dawning of the day, the King of the Hundred Knights went out to see the host of King Arthur. Nigh to the castle where the king was lodged there was a town that was called the Height of Malohaut, and it was not so near that it was not seven English leagues distant. Between King Arthur and the town there was a high hill, that was nearer to the army than to the town. The King of the Hundred Knights went up thereon to survey the army of King Arthur, and it seemed to him that there were more than seven thousand men therein. Forthwithal he returned back to Galehot, and he said to him, "Sir, I have surveyed their host, and they have no more than ten thousand knights". And with intent he said a greater number, for that he should not be blamed by the following of Galehot. And Galehot replied, "Take ten thousand of your knights, such as it pleaseth you, and go to do battle with the king". And he said, "Gladly".

And the King of the Hundred Knights chose ten thousand knights such as he would, both kings and knights, and they armed them at all points, and they rode at a great pace toward the host of King Arthur that had not yet dressed their battles, nor made them ready. Word was brought to the host that the knights of Galehot came in haste. Forthright the

men throughout the host armed them, and Sir Gawain
came to his uncle and he said, " Sire, the knights of
Galehot come all armed and at full speed to encounter
with us, but he cometh not in his own person, and
since he cometh not, neither shall ye go ".

" Nay," said the king, " but do ye go and lead with
you as many men as we have, and dress your battles
and put them in array, and see that all be done dis-
creetly, for they have many more men than we have
as yet."

" Sire," said Sir Gawain, " we shall do as best we
may."

Sir Gawain and the other knights passed the ford,
for the host was lodged on the river bank. And when
they had passed the water, they dressed their battles
and put them in array. And the men of Galehot
came on as fast as they might, and Sir Gawain sent
a company against them to encounter with them.
They came all fresh and desiring the encounter, and
the others received them well, and a great and marvellous stour began.

At first the knights of Arthur rout the followers of Galehot,
but they are outnumbered, and in spite of valorous fighting,
but for the prowess of Gawain all would have been taken
prisoners. Their losses are heavy, and they are obliged to withdraw into Arthur's castle, Gawain himself being severely
wounded.

CHAPTER XXVI

How the Lady of Malohaut accorded unto Sir Lancelot
that he might go to the assembly

NEAR by was the city of Malohaut, and a lady held
it, for her lord was dead, and she had had children
by him. Now she was a discreet lady and much
honoured and beloved by all them that knew her.
And the folk of her land so loved and esteemed her
that when anybody asked them, " Who is your lady ? "
they answered, " She is the best of all ladies ". This
lady held a knight prisoner and she kept him imprisoned
in a cell, whereof the walls were pierced and the
openings were so large therein that he could see all
them that were without, and they without saw him.
The cell was narrow and so high that he might stand
upright therein, and it was the length of a large
stone's throw. And there the lady kept the knight
in prison.

And the evening after the assembly the knights of
the land came to the lady, and they told her the news
of the just, and she asked who had done the best
therein, and they said Sir Gawain, and that, as it
seemed to them, no knight had e'er done better.
The knight that was in prison heard these tidings,
and when the sergeants that guarded him brought
him meat, he asked which knight of the meinie of
the lady was best beloved by her. And they named
a valiant knight that stood well with her.

" I pray you send him to speak with me," said he.

"Right gladly," they replied. "We will tell him ". And they said to him, "The knight that is in prison would fain speak with you ".

And he went to the cell to speak with him, and when the knight saw him, he rose to meet him, and he said, "I have summoned you and I would humbly entreat you that ye beg my lady that she come to speak with me ".

"I will well, fair sir ", said the knight. He went forth from the chamber, and he came before the Lady, and he said to her, "Lady, grant me a boon ".

"What boon ? " said she.

"Lady, grant it me, and I will tell it you."

"Speak," said she. "Surely if ye have need of aught, I will give it you."

"Lady, of your grace," said he, "ye have granted me that ye will speak with the knight that ye hold in prison."

"Willingly. Bring him hither," said she.

The knight went to fetch him, and he brought him, and then he withdrew and left him with the Lady.

"What will ye, fair sir ? " said the Lady. "They have told me that ye would fain speak with me."

"Lady," said he, "in sooth I am your prisoner, and I would pray you that ye let ransom me. For I have heard say that King Arthur is in this land. And I am a poor bachelor, howbeit I am known to those of his fellowship that would speedily give me my ransom."

"Fair sir," said she, "ye know well that I hold you prisoner not from desire of your ransom, but ye know

Lancelot before the Lady of Malohaut

well that ye did a great outrage, and I hold you
prisoner for that ye have merited it."

" And I pray you, lady," said he, " for that,
although I cannot deny the deed, needs was that I
should do it, for I could not leave it be for the sake
of mine honour. But if it were your pleasure to let
ransom me, ye would do well and courteously, for I
have heard say that there hath been to-day an assembly
in this country, and that it will be renewed on the
third day from to-day, as these knights said but now
in this hall. And if ye will ransom me, I pray you
that ye let me go, and I will promise you that at night
I will return to your prison, if I am unharmed in my
limbs."

" This I will do," said she, " on the covenant that
ye will tell me how ye are called."

" That I cannot do."

" Then ye shall not go," said she.

" Let me go, and I will promise you that so soon
as it shall be the time to tell it, I will tell it you."

" Do you promise it ? " said she.

" Yea," said he.

" Then ye shall go," said she, " but pledge me that
in the evening ye will yield you again as my prisoner,
if ye are unharmed in your limbs."

" This I grant you, lady," said he.

And he pledged it her, and she took his pledge.
And he returned to the prison and abided there that
evening and all the next day and the night thereafter.

CHAPTER XXVII

How Sir Lancelot fought in the assembly against the knights of Galehot and how he overcame them

By the time that the day for the assembly has come, Arthur's forces have received many additions. He gives orders that none of his men shall cross the ford, but that all shall await the coming of Galehot's force on their own side of the stream. Galehot prepares to send only a part of his following, drawing them from the men that had not been present in the previous encounter. He himself does not intend to go in person until the third assembly.

THE knights of the country were all come to the host of King Arthur, both they of the city of the Height of Malohaut and of the other lands round about. The Lady of Malohaut had given to the knight that she held prisoner a horse and a red shield and his own arms that he bore when she took him prisoner, for he would have none others. In the morning when it was day he issued forth from the town, and he rode toward the host of King Arthur, and he saw the knights on one side and on the other all armed. And he stopped at the ford and he crossed not over. Hard by the ford was a pavilion wherein King Arthur and the queen and maidens enough to fill it withal were set, and Sir Gawain, so hurt as he was, had let bear him thither.

The knight stopped at the ford, and he leaned upon his lance. And the men of Galehot advanced in full array. In the first battalion rode the king that he had first conquered, and as they drew nigh he left his following, took his shield, and rode before the others all alone. The hangers-on, that were in the hoſt of King Arthur, and the heralds at arms began to shout aloud, " Their knights advance. Lo, they are here ! " And the King Firſt Conquered drew nigh, and the knaves began to call out to the knight of the red shield, " Sir knight, see, one of their knights cometh. What await ye ? He cometh all alone ". Many times they spake to him, and he answered not a word. And the King Firſt Conquered came on right speedily.

Now these base fellows had said so much to the knight that they were vexed, and a jaunty knave came towards him and took the shield of the knight from his neck and hung it on his own ; and yet he moved not. And another knave that was on foot thought that the knight was a fool, and he ſtooped down toward the water, and he took a clod of earth and threw it againſt the nosepiece of his helmet. " What do ye here, old coward ? " said the fellow. " Why ſtand ye here ? " The clod was damp, and the water ran into his eyes. He shut them and opened them for the water that he felt, and he heard the clamour, and he looked and he was ware of the King Firſt Conquered, that was now full nigh. And he ſtruck his horse with his spurs, and he took his lance and fewtered it, and he came to meet the king at a great pace. And the king smote him in the breaſt. His hauberk was ſtrong and close, and it gave way no whit, and his lance was all shivered. The knight smote him so hard on the shield that he bare him to earth, horse and man, all in a heap. And when the horse rose to his feet, the knave that had taken the shield and that had it on his neck seized the bridle. And the knight regarded him not, for, an he would, he might have grasped it. And the fellow, he that had taken the shield, came toward him and hung it on his neck. " Here, sir," said he, " it is better employed on you than I thought." The knight looked down, and he saw that the knave had hung the shield on his neck, and he gave no sign that he was ware thereof, but he took it.

The followers of the king that he had unhorsed pricked on, when they saw that their lord was fallen, and the party of King Arthur made them ready, and when they were ready, they came forth, and they passed the ford. Great and marvellous was the ſtour that began between the followers of King Arthur and those of Galehot. The battalions of King Arthur passed the water in close array, one after other. And the men of Galehot came from the other side, desiring overmuch to encounter with them. And these received them with the points of their spears, and they left there many dead and wounded. And none the less the following of Galehot did passing well, and the followers of King Arthur did better, and needs they muſt, for they were fewer in number, for they were but twenty thousand, and the others were sixty thousand. The fray laſted long, and the battle was good, and many noble feats of chivalry were done there, and the party of King Arthur and the worship-ful knights of his household acquitted them right well. Many were the valorous deeds at arms wrought on that day by the following of King Arthur and of Galehot. But he of the red armour surpassed all, for he won all the tournament. And at night he departed, so that no man knew what became of him.

But Arthur greatly feared to lose his land, for many of his men had failed him, even as his wise clerks had foretold. And he was sore troubled. And on the other hand Galehot spake to his men, and he said that he had won no great honour in fighting against King Arthur. "For the king hath too small a following, and if I should conquer his land now," said he, "I should have not honour but shame therefrom".

"Sire," said his men, "what would ye propose?"

"I will tell you," said he. "It is not my pleasure to fight longer against him in this wise, but I will give him a truce for a year, so that he shall lead all his forces hither at the end of the year, and then shall I win greater honour in conquering him than I should now."

CHAPTER XXVIII

How the Lady of Malohaut went to the court of King Arthur

Arthur has previously had a troublesome dream, which his clerks have told him presages that he will lose worldly renown and the loyalty of those in whom he has trusted. He is now visited by a holy man of great worship, who tells him that the source of his danger is his disregard of the law of God, for he has neglected the poor and honoured the rich, and is still unrepentant for the great wrong that he did King Ban of Benoich in failing to come to his aid. He bids Arthur change his course of life and endeavour by a wise and just rule to win back the affection of his people that they may help him maintain his realm. In all humility the king promises to follow his counsel.

While they talk together the King of the Hundred Knights and the King First Conquered come to Arthur with a message from Galehot. They declare that Galehot is of the opinion that he should win no honour in conquering such a king as Arthur while he has so small a following as that assembled there, for he is at too great a disadvantage. Galehot therefore proposes a truce for a year, on the understanding that at its end they shall meet in the same place, each with all his forces. He will engage not to depart thence till he has conquered the land ; he also boasts that by that time he will have in his meinie the valiant red knight. Arthur accepts the truce, but vows that, if it please God, his land shall never be conquered. He is, however, dismayed at the determination of Galehot to number the red knight among his followers.

After the just Lancelot returns to his cell at Malohaut in great pain from the wounds that he has received. The knights of the Lady of Malohaut bring her reports of the red knight who has surpassed all other combatants, and she, suspecting that he is none other than her prisoner, accompanied by her cousin, a maiden of her household, visits his cell while he sleeps, to discover, if she can, any marks of the combat. When she sees how sadly he is wounded, she becomes so enamoured of his prowess that her cousin leads her away, expostulating with her on giving her love to a stranger knight. And at last she says, " Perchance the knight thinketh more of another than ye suppose. Supposing hath deceived many folk ". " I suppose," replies the Lady, " that he hath set his thought higher than any other man hath e'er set his, and may God, who made him fairer and better than other men, grant him to lead to a good end that whereon he hath thought." She determines within herself that she will find out who the knight is and on what lady he has set his love.

Now the story saith that on a day the Lady let lead Lancelot forth from his prison to speak to him, and when he came before her, he would have sat on the ground at her feet, and she, desiring to do him honour, bade him sit by her side on high. And she said to him, " Sir knight, I have kept you long time a prisoner for the great misdeed that ye did, and I have treated you honourably against the will of my seneschal and of his kindred, and ye should therefore be much beholden to me, if there is much good in you ; and so ye are, as I think ".

" Lady," said he, " I am beholden to you in such sort that I am your knight in all need and in all places."

" Gramercy," said the Lady, " and ye shall give proof thereof. Now therefore I pray you that ye tell me that which I require of you, to wit, that ye tell me who ye are and for what ye long. And if ye would conceal it, wit ye well that it shall never be known apart from here."

" Lady, in God's name, spare me," said he. " So help me God, that ye may never know, for there is no creature living to whom I would tell it."

" Nay ? " said she. " Will ye in no wise tell it ? "

" Lady," said he, " do with me as pleaseth you, for an ye were about to cut off my head, I would not tell you."

" Certes," said she, " then ill betide you, if ye conceal it from me, for by the faith that I owe the being that I love most, ye shall never issue forth from prison before the assembly that shall be held between my lord King Arthur and Galehot of the Stranger Isles. And wit ye well that ye shall henceforth suffer enough shame and misease, and there is yet almost a year to the day of the assembly, and if ye had told me, ye should have been this very day out of prison. And yet I shall know it within a year or at some time, and in spite of you, for I shall go thither where it will be told me."

" Whither, lady ? " said he.

" I' faith," said she, " to the court of King Arthur, where all news is known."

" Lady," said he, " I can do no more about it."

Right so she sent him back to his cell, and she made semblance that she was passing wroth with him and that she hated him, but she did not, rather she loved him more than she was wont, and each day her love grew and increased. Then she summoned her cousin, and she said to her, " See," said she, " that ye tell the knight of the cell that I hate him more than I hate any other man, and that I shall let work him all the ill that the body of man can suffer ". Thus spake the Lady to her cousin for to conceal her thought, and anon she made her ready to go to the court of King Arthur to learn who the knight was. And she would fain go richly beseen.

On the fourth day the Lady departed for the court, and she left her cousin in her stead, and she said to her, " Fair cousin, I go to the court of King Arthur. And I have made semblance to the knight in prison that I hate him bitterly for that he would not tell me his name, but I might never hate him, for he is too worshipful. I therefore beg and require you, as ye hold my love and your honour dear, that ye seek and purvey for him whatsoever ye deem that his heart desireth, save your own honour, and that ye give him back to me ". And she promised it her.

Forthwithal the Lady departed, and she went her way till that she found the king at Logres, the which was the chief city of his realm. And when he heard her say that she came, both he and the queen went to meet her, and they received her with great joy.

But before that they entered into the city there was not a knight to whom a gift from the king was not given, and the queen did as much for the ladies and the damsels, and this was for the sake of the Lady of Malohaut. And the king suffered her not to alight save in his dwelling, for much she had aided him in his great wars.

The king and the queen made great joy and glad cheer of the Lady. And that night after supper they were all three seated on one couch, and the king said to the Lady of Malohaut, "Certes, lady, 't was with great effort that ye came hither, so far from your own land, and I wit well that it was not without cause, for ye are not wont to fare far from your own country".

"Certes, Sire," said the Lady, "I came not without cause, but it was anent a great matter, and I will tell it you. Sooth to say I have a cousin who hath been deprived of her lands by a neighbour, and she hath found no knight that would take her quarrel upon him, for her neighbour is a good knight and of high lineage. And she hath no help save in me. Wherefore I desire that ye will so far aid me that I may have the good knight of the red armour that won the joust between you and King Galehot, for men tell me that none would better do battle for her. For this I have come to you, and great need have I of your aid."

"Fair lady," said the king, "by the faith that I owe my lady the queen, that I love more than any other being alive, never to my knowledge was I acquaint with this knight whereof ye speak, nor is he of my household or of my land, as I think. And I

would fain see him, and Sir Gawain, my nephew, is
one of forty knights, the beſt of my household, that
are in queſt of him, and they set out nigh a fortnight
since, and they will not return again to my court
till that they have found him."

Then the Lady began to smile because of the
knights that were seeking him, for that their queſt
was foolishness. And the queen saw her, and she
thought within herself that the Lady never smiled
for naught, and she said to her, "Certes, lady, me
thinketh that ye know better where he is than either
I or my lord the king".

And she made answer, "By the faith that I owe
my lord King Arthur, whose liege lady I am, and you,
who are my lady, I came hither for naught else save
to hear who he is, for I thought to learn tidings of
him".

"Certes," said the queen, "I thought as I did,
for that I saw you smile when my lord spake thereof."

"Lady," said she, "it was for that I made mock
of myself, and for that I laboured overmuch for
naught. But since after coming hither I can hear
no news of him, I ask you leave to depart, and I will
go away in the morning, for I have much to do in
my own country."

"What," said the king, "then ye think to go away
now ? So soon shall ye never leave, but bear the
queen company for a se'nnight or a fortnight, and
then shall ye take with you the beſt of my knights,
him that pleaseth you moſt, to do your battles. For
wit ye well, ye are one of the ladies that I would moſt
honour on earth, for ye have aided me in my need."

" Sire," said she, " gramercy, but I can in no wise
remain, neither will I take a knight away with me,
since I cannot have him whom I seek, for I have
others enough."

So much the king and also the queen begged her
that she abided unto the third day, and then she
departed with the good accord of them both, and
she fared back to her country, for much she longed
to return and to see him for whom all the most valorous
knighthood of the world was in quest, and much she
boasted that she had in her keeping that which none
other might have.

CHAPTER XXIX

How Sir Lancelot paid the Lady of Malohaut his ransom

THUS the Lady came back merry and joyous, and she
came to her cousin and made known to her that she
had gone to the court of King Arthur for that she
feared that her prisoner was of his court or of his
country, and that the king would be offended with
her because of him.

" Now have I learned this much," said she, " that
he is not of the household of the king nor of his country.
But how have ye fared, ye and the knight ? "

" Right well, lady, thanks be to God," said she.
" He hath had all whereof he had need."

Thereafter within a while she let take him from the cell, and she spake to him after the manner of a woman that is passing wroth.

"Sir knight," said she, "ye refused the other day to tell me your estate, and I have since learned so much thereof, that now, an ye list, I would grant you your ransom."

"Gramercy, lady," said he, "I would gladly redeem me, if I might come to your terms of ransom."

"Know ye what your ransom will be?" said she. "I will give you three behests, and if ye obey not one thereof, never, so help me God, shall ye issue forth from my prison, not for all that ye have or all that ye ask. Now choose one of the three, if ye would e'er issue forth from my prison."

"Lady," said he, "tell me your pleasure, and since I am come to this pass, I must needs accept it, whatever it be."

"I will tell you," said she. "First, if ye will tell me who ye are and how ye are called, ye shall be free of my prison. And if ye will not tell me this, then tell me who is your love. And if ye will tell neither one nor the other, then tell me if ye think ever again to do such deeds at arms as ye did the other day at the assembly."

When the knight heard her, he began to sigh heavily, and he said, "Ye must hate me out of measure, lady," said he, "and well am I ware thereof, seeing that ye would not set me free save with shame. Lady, in God's name, when ye have made me speak to my grief and your pleasure, what surety shall I have that ye will let me go free?"

"I pledge you faithfully," said she, "that so soon as ye shall have chosen one of the three ransoms, ye shall go free. Now the going or the staying lieth with you."

Then the knight began to weep piteously, and he said, "Lady, I see that I must needs escape by a shameful ransom, and I must needs suffer it as best I may, if go I would. And since it is thus, it liketh me better to speak to my own shame than to that of another. For wit ye well, I will in no wise tell you who I am or how I am hight. And if I love, so help me God, ye shall never know whom, if it lieth in my power. Therefore I must needs tell you the other, and I will tell it, whatever shame I may have therefrom. Know then this much in sooth, that I think to do greater deeds at arms than I have ever done, if I am commanded. Now have ye made me tell my shame, and I shall go forthwith, if it is your will".

"Ye have said enough," said she. "Now ye may go when it pleaseth you, for now I can take better cognisance of you than ever I did. But forasmuch as I have treated you with honour in your captivity, I pray you that ye will grant me a guerdon that will trouble you no whit, and I ask it more for your sake than for mine."

"Lady," said he, "speak your will, and ye shall have that which ye ask, if it may be had."

"Gramercy," said she. "I pray you that ye abide here until the assembly, and I will make ready for you a good horse and such arms as ye would bear, and ye shall go to the assembly from here, and I will tell you on what day it will be."

" Lady," said he, " I will do your will."

" Now I will tell you what ye shall do," said she.
" Ye shall abide in your cell, and ye shall have whatsoever ye desire, and I will often bear you company,
I and my cousin. But I will that none know that
ye have paid me your ransom. Now tell me what
arms ye would bear."

And he said black arms. Then he went away into
his cell, and the Lady let prepare for him secretly
a shield all black and a horse of the same colour and
likewise a coat of mail and housings. Thus abided
the knight with the Lady.

And King Arthur remained in his land, and he did
honour to his folk even as his master had taught him,
so that ere the half year was passed he had so regained
their hearts that he had built more than a thousand
dwellings on the field, and they were so bestirred
within them that they would liefer die in battle than
that the king should lose his realm while they lived.
Thus they turned them with their whole hearts to
the king for the great kindness that he had shown
them, and a fortnight before the truce was ended
they thronged to him in the field in as great numbers
as they might. And then on the other hand Sir
Gawain and his companions came back from the quest,
where they had accomplished naught, and they were
sore ashamed thereat. But the great need of the
king had led them back. Thus came the king prepared
to defend his realm.

And on the other side Galehot came with great
puissance, seeing that for one man that he had led
before he brought back two, so that the nets of iron

that had enclosed the firſt hoſt might not enclose the half of this.

CHAPTER XXX

How Sir Lancelot went the second time to the assembly, and how he behaved him there

On the firſt day of the assembly neither side gains the maſtery. Gawain accomplishes many deeds of valour, but is so severely wounded that reports of his death are spread abroad. The news reaches Lancelot in his prison. He chides the Lady of Malohaut for not having told him the day of the juſt. She promises that on the day after the morrow, when the assembly is renewed, he shall go equipped in black armour. On the following day, unknown to him, she herself goes to the field and joins the king and queen.

THE cousin of the Lady of Malohaut, who had abided in her lodging, that evening made ready his arms for the knight. On the morn he rose early, and the maiden aided him to arm him, and when she had commended him to God, he parted from her, and that morning he fared on his way till that he came to the field at sunrise. And he ſtopped on the river bank, and he leaned on his spear in the same place where he had been at the other juſt. And anon he looked toward the tower where Sir Gawain lay hurt, and this he did because of the ladies and the damsels that he saw there, for the queen was come there and the Lady of Malohaut and a great plenty of other ladies and damsels. And the following of Arthur, they that desired the encounter, were already armed, and they passed over the water in close array. And the following of Galehot did likewise. And within a while the field was covered with many a juſt and many a fray.

And ever the knight ſtood in thought and leaned on his spear, and he looked full tenderly toward the tower where the ladies and the damsels were. The Lady of Malohaut was ware of him, and she knew him right well, and she began to speak in the hearing of all the other ladies. " Look," said she, " at the knight that I espy on the river bank. Who can he be ? He neither harmeth nor helpeth us." Then all, both knights and ladies, began to look toward him. And Sir Gawain asked if he might see him. And the Lady of Malohaut said that she would so dispose him that he might see the knight. Then she herself prepared a seat for him beside a window so that he might see well all down the field. And he looked and he saw the black knight, that leaned on his shield and his spear in thought, and he said to the queen, " Lady, lady, do ye remember when I was wounded laſt year and lay here that either this or another knight ſtood thus in thought on the river bank ? But he bore red arms, and it was he that won the juſt ".

" Fair nephew," said she, " it may well be. But why say ye so ? "

" Lady," said he, " I say it, because I would that this were he, for I never beheld such deeds of prowess of any knight. And we shall see enough of them here."

Long time they talked of the knight, but he ne'er changed his poſture.

On that day Galehot wore not the arms of a knight, but he did on a habergeon, short like that of a sergeant, and he had a cap of iron on his head, and his sword girt, and a short and thick club in his hand, and he sat a horse such as beseemed a man of worship, for no man in the world had more horses that were good and fair.

And so they were arrayed for the battle in the field on one side and on the other. And ever the black knight ſtood in a ſtudy on the riverside. The Lady of Malohaut, that knew him right well, spake to the queen, and she said, " Lady, ye would do well to require of that knight to do deeds of arms for love of you, and to show you whose knight he is, whether ours or theirs. Then we shall see what he would do, and if there is aught of valour in him ".

" Fair lady," said the queen, " I have enough else to think on, for my lord the king is in peril of losing to-day all his land and all his honour, and my nephew lies in such plight as ye may see. And before my eyes is so great mischance that I have no longer desire nor reason for the challenges or for the pleasantries that I was wont to make. For I have enough else whereon to set my thought. But do ye and these other ladies here, if they liſt, send word to him."

" I' faith, lady," said she, " I am all ready, if he be summoned by another. An ye will, do ye summon him, and I will bear you company."

" Certes, lady," said the queen, " dismay you not for that I will not send to him. Do ye and these other ladies send for him, if ye liſt."

Then the Lady of Malohaut said that if the other

ladies would send for him, she for her part would send also, and they were all accorded thereto. And the queen gave them one of her maidens to carry the message. The Lady of Malohaut devised the message, and Sir Gawain added thereunto two of his spears and a squire to bear them. Then the Lady of Malohaut said to the maiden, " Damsel, ye will go to that knight yonder, that is in a ftudy, and ye will say to him that all the ladies and the maidens of the household of King Arthur and of the chamber of the queen greet him, and they pray and entreat him that if he hopeth ever to have welfare or love in a place where any one of them hath influence or power, then let him take arms to-day for love of them, in such wise that they shall be beholden to him. And give him these two spears that Sir Gawain sendeth to him ".

Forthwith the maiden mounted on her palfrey, and the squire that bare the two spears followed her, and they came to the knight, and the maiden gave him her message. And when he heard her speak of Sir Gawain, he asked where he was, and the maiden said, " He is in that tower with many ladies and maidens ". And he took leave of the maiden, and he said to the squire that he would follow him. And he looked down at his legs, and he dressed him in his ftirrups, and it seemed to Sir Gawain, who looked upon him, that he had grown half a foot in height. Then the knight gave a glance toward the tower, and he turned him, and he came pricking down the field. And when Sir Gawain saw him, he knew him for that he bore his arms so well, and for that he was as swift and as slender as a sparrow-hawk. And he said to the queen,

" Lady, lady, see the knight that in all the world
hath not an equal, for never have I beheld one that
jufted and bore his arms so well and so nobly as he ".

Then all the ladies and the maidens ran to the
battlements to see him, and he came riding on amain
as faft as his horse might carry him. And at the right
and at the left he was ware of many a fair juft and many
a fierce mêlée. For a large part of the nimble bachelors of King Arthur had already entered the lifts to
do deeds at arms, and of the hoft of Galehot there
came here twenty, here thirty, here forty, here one
hundred, in one place more and in another less. And
he passed by all the mêlées and spurred on againft
a great company that he saw come, wherein there
might well be an hundred knights. And he hurtled
among them, and he smote a knight so hard that he
bare him to the ground, him and his horse, all in a
heap. And when his lance brake, he dealt blows with
the truncheons so long as they lafted up to the point.
And then he turned him to his squire, who carried
the two lances, and he took one, and he hurtled again
among them so openly that all the others left their
jufting and their valiances to watch him. And he
did such deeds of prowess with his three lances so
long as they lafted that Sir Gawain bare witness that
no man to his knowledge could do so much. And so
soon as they were all three shivered to bits, he went
back to the riverside to the same place where he had
been afore, and he turned his face toward the tower
and looked upon it full tenderly.

Sir Gawain spake thereof to the queen, and he said,
" Lady, ye see that knight. Now wit ye well that

he is the moſt worshipful man in the world. But ye
erred in the message that was sent to him, when ye
would not be named therein, and perchance he hath
counted it to you for haughtiness, for he seeth that
it is your affair more than that of any others, and he
thinketh mayhap that ye eſteemed him lightly, since
ye deigned not to bid him take arms for love of you ".

" I' faith," said the Lady of Malohaut, " he maketh
it plainly known to the reſt of us that he will do no
more for us. Now let her who will send for him,
for our challenging is ended for to-day."

" Lady," said Sir Gawain to the queen, " seemeth
it to you that I have spoken reason ? "

" Fair nephew," said she, " what would ye have me
do about it ? "

" Lady," said he, " I will tell you. He hath much
who hath on his side a man of worship, for by a single
man have many great adventures that were turning
to naught been led to an end. And I will tell you
what ye shall do. Send your greeting to him and
tell him that ye cry him mercy for the kingdom of
Logres and for the honour of my lord the king and
for our own, whereto ill will befall to-day, if God and
he give not heed thereto. And if he e'er hope for
honour or welfare or joy in any place where ye have
worship, let him now for love of you do such deeds
at arms that ye will be beholden to him therefor,
and that it may appear by his deeds that he hath
brought succour to the honour of the king and to
your own. And wit ye well that if he will give his
defense, my lord the king will never be discomfited
to-day for all the power of Galehot. And I will send

him ten lances, whereof the steel is sharp and cutting, and the shafts are short and thick and strong, wherewith ye shall see to-day many a joust fought. And I will send him three strong and good horses that I have, and they shall be all trapped with my arms, and I know that if he will do all in his power, he alone will perforce put the enemy to flight to-day."

Thus Sir Gawain devised, and the queen said to him that he send to the knight from her and in her name whatsoever message he desired, for she consented unto it. And the Lady of Malohaut made such joy thereat that but a little and she would have leaped for gladness, for now she deemed that she had attained that which she had ever secretly sought. Then Sir Gawain summoned the maiden that had carried the message, and he sent her to the knight that was in thought. And he devised the message even as he had told it to the queen. Then he called four of his squires, and he bade them take to the knight three of his horses all trapped, and a fourth he bade carry a set of ten of his lances, the strongest that he had. Forthright the maiden departed, and she told the knight the word that Sir Gawain and the queen sent him, and she gave him the gifts. And the knight asked the maiden, "Where is my lady?"

"Sir," said she, "she is up yonder in that tower with a great company of ladies and maidens, and Sir Gawain lieth there hurt, and know well that ye will be well observed."

And the knight said to her, "Say to my lady only that thus it shall be, even as it pleaseth her, and to Sir Gawain return my great thanks for his gift".

Then he took the ſtrongeſt of the lances that the
squire carried, and he bade them all follow him. The
maiden took leave of him, and she returned and gave
to the queen and to Sir Gawain the message that the
knight had sent them. And the Lady of Malohaut
began to laugh heartily at the whole matter.

And the knight rode at a great pace ſtraight down
the field, where many good knights were already
assembled both on one side and on the other. And
he passed by all the encounters and made semblance
that he saw none of them. And he rode ſtraight to
the company that the King Firſt Conquered led,
wherein there were full twenty thousand knights.
And he turned the head of his horse toward them,
and heart and body and will withal, and he hurtled
among them so faſt as his horse might carry him,
and he dealt ſtrokes there where him seemed that they
were beſt employed, so that before his lance naught
that he pursued, neither knight nor horse, endured,
but he felled them all to the ground in a heap, and
he shivered their lances to bits.

CHAPTER XXXI

How Galehot took Sir Lancelot to his tent

So dismayed were his enemies at the marvels that he
wrought that the greater part of them gave aback
and betook them ſtraight to their tents much caſt
down. When Galehot was ware of them he marvelled

greatly what this might be, for well he knew that his following was the larger, and he came to meet them that went fleeing, and he asked them what this was.

"What, sire?" said a knight that had no will to juſt. "Down yonder is a knight that surpasseth all others single-handed. No man can endure againſt him. Not even the knight of laſt year is worth aught in comparison of him, and naught can weary him, for he hath not paused since the morning, and he is as ſtrong and as fresh as if he had not yet borne arms."

"Now, perdy, that shall I see in good time," said Galehot.

Then he went to his great hoſt, and he separated therefrom ten thousand men and he left thirty thousand of them, and he said to King Baudemagus, "See, as ye hold dear your own honour and mine that my hoſt move not from here till that I come to seek you. And you," said he to the ten thousand, "do you hold yourselves softly apart far from the others till that I come to you".

Right so he went to the battle with such arms as he had, and he made all them that had fled return with him, and already his followers were brought to such a pass that they truſted not in themselves. But when King Clamadex saw them come, he took heart, and he raised his battle cry on high and rode again hard at his enemies. And Galehot commanded his men that he led to ſtrike into the press at full speed as faſt as they might go. "And have no fear," said he, "that you will not be well succoured in need." And they let their horses run at the bidding of their lord, and they hurled into the midst of their enemies, and then they encouraged all their men, and well they cried aloud the cry of Galehot so that they on the side of King Arthur thought that a great company had succoured their enemies, and the party of the king would have been sore routed, if the black knight had not been there. But he alone so took the charge of the battle upon him that he protected them in every need, and in every need he was ready both for defense and for pursuit. There was his horse killed under him, and he was left on foot, and this was the last of his horses, and the press was so thick about him that no one might lightly come to him to remount him. And there where he was on foot he did so well that no man could hold him for a coward or a laggard, for even as a standard he was exposed to all his foes. And he dealt blows to the right and to the left without rest. His sword was not seen save in giving strokes. He did wonders to behold.

When Galehot was ware of the marvels that he wrought, he wondered that a single knight could achieve them, and he said within him that not to win all the lands that are under heaven would he have so valiant a man slain by his strokes. Then he pricked his horse with the spurs, and he hurled into the press, club in hand, to drive the mêlée away from him, since that he was on foot. And with great travail he made his party draw back. Then he called the knight, and he said, " Sir knight, now have no fear ". And he replied with all hardihood that he had none. " Now harken," said Galehot, " to what I will tell you. I would have you learn somewhat of

my custom. Know that I forbid all my men as they
love me to lay hand upon you or to pursue you so
long as ye are on foot. But if ye should withdraw
and give over doing deeds of arms through cowardice,
I would not assure you that ye should not be taken.
But so long as ye bear arms, ye shall find none to take
you. And even if your horse is dead, be not dismayed,
for I will give you as many horses as ye can use to-day,
and I will be your squire all this day long. And if
I cannot weary you, then no man living will e'er
do so."

Then he alighted down from his horse and gave
it to the knight, and he mounted therewithal, and
he returned to the mêlée as swiftly as if he had not
dealt a blow on that day. Galehot mounted on a
horse that was led to him, and he came back to his
host, and he took the ten thousand men and he bade
them go before to the field. And when they came
into the field there was a mighty noise, and the others
rode to meet them so fast as ever they might. But
the party of Galehot came so hard that in their
coming they smote down many that day. And at
their coming the good knight was borne to the ground,
and his six fellows likewise that had been all day nigh
him. Then Galehot came forward, and he remounted
him on the horse whereon he himself sat, for he
deemed the other unworthy. So soon as the knight
was remounted on horseback, he rode back to the
press as fresh as he had been afore, and he began to
work more noble deeds of arms, as Galehot attested,
than any other man could do, so that all men marvelled
at him.

So he ever did well till nightfall, and never was there an hour that he and his fellows had not the better of the battle. When it drew toward evening then they began to depart on one side and on the other, and he went away so privily as he might, and he turned him up the meadow between the hill and the riverside. Galehot, that watched him closely, saw him go, and he spurred after him, and he followed him at a diſtance along the curve of the hill till that he overtook him in the valley. And he rode along by the side of the knight so courteously as he might, and he said, "God's benison be with you, sir". And he looked askance at him, and he scarce returned his greeting.

"Sir," said Galehot, "who are ye?"

"Sir, I am a knight, as ye may see."

"Certes," said Galehot, "ye are a passing good knight, the beſt that liveth, and ye are the man that I would moſt honour in all the world. And I am come to you to pray you of your courtesy that ye come to-night to lodge with me."

And the knight said to him, as if he knew him not nor had ever seen him, "Who are ye, sir, that prayeth me thus to lodge with you?"

"Sir," said he, "I am Galehot, the son of the Fair Giantess, lord of all this people againſt whom ye have this day defended the kingdom of Logres, that I had undertaken to conquer, and conquered I should have, if it had not been for your person."

"How is this?" said the knight. "Ye are an enemy of my lord King Arthur, and yet ye pray me to lodge with you. With you, please God, I will by no means lodge to-night."

"Ah, sir," said Galehot, "I would do much more for you than ye think, and indeed 't would not be for the firſt time. And I pray you again in God's name that ye lodge with me to-night upon this covenant that I do at your commandment whatsoever ye may ask me."

Therewithal the knight ſtood ſtill, and he looked hard at Galehot, and he said, "Certes, sir, ye are a good promiser. I know not how it is with the keeping".

And Galehot made answer, "Sir, know that there is no mighty man in the world that promiseth less than I. And again I tell you that if ye come to lodge with me, I will give you that which ye ask of me, and I will give you whatever surety ye demand of me with your lips".

"Sir," said the knight, "ye are held for a man of great worship, and it would not be to your honour to promise aught wherefor ye would not in the end keep your pledge."

"Sir," said Galehot, "have no doubt thereof, for I would not do it to win all the kingdom of Logres. And I will promise you as a loyal knight—for I am not king—that I will give you whatsoever ye ask of me to have your company to-night, and if I may have it longer, I shall keep it. And if ye have not a sufficient surety from me, I will pledge you what ye will."

"Sir," said the knight, "me seemeth that ye desire much my company, if your heart is even as your words. I will lodge with you to-night, but do ye promise to give me what I ask of you, and ſtill another surety I would require of you."

Thus they made covenant each to other, and Galehot promised to keep his covenant. Then they went to their host, and the people of King Arthur had already repaired to their tents.

And Sir Gawain had seen the knight go, and he was sore grieved that he went away, and if he had been in sound health, he would have set great pains to retain him. And he had sent to the king to come to him, for he would counsel him to follow after the knight till that he might keep him. While that he awaited the king, he looked across the meadows, and he saw Galehot come, his right arm around the neck of the knight, and he led him between the hill and the river so that the following of King Arthur was ware of them. And when Sir Gawain saw them, he knew well that Galehot had kept him, and he said to the queen, who was there, "Ah, Lady, lady, now ye may well say that your folk are discomfited and slain. Look ye, Galehot hath won yonder knight by his wit". The queen looked, and she saw the knight that Galehot led away with him, and she was wroth, nor could she utter a word for a long time. And Sir Gawain had such sorrow thereat that he swooned thrice in less time than a man may go a small stone's throw. And the king came there, and he was ware of the knight that Galehot led away, and he had such grief thereat that he nigh fell to the ground, and he could not refrain from weeping. Great was the sorrow in the host of the king that all alike made for the good knight that Galehot led away with him.

CHAPTER XXXII

Of the pledge that Sir Lancelot required of Galehot,
and how Galehot did him honour

AND they two rode on their way, and when they drew nigh to the host, the knight called Galehot, and he said, " Sir, I go my way with you. But I require you before that I enter into your host that ye let speak with me the two men wherein ye most trust in the world ". And he granted it him.

Forthright Galehot parted from him, and he said to two of his men, " Follow me, an ye would see to-night the richest man in the world ".

And they said to him, " How is this, sir, are not ye the richest man alive ? "

" Nay," said he, " but I shall be ere I sleep."

These twain were the King of the Hundred Knights and the King First Conquered ; they were the two men in the world wherein he most trusted. And when they saw the knight, they made great joy of him, for they knew him well by his arms. And he asked them who they were, and they named them so as ye have heard. And he said to them, " Sirs, your lord doth you great honour, for he saith that ye are the two men wherein he trusteth and believeth most. And we have made an agreement, he and I, that I would that ye should hear. For he hath pledged me that if I lodge with him to-night, he will give me whatsoever I demand of him. Do ye ask him ". And he said that it was true.

"Sir," said the knight, "I would ſtill have the pledge of these men of worship."

And Galehot accorded thereto. "Tell them the manner thereof," said he.

"They shall promise me," said he, "that an ye fail me of this covenant, they will leave you and will come with me wheresoever I will, and they shall serve to work harm to you and to aid me, and they shall owe me what they now owe you, and they shall owe you what they now owe me as their mortal foe."

And Galehot bade them promise it. And the King of the Hundred Knights, who was his seneschal and his cousin germain, said to him, "Sir, ye are so worshipful and so discreet that ye ought to under-ſtand well what ye command us, for this is too great a thing to do".

"Dismay you not thereat," said Galehot, "for thus it pleaseth me, and I wit well what I do. But pledge him even as he saith."

And they both promised even so.

Galehot summons his barons to welcome Lancelot, and all joyfully hail him as the flower of knighthood and hold high revelry that evening in the tent of Galehot. That night Galehot has four couches prepared in his chamber, one larger and richer than the reſt for Lancelot, and the others oſtensibly for his attendants. When he knows that Lancelot is asleep, he himself occupies the couch neareſt that of Lancelot.

That night the knight slept heavily, and ever he made moan in his sleep, and Galehot, that scarce slept, heard him well and thought all the night through on how he might keep him. On the morn the knight arose, and he heard mass, and Galehot was already arisen softly, for he would not that the knight should perceive him. And when they had heard mass, the knight called for his arms, and Galehot asked him wherefore. And he said that he would go away. And Galehot said to him, " Fair, sweet friend, bide yet a while, and think not that I would deceive you, for there is naught that ye would dare ask that ye would not have it for the abiding. And wit ye well that ye can have the company of a more powerful man than I, but ye will never have that of a man that loveth you so well. And since that I would do more than all the world to have your company, well I deserve above all others to have it ".

" Sir," said the knight, " then I will abide, for better company than yours could I never have. And now I will make known to you the gift wherefor I will abide, and if I have it not, ye would in vain speak more of my remaining."

" Sir," said Galehot, " speak boldly, and ye shall have it, if it be in my power."

And the knight called the two that were his sureties, and he said in their presence, " Sir, I demand that when ye shall have the maftery over King Arthur so that he may by no means rescue him, so soon as I shall summon you, that ye go to him to cry him mercy and that ye put you wholly in his power ".

When Galehot heard this, he was overmuch amazed, and he began to ponder thereon, and the two kings said to him, " Sir, on what think ye ? Here is no room for thought. Ye have gone so far that there is no turning back ".

" What," said he, " think you that I would fain

retract? If all the world were mine, yet I should not fear to give it all to him. But I thought on the noble word that he hath said, for never man spake one so noble. Sir," said he, " so help me God, ye shall have the boon. For I could do naught for you whereof I should be ashamed. But I pray you that ye take not your company from me to give it to another, since I would do more than any other man to have you."

And the knight promised it him. Thus he remained, and the dinner was prepared, and they went to sit at meat, and in the host of Galehot they made joy of the knight that had remained, they who knew not of the covenant. And in the hostel of King Arthur they made great dole thereat.

CHAPTER XXXIII

How peace was made between Galehot and King Arthur

THUS that day passed, and on the morrow Galehot and his following arose, and they went to hear mass. And Galehot said, " Sir, this is the day of the just. Would ye bear arms ? " And he made answer that he would. " Then I pray you," said Galehot, " that ye wear my arms for the beginning of our fellowship." And he made answer that he would right willingly. " But ye will wear no arms save those of a sergeant." " Gramercy," said Galehot. Then they let fetch the arms, and they armed the knight with all save the hauberk and the greaves, which were too large and broad.

Then the party of Galehot armed them, and the party of Arthur likewise, and as many as were there entered the lists. And King Arthur had commanded that none of them pass the water, for he feared that he would be discomfited, and all for the good knight that he had lost. But no command could keep the nimble young bachelors from passing the water, and in short while there were in many places good justings and fierce encounters, and thus they began to come together on one side and on the other. And when the people of Galehot perceived that their party had the worse, then they succoured them, and in the same way did the party of King Arthur. And the king was by his standard with forty of his most worshipful knights, that he had commanded to lead the queen to safety, if they saw that the battle turned to discomfiture.

When all the host of King Arthur was assembled, then there came to encounter with them the good knight armed with the arms of Galehot. And all that saw him thought that he was Galehot, and they said, " See, here is Galehot ! " But Sir Gawain knew him, and he said, " This is not Galehot, but it is the good knight that wore the black armour the day before yesterday. I know him well ". Thus said Sir Gawain of the good knight. And so soon as he was come to the justing, the followers of Arthur nevermore held themselves of aught but small account, for greatly were they put to the worse by the good knight that was against them, and none the less he spared them oft.

And when that he had routed them, he remained in their midst in the path because of the others that all desired to follow them. Then he looked about him and he began to cry aloud for Galehot. And Galehot came spurring toward him, and he said, " Fair, sweet friend, what would ye ? "

" What ? " said he. " I would a marvel."

" Tell it me boldly," said Galehot.

" Sir," said the knight, " is it enough ? "

" Yea, certes," said Galehot, " speak your pleasure."

" Sir," said the knight, " keep your covenant with me, for now is the place."

" Now, before God," said Galehot, " that irketh me not, since it pleaseth you."

Forthright Galehot pricked straight to the standard where the king was, whose heart nigh burst with grief for his people that he saw discomfited. And the queen was already mounted on her horse, and the forty knights had given spurs to their horses and led her away, for they had now no hope of recovery. And they would fain have carried Sir Gawain away in his litter, but he said that he had liefer die on the spot than see all joy dead and all honour put to shame, and he swooned so oft that all that saw him thought that now he was dying.

When the good knight saw Galehot go to do himself such great mischief for his sake, he thought and said that never had he had so good a friend and so true a comrade, and he felt so great pity for him that he sighed from the depths of his heart and wept beneath his helmet, and he said between his teeth, " Fair Lord God, who can recompense this ? "

Galehot crying mercy of King Arthur

Galehot rode so far as the ſtandard, and he asked
for King Arthur, and the king came forward all dismayed as one that thought to lose all earthly honour.
And when Galehot saw him, he said to him, " Sir,
dismay you not, but come hither, for I would speak
with you ". Then began all to say, " This is Galehot".
And the king marvelled greatly that this could be,
and he came forward. Even so far off as Galehot was
when he saw him, he alighted down from his horse
to the ground, and he kneeled before the king, and he
clasped his hands and said, " Sire, I come to you
to set right that wherein I have done you wrong,
and I repent me, and I put me wholly at your
mercy ".

When the king heard this, he had great joy, and he
raised his hands to heaven, and he was so glad thereat
that he could scarce believe him. And none the less
he made glad cheer, and much he humbled him before
Galehot, and he said to him, " Rise up, fair, sweet
sir ". Galehot raised him up from his knees whereon
he ſtill was, and each kissed other, and they made
great joy each of other.

And Galehot said to the king, " Sire, do your
pleasure with me, and fear naught, for I shall put
myself in your power, and shall go thither where it
pleaseth you, and if ye will, I will bid my following
withdraw, and I will come back to you ".

" Go then," said the king, " and come aback speedily,
for I would fain speak with you."

Forthright Galehot went to his party, and he bade
them withdraw. And King Arthur sent for the queen,
who had gone on her way making great dole. And

the messengers followed after her till they overtook
her, and they told her the great joy that had befallen
them, and she could not believe them till she saw the
true tokens that the king sent her, and then she
turned back with glad cheer. So faſt spread the news
that Sir Gawain heard it, for the king himself told
him with his own lips, and he rejoiced thereat beyond
all men, and he said, " Sire, how can this be ? "

" I' faith," said the king, " I know not. Such hath
been the pleasure of our Lord."

Passing great was the joy of King Arthur, and he
marvelled how this might have befallen. And Galehot
sent his men away, and he said to his companion,
" Fair, sweet comrade, what will ye that I do ? I
have done your bidding, and the king hath commanded
me to return to him. But I will attend you to our
tents, and I will bear you company for a diſtance,
for little have I done for you, and then I will return
to the king ".

" Ah, sir," said the knight, " do ye go to the king
and bear him company all that ye can, for ye have
done me greater service than I can ever repay. But
this much I pray you in God's name, that no living
being learn where I am."

And Galehot promised it him. Thus talking they
rode to their tents, and it was known through all
the hoſt of Galehot that peace was made and how,
and the moſt part of them were grieved thereat, for
better they would have liked war.

CHAPTER XXXIV

How Galehot promised the Queen that she should see Sir Lancelot

Galehot returns to the pavilion of Arthur, where he is joyfully received by the king and the queen, as well as by Sir Gawain. He passes the next few days at court with daily visits to his tent, where he has left Lancelot with the two kings to bear him company. On his first visit Lancelot begs him to remain with Arthur and to comply with all his behests, but he requires Galehot to promise never to ask him his name until he chooses to tell it. On his next visit Galehot learns from the two kings that Lancelot has passed the night in weeping and lamenting. Galehot accordingly charges him with concealing some secret sorrow. But Lancelot makes paltry excuses and does not reveal the true cause of his grief. Galehot again commits him to the keeping of the two kings before going back to the pavilion of Arthur.

AND Galehot went his way to the court of King Arthur. And all made the greatest joy of him that they might. And after dinner Galehot and the king and queen gathered about the couch whereon Sir Gawain lay, and anon Sir Gawain spake to Galehot. " Sir," said he, " let it not irk you, if I ask you somewhat."

" Certes," said Galehot, " it will not."

" Sir, this peace that is made between you and the king, tell me, by the being that ye love most, by whom was it made ? "

" In sooth," said Galehot, " ye have so conjured me that I would not lie about it. A knight made it."

" Who is he ? " said Sir Gawain.

" So help me God, I know not," said Galehot.

"Who was he with the black armour?" said the queen.

"Lady," said Galehot, "he was a knight."

"Ye can say so much," said Sir Gawain, "even if ye would keep your pledge."

"Sir," said Galehot, "I have kept my pledge to you when I told you that it was a knight, and more I will not tell you now. And I should have told you naught, if ye had not conjured me by the being that I love moſt; and know that the being that I love moſt made the peace."

"Perdy, it was the black knight," said the queen. "Now, show him to us."

"Who, lady? I can show him to you as well as I can any man whereof I know naught."

"Hush!" said she. "He tarrieth with you, and yeſterday he wore your arms."

"Lady, lady," said he, "that is true. But I have not seen him since the firſt time that I left my lord Gawain, that is here."

"What," said the king, "know ye not him of the black armour? I thought that he was of your land."

"Before God, Sire," said Galehot, "he is not."

"Sir," said the king, "neither is he of mine. For it is long while since I have heard speak of any loſt knight of whom the pennon was not known."

Right hard both the king and the queen pressed Galehot to let them know the name of the knight, but no more could they draw forth from him. And Sir Gawain, fearing that he was vexed thereby, said to the king, "Sire, leave speaking thereon, for certes, whoe'er the knight be, he is a man of worship, nor in

194

this world is there a knight that I would so fain resemble". Greatly Sir Gawain esteemed the knight, and he thought within him that in sooth it was the black knight that had made the peace between them twain, and that for him Galehot had turned his honour to shame at the moment when he saw that he had the mastery over all. And he told the queen that thus it was, and Galehot was the more honoured therefor, nor as it seemed to them might they sufficiently esteem him.

Long time they talked of the black knight. And within a while the queen rose and said that she would go to the turret of Sir Gawain, wherein was her chamber, and Galehot attended her. And when they were mounted up to the tower, the queen took Galehot into her counsel, and she said to him, " Galehot, I love you well, and I would do more for you than mayhap ye think, and it is true that ye have in your company and in your keeping the good knight. And by chance he is one that I know well; so I pray you, as ye hold my love dear, on the pledge that whatsoever I shall e'er be able to do for you I place at your disposition and in your control, that ye bring it about that I may see him ".

" Lady," said Galehot, " he is not now in my power, nor hath he been since the peace was made between me and my lord."

" Certes," said the queen, " it cannot be that ye know not where he is."

" And if he were now in my tent, there would be need of another will than mine. It may even be that he is not now in this land."

"And where is he ? " said the queen.

"Lady," said he, "I suppose that he is in my country, and wit ye well that since ye have prayed and conjured me, I will do all in my power that ye may be eased by seeing him."

"So much know I well," said the queen, "that if ye do your utmost, I shall see him. Now I trust to you therein, and do ye deal so that I shall ever be beholden to you. For he is the man in all the world that I would most gladly see, not for that I hope to become acquaint with him for aught save good, but for that there is no man or woman that would be the worse for knowing a man of worship."

"Lady, that wit I well," said Galehot, "and ye may be assured that I shall do all in my power."

"Gramercy," said the queen. "Now, away, and so do that I may see him so soon as may be. And if he is in your country, I pray you send to fetch him by day and by night, so that he be here the soonest that he may."

CHAPTER XXXV

How Galehot told Sir Lancelot that the Queen would fain see him

THEREWITHAL Galehot left the queen, and he betook him to the king and to Sir Gawain and the other knights that were there, and the king said to him, "Galehot, now are we free of our hosts, for we have here none save the people of our own households.

196

Let draw your meinie near mine, and I will let draw mine near yours, and thus we shall be nearer one to the other ".

"Sire," said Galehot, "I will bring my people before you on the riverbank in such wise that my tent shall be opposite yours, and a boat shall be made ready whereby we shall pass from there here and from here there, and I will go forthright."

"Certes," said the king, "ye have well said."

Anon Galehot went to his tent, and he found his comrade in a ſtudy. And he asked him how he fared. And he said well, but that fear was maſtering him. And Galehot said to him, " Sir, in God's name, of what are ye afraid ? "

" Sir," said he, " leſt I be known."

"Now think not thereon," said Galehot, "for by the faith that I owe you, ye shall never be known save at your pleasure."

Thereupon he told him what the queen had said, and how she had put him to entreaty that she see the good knight, and how he had answered her. " And wit ye well," said he, " that she desireth naught so much as to see you. And my lord the king hath prayed me that I make my following draw nigh his, so that my tent shall be opposite his own, for we are too far one from other. Now tell me what ye will that I do, for it lieth in your will and in your pleasure."

" Sir," said he, " I counsel you to do what my lord the king asketh of you, for it will advantage you much."

" Fair, sweet friend," said Galehot, " and what shall I reply to my lady concerning that which I have told you ? "

"Certes," said he, "I know not." And he began to sigh and the tears came to his eyes, and he turned him away, and he was so moved within him that he knew not where he was.

And Galehot said to him, "Sir, have no fear. But tell me plainly how ye will that it shall be, and know well that it shall be even as ye will. For I had liefer anger half the world than you alone, and it is for love of you that the king hath mine. So tell me what pleaseth you ".

"Sir," said the knight, "I would follow whate'er ye counsel, for from henceforth I am in your keeping."

"So help me God," said he, "I see not how ye can be the worse for seeing my lady."

"Sire," said the knight, "I shall have enough pain and joy therein."

Then Galehot was ware of his ſtate, and he held him so short that the knight granted that which he asked. "But," said he, "it needs muſt be so privily that none know thereof, and say to my lady that ye have sent to fetch me."

"Leave the reſt to me," said Galehot, "for I mean to ponder well thereupon."

Right so he called his seneschal, and he bade him, so soon as he should be gone to court, to let take his pavilion and his tents and his nets of iron, and carry them all opposite the following of the king, and lodge them so near that there should be naught betwixt them twain save the river. Anon he went to court with a small following, and the queen was already issued forth from the tower. And when she saw

Galehot come, she sprang forward to meet him, and she asked him how he had sped on his errand.

"Lady," said he, " I have wrought so well that I fear me that your prayer will take from me the being that I moſt love in the world."

" So help me God," said she, " ye will lose naught through me that I shall not pay it back to you two-fold. But what will ye lose thereby?"

"Lady," said he, "him himself whom ye demand, for I fear leſt somewhat may befall wherefor he will be angered with me, and that I shall lose him forever."

"Certes," said she, "that could I never give back to you. But, if it please God, by me ye shall ne'er lose him, and he would not be courteous, if he worked you ill for love of me. But none the less, when will he come?"

"Lady, so soon as he can," said he, "for I have sent to fetch him at full speed."

" Now we shall see," said she, " for he will be here on the morrow, if ye will."

"Lady," said he, "he would not be here, if he set out now from the place where he is. And I would that he might be here even to-night."

That night Galehot went back to see his comrade, and he told him what he had found, and that the queen was passing desirous to see him, and he felt in his heart fear and joy. And when that they had taken counsel for a long time together, Galehot by his leave came back to the king, and the queen drew him aside and asked him if he had heard any tidings of the knight, and he said none yet. And she said smiling, " Fair, sweet friend, hold not far from me that which ye might speed toward me ".

" Lady," said he, " so help me God, I should not see him less gladly than ye."

" I wend", said she, " that ye set greater store thereby than I. That is the reason," said she, "wherefor I fear that ye may make me pay dear for him. And ever it befalleth that the thing most desired is the most denied. But there are folk that against their will grant to another the use of that which they themselves love. And none the less have no fear, for never through me will ye lose aught that ye have had."

" Lady, gramercy," said Galehot, " for I suppose that ye can aid me more than I can aid you."

So talking they passed the day, and that night Galehot returned to the tent of the king, and the king would not that he departed from him. On the morn full early Galehot went back to his comrade, and he recounted to him the words of the queen, and he said so much to him that he took comfort from the fears that he had had, and he led not so sorry a life as had been his wont, and his countenance that had been pale and downcast, and his eyes that were red and swollen returned to their beauty. And Galehot was glad thereof, and he asked him, " Sir, if my lady asketh me about you, what shall I answer her ? "

" Sir," said he, " whate'er seemeth best to you, for henceforth the matter resteth with you."

Thus Galehot went to his comrade in the morning and in the evening. And each time that he returned the queen asked him what he had found. That night Galehot went there where he was wont, and on the morrow he rose right early, and he went to his comrade, and he said to him, " Sir, this is the end ; to-day it is fitting that the queen see you ".

" Sir," said he, " in God's name, let none know thereof save only we and she, for there are those in the court of my lord the king that would know me well, if they should see me."

" Now have no care," said Galehot, " for I will take thought thereon."

Therewithal he again took leave of him, and he called his seneschal. " Look well," said he, " if I send for you hereafter, that ye come to me, and lead my comrade with you in such wise that none may know save you that it is he." " Sir," said he, " as it pleaseth you." Right so Galehot repaired to the tent of the king, and the queen asked him what tidings.

" Lady," said he, " good and fair. The flower of all the knights of the world is come."

" Ah, God," said she, " how shall I see him ? I would fain see him in such wise that none know that it is he save ye and I, for I would that none others have pleasure therein."

" I' faith," said Galehot, " thus it shall be. For he said that for naught on earth would he that any of the household of the king should know him."

" What ? " said she. " Then is he known here ? "

" Lady," said he, " some folk that know him might see him."

" Ah, God, who can he be ? " said she.

" Lady," said he, " before Heaven, I know not, for never hath he told me his name nor who he is."

" Nay ? " said she. "Then, perdy, here is a marvel. Now am I the more eager to see him."

"Lady," said he, "ye shall indeed see him to-night, and I will tell you how. We will go down yonder to make merry, and I will show you a place hard by the meadow, where there are many bushes, and we shall have the least following that we may, and ye shall see him there a little before it draweth toward evening."

" Ah," said she, " well have ye devised, fair, sweet friend. Now would that it pleased our Lord that it were already eventide ! "

Then they both began to laugh, and the queen embraced him and made great joy out of measure. And the Lady of Malohaut espied them, and her seemed that matters sped faster than they were wont, and she gave great heed thereto, and she saw no knight come thither that she looked him not well in the face. The queen made passing great joy of the knight that was to come, and long it seemed to her that the evening tarried, and she set her to talk and to devise how to forget the day, the which was irksome to her.

CHAPTER XXXVI

How Galehot led Sir Lancelot to the Queen in the meadow, and how the Queen kissed Sir Lancelot in token of her love

IN such wise the day passed till after supper the gloaming came. The queen took Galehot by the hand, and she called the Lady of Malohaut to her and

the maiden, Lore of Carduel, and only a single damsel
from them that she had about her, and she took her
way down the meadow thither where Galehot had
said. And when they had gone a little space, Galehot
looked and he saw a squire, and he called him, and he
told him to go to his seneschal and bid him come to
him, and he showed him to what place. And when
the queen heard him, she looked at him and she said,
" What," said she, " is he your seneschal ? "

" Nay, lady," said he, " but he will come with the
seneschal."

Anon they passed under the trees, and Galehot
and the queen sat apart from the rest on one side,
and on the other the ladies, that wondered why they
were so secret.

And the squire went to the seneschal and gave him
the message, and he took the knight forthright with
him, and they passed beyond the water and came
straight down the meadow, even as the squire had bade
them. And they were both so fair knights that in
vain might fairer be sought in any country.

When they drew nigh, both they and the ladies
regarded each the other, and so soon as the Lady of
Malohaut espied the knight, she knew him, for she
had had him many a day in her keeping. And for
that she would not that he knew her, she bowed her
head, and she drew near the damsels, and the knight
passed before them, and the seneschal greeted them.
And Galehot said to the queen, " Lady," said he,
" ye see here the best knight in the world. Which
seemeth to you to be he ? "

" Which is he ? " said the queen. " Certes," said

she, " they are both well favoured knights. But I
see none that would seem to have in his person half
the prowess that the black knight had."

" Lady," said Galehot, " now wit ye well that he is
one of these two."

Right so they came before the queen. The knight
trembled so that he might scarce salute her. And he
so loſt his colour that she marvelled greatly thereat.
Then they both kneeled down, and the seneschal
saluted her, and so also did the other, but timorously,
and he fixed his eyes on the ground like a man abashed.
And then the queen thought within her that this
was he. Galehot said to the seneschal, " Go and bear
those maidens yonder company, for they are more
alone than is meet ". And he did even as his lord
commanded him.

And the queen took the knight by the hand even
as he kneeled, and she seated him before her, and she
made him fair semblance, and she said to him smiling,
" Sir, much have we desired you, and now at laſt,
thanks to God and to Galehot here, we see you.
And nevertheless I know not even yet if ye be the
knight for whom we have asked, but Galehot hath
told me that ye are he. But I would ſtill fain hear
from your own lips who ye are, if it were your pleasure".

And he made answer that he knew not who he was,
and never once regarded he her in the face. The
queen wondered greatly what ailed him, and yet she
suspected in part what it was. And Galehot, when
that he saw him so abashed and dismayed, thought
within him that the knight would sooner tell his thought
if he were alone with the queen. And he looked

Lancelot questioned by Guinevere

toward the ladies, and he said on high so that all might hear him, " Certes," said he, " now am I in sooth a churl that all these ladies have but a single knight to bear them company." Therewith he arose and went there where the ladies sat, and they rose to meet him, and he seated them again, and then they began to talk of many things.

And the queen put the knight to the question, and she said to him, " Fair, sweet sir, why hide ye yourself from me ? Surely there is no reason therefor. And even though there were, thus much can ye tell me, if ye are he that won the assembly the day before yesterday ".

" Lady," said he, " nay."

" What, did ye not wear black armour ? "

" Lady, yea."

" Then are ye not he to whom Sir Gawain sent the three horses ? "

" Lady, yea."

" Then wore ye not the arms of Galehot on the last day ? "

" Lady, yea."

" Then ye are he that won the first day and the second ? "

" Lady," said he, " in truth I am not."

Then the queen saw that he would not make avow that he had won it, and she esteemed him highly therefor. " Now tell me," said she, " who made you knight ? "

" Lady," said he, " ye."

" I ? " said she. " When ? "

" Lady, do ye remember that a knight came to my

lord King Arthur at Camelot, that was wounded through the body with two truncheons of lances and had a sword through the head, and that a young squire came to the king on a Friday in the even, and he was made knight the Sunday thereafter ? "

"That," said she, "I remember well. And, as ye hope for God's mercy," said she, "were ye the youth that the damsel clad in a white robe brought to the king ? "

"Why say ye so ? " said he.

"Because," said she, "ye say that I made you knight."

"Lord love me, lady," said he, "it is sooth." For it was then the custom in the kingdom of Logres that none might be made knight without the girding on of the sword. And he of whom he held the sword made him knight. "The king gave me the accolade, but, wit ye well, he gave me no sword, but I hold it of you. Therefore I say that ye made me knight."

"Certes," said she, "I am right glad thereof. And whither went ye thereafter ? "

"Lady, I went to give succour to the Lady of Nohaut, and anon there came thither Sir Kay, that did combat with me."

"And in the meantime sent ye me aught ? "

"Lady, yea," said he. "I sent you two maidens."

"Yea, in sooth, it is true," said she. "And when ye rode on your way back from Nohaut, whither went ye thereafter ? "

"Lady, to the Dolorous Gard."

"And who conquered it ? "

"Lady, I entered therein."

"Ah," said she, "then wit I well who ye are. Ye are called Lancelot of the Lake."

And he was silent. "I' faith," said she, "in vain ye conceal it. Short time since it was first known at court." Then she asked him why he had suffered an insolent knave to lead him by the bridle.

"Lady," said he, "I suffered it for that I had no control over my heart or my body."

"Now tell me," said she, "were ye afore at the tournament?"

"Lady, yea."

"And what armour wore ye?"

"Lady, all red."

"Now, by my head," said she, "ye speak soothly. And the day afore yesterday at the assembly wherefore did ye such noble deeds of arms?"

And he began to sigh heavily. The queen pressed him hard, as one that wist well how it was with him.

"Tell me truly," said she, "how it is with you, for I will never discover it to no man. And I wit well that ye have done this for the sake of some lady or damsel. Now tell me who she is, by the faith that ye owe me."

"Ah, lady," said he, "I see that I must needs say it. It was ye."

"I?" said she.

"In sooth, lady."

"For me ye never brake the three blades that my maiden brought you, for I had held me well aloof from the message."

"Lady," said he, "I did for them that which I ought, and for you that which I could."

"Now tell me," said she, "all these exploits that ye have done, for whom did ye them?"

"Lady, for you."

"What," said she, "love ye me then so well?"

"Lady," said he, "I love not so well myself or another."

"And since when," said she, "have ye loved me so well?"

"Lady," said he, "since that I was called knight, and yet I was not."

"And by the faith that ye owe me, whence came the love that ye have for me?"

At these words that the queen spake it befell that the Lady of Malohaut coughed,[1] knowing what she did, and she raised her head that she had held bowed. He, that had many times heard her, heard her now, and he looked at her, and he knew her, and he had such fear and pain in his heart that he might not make answer to that which the queen asked of him, and he began to sigh right heavily, and the tears fell down his face so fast that the samite wherewith he was clad was wet as far as his breast. And the more he looked at the Lady of Malohaut, the more was his heart at misease. Of this the queen was ware, and she saw that he looked piteously toward the ladies, and she checked him. "Tell me," said she, "whence came this love, for I ask you."

He enforced him to speak so far as he might, and he said, "Lady, since the time that I have said."

"And how came it?" said she.

"Lady," said he, "ye made me love you, ye who made me your love, if your mouth erred not."

" My love ? " said she. " And how ? "

" Lady, I came before you when I had taken leave of my lord the king, armed at all points save for my hauberk, and I commended you to God, and I said that I was your knight in whatsoever place I might be, and ye said that ye would fain have me for your love and your knight. I said ' God be with you, lady,' and ye said, ' God be with you, fair, sweet love,' and never thenceforth hath the word left my heart, and it is the word that will make me a man of worship, if so be that ever I am one. And never thereafter, lady, have I been in great mischance that I have not bethought me of this word. This word comforteth me in all my griefs ; this word hath protected me from all ills and sheltered me in all peril; this word is my solace in all travail; this word maketh me rich in all my great poverty."

" I' faith," said the queen, " 't was a word spoken in a happy hour, and God be praised that He led me to speak it. But I took it more lightly than ye did, and to many a knight have I said it where I thought of naught beyond the saying. Yet your thought was not base, but it was gentle and debonair, and good hath come to you therefrom, for it hath made you a man of worship. And none the less such is not the custom of knights, who make fair semblance to many ladies of that which they have little at heart. And your bearing showeth me that ye love I know not which of those ladies yonder more than ye love me. And ye have wept enough, and ye dare not look at them directly. So I well perceive that your thoughts are less for me than ye make semblance that they are.

209

14

Now by the faith that ye owe the being that ye moſt love, tell me which she is."

"Ah, lady," said he, "in God's name, I cry you mercy. So help me God, in sooth none of them hath my heart in her keeping."

"This availeth you no whit," said the queen. "Ye can hide naught from me, for I have seen many such signs, and I perceive that your heart is there, even though your person is here."

And this she said to see how far she might put him at misease, for well she discerned that he thought not on love save for her alone, even had he done naught for her but on the day when he wore the black arms. But she delighted to see his misease, and he was so tormented thereby that but a little and he would have swooned, but the dread of the ladies, who looked at them, withheld him. The queen herself feared when she saw him grow pale and change colour, and she took him by the shoulder leſt he should fall. Then she called Galehot. He sprang up and came running toward her, and he saw that his comrade was thus moved, and he felt as aggrieved in his heart as he might be, and he said, "Ah, lady, tell me, in God's name, what aileth him". The queen told him what she had set forth to Lancelot.

"Ah, lady," said Galehot, "in God's name, I cry you mercy. Ye might well deprive us of him, if ye diſturb him thus, and that would be a loss beyond measure."

"Certes, 't would be mine," said she. "But know ye why he did such feats of prowess ?"

"Nay, lady," said he.

" In sooth, for me," said she, " if he hath told me the truth."

" Lady," said he, " so help me God, ye should well believe him, for even as he is the moſt worshipful of men, so is his heart truer than that of any other."

" Say ye," said she, " that he is the moſt worshipful of all men ? In sooth, if ye knew what he has done at arms since he was made knight even as I know it, ye would well say so."

Then she recounted all his aĉts of chivalry even as he had told them to her, and that he had borne the red arms the other year at the other tournament. " And know well," said she, " that he did all this for the sake of a single word that I spake to him." Therewith she told him even as ye have heard the word that she had said.

" Ah, lady," said Galehot, " for God's sake and for his own great deserts have mercy upon him, even as I have done that which ye asked of me."

" What favour will ye that I show him ? " said she.

" Lady, ye know well that he loveth you above all else and hath done more for you than any knight could do for you in all his life. Know too that the peace betwixt my lord the king and me had never been made, if he had not been here and made it all alone."

" Certes," said she, " I doubt not that he hath done more for me than I can recompense, even if he had wrought no more than the peace, nor could he require of me aught that I would refuse him. But he requireth naught of me, and he is sad and downcaſt —I know not wherefore,—and he no sooner ceaseth

211

weeping than he looketh toward these ladies. Nevertheless, I distrust him not that he loveth any one of them, but he feareth perchance that one of them knoweth him."

"Lady," said Galehot, "of this there is no need even to speak. But take pity on him, for he loveth you more than himself, and, so help me God, I saw in his bearing when he came naught save that he feared to be known, and never hath he discovered more than that to me."

"I will show him such mercy as ye desire," said she, "for ye have done that which I asked of you, and I ought to do that which ye will. But he beggeth naught of me."

"Certes, lady," said Galehot, "he dareth not, for no man may love where he feareth not. But I entreat you for him. And if I entreated you not, ye should still purvey for yourself, for a richer treasure could ye never win."

"In sooth," said she, "I believe it well, and I will do whatsoever ye bid me."

"Lady, gramercy," said Galehot. "I pray you that ye grant him your love, and that ye take him henceforth for your knight, and that ye become his loyal lady for all your life days. Thus will ye have enriched him more than if ye had given him all the world."

"Certes," said she, "thus I grant him that he be all mine and I all his. And let any misdoing or disloyalty to the affiance lie in your amendment."

"Lady," said Galehot, "gramercy. Now it behooveth that the service begin."

"Ye may devise naught," said the queen, "that I shall not do it."

"Lady, gramercy," said he. "Then do ye kiss him in my sight for the beginning of true love."

"As for kissing," said she, "I see not that this is either the place or the time. And doubt not that I would be as fain for it as he would be, but yonder are those ladies, who marvel much that we are gone so far, and it could not be that they would not see it. And yet, if it is his pleasure, I will kiss him gladly."

And the knight was so glad that he could answer naught save, "Lady, gramercy".

"Ah, lady," said Galehot, "doubt not his will thereto, for it is wholly there. And wit ye well that none will see it. Now let us three draw together even as if we were taking counsel together."

"Now wherefore should I wait for entreaties?" said the queen. "More do I desire it than either ye or he."

Therewithal they all three drew together and made semblance that they took counsel. The queen saw that the knight durſt do no more, and she raised his chin, and she kissed him full long in the presence of Galehot,[1] so that the Lady of Malohaut was ware that she kissed him. And thereupon the queen, that was a passing discreet and noble lady, began to speak.

"Fair, sweet love," said she to the knight, "I am all yours. Thus much have ye wrought, and great joy have I thereof. Now look well that the matter be kept so secret as need be. For I am one of the ladies in the world of whom the greateſt good hath been said, and if my fair fame should be lessened through you, then would love have made me base and low. And you, Galehot, who are moſt discreet, I entreat likewise, for if ill came to me therefrom, it would be through you alone. And if I have welfare and happiness therefrom, ye will have given it me."

"Lady," said Galehot, "he could ne'er be the cause of misfortune to you, and I have well done that which ye commanded. Now 't would be fitting that ye should grant me my will even as I have granted you yours. For I said to you yeſterday that ye might at some time aid me more than I might aid you."

"Speak boldly," said she, "for there is naught that ye dare ask of me that I would not do."

"Lady," said he, "then ye have granted me that ye will give me his company forever."

"Certes," said she, "if he ſhould fail you in this respeᶜt, then would ye have ill employed the great toil that ye have expended on him."

Thereupon she took the knight by the hand, and she said to Galehot, "I give you this knight forever, save that I have him afore ye. Now do ye promise it likewise," said she. The knight promised it. "And know ye," said she to Galehot, "whom I have given you? Lancelot of the Lake, the son of King Ban of Benoich." And thus she made known the knight, who was much abashed thereby. Then Galehot had the greateſt joy that he had ever had, for he had heard it said oft-times, as words go, that the beſt knight in the world was a poor man, and well he knew that King Ban had been a man of gentle lineage and puissant of friends and of lands.

Thus the firſt meeting of Lancelot and the queen was by means of Galehot. And Galehot had never known him save by sight, and therefore Lancelot had required him to promise that he would not ask his name till that he told it to him or another for him. Then they arose all three, and already it drew faſt toward night, but the moon was arisen, and it was so light that they might see clearly the length of the meadow. Forthwithal they all took their way back together up through the meadow to the tent of the king. And the seneschal of Galehot came after them with the ladies till they came ſtraight to the pavilions of Galehot, and then Galehot sent his comrade to his tent, and Lancelot took leave of the queen, and he went away with the seneschal.

And Galehot accompanied the queen to the pavilion of the king, and when the king saw them, he asked whence they came. " Sir," said Galehot, " we come from seeing the meadows with these few people here." Then they sat them down and they talked of many things, and Galehot and the queen had full great ease. Within a while the queen rose and went to the tower, and Galehot attended her thither. And then he commended her to God. Then he went away to take leave of the king. And then he went to his comrade, and they reſted that night in one bed, and they talked all the night long of that whereof their hearts had full great ease.

CHAPTER XXXVII

How the Saxon Hold was taken, and how Sir Lancelot was entreated of the Queen to abide in the fellowship of the King

After the queen has gone to her chamber, she ſtands by the window looking out, loſt in thought. The Lady of Malohaut comes to her side, and adroitly implying that she knows of her love for Lancelot, admits that she held Lancelot in captivity, sent him to the assembly, and came there herself to incite him to feats of valour solely that Guinevere might be led to return the love from which the Lady had already suspeſted that he was suffering. She begs the queen to keep her at court as a confidante during the absence of Lancelot. Guinevere gladly consents, and secretly resolves that she will induce Galehot to choose the Lady of Malohaut for his lady and his love. At their next meeting with Galehot she learns that neither he nor the Lady are loth to the arrangement. Many secret meetings between the two pairs of lovers follow in the meadow, until at length Gawain is so far recovered of his wounds that Arthur decides to break up the encampment and return to Logres. Galehot also is recalled to Sorelois by his own affairs, but agrees to come with Lancelot to the firſt tournament that Arthur shall hold in Logres.

Galehot takes Lancelot to Sorelois with him. Sorelois is a beautiful and fertile land nearer to the kingdom of Logres than to the Far Away Isles, which form the principal domain of Galehot. On one side it is bordered by the river Assurne, which separates it from the territory of Arthur, and on the other it is washed by the sea. It can be entered by only two passes, each of which is proteſted by a valiant knight and ten other armed men. Within this land Lancelot lives in complete privacy, but his love for Guinevere keeps him reſtless and unhappy. He is somewhat cheered ere long by the arrival of his cousin Lionel, whom the Lady of the Lake sends to remain in Sorelois until the time for his knighting.

Meanwhile Arthur, who does not know that the red knight of the firſt assembly is Lancelot, reminds Gawain of his relinquished queſt for him, and Gawain with a number of companions accordingly sets out in search of him. The queen, however,

The cleft shield

Lionel before Guinevere

[*face p. 217*

first privately reveals to Gawain that the red knight is Lancelot and that he is to be found in the company of Galehot.

One day there arrives at court a maiden bearing a shield that hangs from her neck upside down. She comes before the queen and greets her from the fairest and the most discreet damsel in the world, who bids her keep the shield for love of her and of another whom the queen loves better; the shield, the maiden adds, will heal her of the greatest grief that she has ever had, and will bring her the greatest joy that she has ever known. The maiden who sends the shield proves to be the Lady of the Lake. It is split throughout the entire length into two halves, separated by a handbreadth and held together merely by a buckle; on one half the figure of a knight richly armed is painted, and on the other that of a fair lady, each with arms extended toward the other. The queen begs the damsel to explain the significance of the shield. "Lady," the maiden replies, "this is, I ween, the best knight of those now living, and so much hath he wrought by prowess and by love that the lady gave him her love, and this is ye, lady, and your love, that is the most worshipful man in the world. And ye are depicted on the two parts of the shields that ye see here disjoined, and when it shall befall that your love is all perfected, then know that this shield will reunite as if it had ne'er been cleft. And know that then ye shall be free of the greatest sorrow that hath e'er befallen you, and ye shall have the greatest joy that ye have ever had. But this shall not be ere the best knight that is now without the court of King Arthur shall belong to his household". The queen is overjoyed at these tidings, for she knows well who this knight is.

As the months go by and no word comes to Sorelois from Guinevere, Lancelot becomes more and more disconsolate, and Galehot decides that a meeting with her must be arranged. At his suggestion Lionel is sent to court to tell Guinevere of the condition of Lancelot and to beg that she grant him an interview.

On hearing the message Guinevere and the Lady of Malohaut take counsel together as to how they can see their lovers. While they are forming their plans, news comes to court that the Saxons and Irish have invaded Scotland and are devastating the country. Arthur summons his hosts to gather within a fortnight at Carduel. The queen accordingly sends word to Lancelot that he and Galehot must also come thither, but secretly, and that Lancelot must carry a pennon that she sends him, as well as the wonderful shield that he bore at the laſt assembly. To the king she gives the advice not to send for Galehot to join his hoſts until he is sure that his need of him is great.

Before Lionel returns from his errand, Gawain, who has learned that Lancelot is in Sorelois, has succeeded in effecting an entrance to the land. He is joined later by Hector, the half-brother of Lancelot. Shortly after this Gawain learns of the Saxon invasion and proposes that the four knights go together to the war. Galehot, mindful of the message from Guinevere, that Lionel has in the meantime brought, insiſts that they go in disguise. The knights proceed to a caſtle, called the Saxon Hold, to which Arthur has already laid siege. The caſtle, however, is in the possession of an enchantress, Camille, who by her arts has won the love of Arthur. He nevertheless continues the siege and engages in the firſt battle, which takes place the day after the arrival of the four knights. The queen and the Lady of Malohaut watch the fighting from a tower and recognise Lancelot, who does marvellous deeds at arms. The queen from time to time sends him messages, and when at length darkness puts an end to the battle, which has resulted disaſtrously for the Saxons, she and the Lady of Malohaut come down from their tower and greet Lancelot and Galehot.

That night Arthur is decoyed by the promises of Camille into her caſtle, where she betrays him into the hands of her knights, who at once take him prisoner. Guinevere profits by his absence for the night to make an assignment with Lancelot. "And toward midnight the queen arose and she came to the shield that the damsel from the lake had brought to her, and she found it whole without a cleft, and she was right glad thereat, for now she knew that she was the beſt beloved of any lady."

When the news of Arthur's captivity comes to the hoſt, Lancelot, Galehot, Gawain, and Hector set out to rescue him. They, too, are duped by the enemy and are made prisoners in the caſtle of Camille. All except Lancelot are docile captives, but he refuses to eat or drink, and finally in his anguish of mind he goes mad and becomes so violent that Camille orders his release. He wanders into the encampment of Arthur, where he is recognised by Guinevere. She sends the Lady of Malohaut to bring him to her that she may tend him, but he threatens the Lady with ſtones when she approaches him. When Guinevere comes to him, however, he allows her to take

him by the hand and lead him to her chamber. Here she tends
him carefully, but he continues to rave until the Lady of the
Lake herself appears and reſtores him to reason by means of a
magic salve and by the virtue of the magic shield that he has
worn in the conteſt and that she bids him hang at his neck. As
soon as he has recovered, he demands his arms and goes out
to join the following of Arthur in an attack upon the Saxons.
By the power of his enchanted shield he succeeds in entering the
caſtle of Camille and in setting free Arthur and the other
knights. The magic books of Camille are deſtroyed, and she
puts an end to her own life. Gawain reveals to Arthur that
his liberator is Lancelot, who is none other than the long
sought red knight.

Thus was the Saxon Hold taken. And the king
descended therefrom and a great part of his following.
And Gawain came out of the tower, and he came to
the king, and he said to him, " Sire, ye are not aware
that ye will lose Lancelot, if ye take not heed ".

" How ? " said the king.

" Certes," said he, " Galehot will lead him away so
soon as ever he may, for he is more jealous of him than
is knight of young and beauteous lady that he loves.
But I will tell you what ye should do. Command
that the gate be closed and that none go forth save
by my consent alone, and do ye on our oath entruſt the
gate to me and to Kay the seneschal and to Gaheriet,
my brother, and to Sir Ewaine. And we will set
such a guard there that none shall enter in or go out
without our will."

Then the king came into the great hall, and he took
Galehot by one hand and Lancelot by the other, and
he led them into the great tower, and they seated them
on a couch, and he let unarm them. Then the king
called Sir Gawain and took his oath, and so likewise that of Sir Ewaine and of Kay and of Gaheriet.

And when that Galehot heard it, he knew well what it was, and he sighed heavily within him. Then he told to Lancelot a part of that which would betide.

"Fair comrade," said Galehot, "I know in sooth that I am come to the place where I shall lose you."

"How?" said Lancelot.

"For that the king", said he, "will pray you to abide in his household, and what shall I do that have given me wholly, body and soul, to loving you?"

"Certes," said Lancelot, "I ought to love you more than all other men in the world. And so I do, and never, if it please God, shall I remain here, unless force compelleth me to remain. But how shall I refuse aught that my lady commandeth?"

"To that point I will never force you," said Galehot, "for if she willeth it, so be it. Perforce it must be."

Thus they two talked long together, and they made semblance of greater cheer than their hearts gave them. And the king let summon the queen. And she came right gladly, and when she came to the tower, all rose to meet her, and she left all the others, and she threw her arms about the neck of Lancelot and kissed him in the sight of all that were there, for that she would fain deceive them that none might think that which was. And none saw it but esteemed her the more therefor. And he stood all abashed, and she said, "Sir knight, I know not who you are, but I know what to offer you for the love of my lord and for mine honour which ye have maintained to-day. But first for his sake and afterwards for mine own I grant you my love and myself as loyal lady to loyal knight".

" Gramercy, lady," said he.

And when that the king heard her, he was glad for that she had spoken thus of her own will.

" Lady," said the king, " know ye who this knight is ? "

And she said, " Nay ".

" Know," said he, " that he is Lancelot of the Lake, he who won the two jufts between me and Galehot yonder."

And the queen made semblance, when she heard this, that it came to her as a marvel, and she crossed her many times.

And anon when supper was ready, they sat at meat. And when they had eaten, the king summoned the queen for counsel, and he said to her, " Lady, I would pray Lancelot to remain with me and to be of the fellowship of the Round Table, for his prowess hath been well proved. And if he will not ftay for me, then do ye fall at his feet ".

" Sire," said she, " he is the knight and the companion of Galehot, and it is meet that ye should entreat Galehot that he suffer it."

Then the king came to Galehot, and he begged him in all courtesy to grant that Lancelot be of his household and abide with him and belong to his fellowship. " Ah, Sire," said Galehot, " I came with all my might to you in your time of need, for 't was all that I could do. And, so help me God, I could not live without him, and how would ye take my life from me ? " And this he said, for that he had no thought that the queen desired it. And the king looked at the queen, and he said to her, " Lady, do ye pray him therefor ". And forthright she fell on her knees at his feet, and he was sore grieved thereat, and he bided not for the reply of Galehot, but he sprang up, and he said, " Ah, lady, I abide at the pleasure of my lord and at yours ". And he raised her up by the hand. " Gramercy, sir," said she.

" Sire," said Galehot to the king, " thus ye shall never have him. It liketh me better to be poor and at ease than to be rich and at misease. Keep me with him, if ever I did aught that pleased you. And in sooth ye should do this for him and for me, for wit ye well that all the love that I have for you I have for his sake."

And the king rose, and he thanked him, and he said that he would keep them both, not as his knights, but as his companions and his seigneurs.

Thus kept the king Lancelot and Galehot for his companions. And to honour them both there was such cheer made in the household of King Arthur that none could e'er conceive greater. And on the morrow the king said that he would hold high court even in the Saxon Hold for joy of Lancelot. And he held a great and rich court, and it was the sixth day before All Saints' Day. In such joy abided the king and his household all the days of the festival until the third day after All Saints' Day, and then he departed from the Hold, and he left his guards there, and he went slowly back toward Britain. And when he came to Karaheu, Galehot took leave of him and prayed him that he might lead Lancelot into his country with him. And the king granted it him, though he was loth. And the queen would have it

Guinevere begging Lancelot to join the Round Table

[*face p. 222*

thus, and she said to the king that Advent would ere long be here, and she wrought so that he granted it on condition that they promise faithfully that they would be with him on Chriſtmas Day.

CHAPTER XXXVIII

Of the marvellous dreams of Galehot, and how his caſtle, that hight the Orgulous Gard, fell to the ground

Galehot departs from court for his own country, taking Lancelot with him. He is obviously heavy hearted, and when Lancelot queſtions him as to the reason for his depression, he explains that he foresees that they will not be able long to hold fellowship together, for the queen will certainly desire Lancelot to dwell in the household of the king, and Lancelot will not dare refuse her. Galehot himself cannot take up his abode at the court of Arthur, for his people would oppose it. So he is convinced that separation from Lancelot is inevitable. Lancelot sorrowfully admits that Galehot has done more for his sake than ever one man did for another, but that, although he never willingly would cause Galehot pain, if Guinevere bids him remain at court, he muſt do so. They ride on speaking no more of the matter, but Galehot remains deeply depressed.

AND Galehot and Lancelot entered a foreſt called Glorinde. And Lancelot prayed and conjured Galehot by the being that he loved moſt to tell him the truth and wherefore he had been so long in thought, for he had ne'er seen him so diſtraught as he had been on this road. "And I pray you, sir," he said, "an I ever did you a service that pleased you, that you tell me the truth without concealment. Nor should ye ever hide aught from me, for wit ye well that I love you above all men who ever lived, and well I may, for I have no welfare save from you alone."

"Fair, sweet comrade," said Galehot, "I love you and I have ever loved you more than all the world, and my heart cannot hide itself from you. And so I will tell you that which I would never dare tell any man. Into this grief and into this distress wherein I have been so long a time, two evil dreams have cast me, that came to me day before yesterday in a vision. For in my sleep me seemed that I was in the dwelling of my lord King Arthur in a great company of knights. And there issued forth from the chamber of the queen a serpent, the largest that I have ever heard tell of. And he ran at me and he spread upon me fire and flame, so that I lost the half of my limbs. Thus it befell me the first night. And the night thereafter me seemed that I saw two hearts in my body, and they were so alike that one might scarce be known from the other. And even as I looked, I lost one. And when it had departed from me, it became a leopard, and he betook him to a forest to a company of wild beasts. And then my heart and all my other limbs withered, and it seemed to me in my dream that I died. Such were the two dreams that I have told you, and never shall I be at ease till that I know for a certainty their signification. And I already know a large part thereof."

"Sir," said Lancelot, "I suppose that no clerk can tell you about an event that is to come?"

"Yea," said Galehot, "he could."

Thus they talked long together till that they came

to the water of Assurne. And when they had crossed
it, Galehot turned to a road at the right that led him
toward a castle of his that he had let build short while
since. And it was set on the strongest piece of land
that he had in his domain. And he himself had
called it the Orgulous Gard, for the beauty and
strength that it had. And he had boasted that he
would put King Arthur there, when he should have
taken him. And the castle was set high on a rock,
and beneath it there flowed a rushing water, that
emptied into Assurne at least half a league distant,
and it was called Terence.

To this castle Galehot turned him with intent to
pass the night in one of the many fair dwellings that
he had there. And it was a Welsh league distant,
and clearly they saw it and the strong, mighty tower
that was well machicolated. And Lancelot began to
speak privily, and he said to Galehot, " Certes, it
appeareth that this castle was built by a jocund and
orgulous lord, for never have I beheld one so well
beseen or so fair ".

And Galehot began to sigh. " Fair, sweet comrade,
fair, sweet friend, if ye knew with how high a heart
it was begun, well would ye say thus. Certes, at the
time when I began it, I was set on conquering the
world. And I will show you soon a great marvel,
wherein I did as a fool, for my great pride mounted
as speedily as it hath fallen. For my emprise was
orgulous beyond measure, whereof a large part is
brought to naught. For in this bailey and on this
tower there are one hundred and fifty crenels by count,
and I had undertaken to conquer so much that I

should bring one hundred and fifty kings under my signory. And when I should have conquered them, I would lead them all into this castle. And then I would let crown me. And in honour of me the kings should all wear their crowns, and I would hold a court so great that all the world should speak of me after my death. And I would do yet more. I would let put on each crenel of this castle a candlestick of silver as tall as a knight, with thick branches on high. And on the day of my coronation, after the dinner the crowns of the kings that I had conquered should be put there, each one on a candlestick, and mine should be placed on the pinnacle of the tower that ye may see from here. And thus should all the crowns rest there until nightfall. And then on each candlestick should be placed a lighted taper so that no man might extinguish it, and they should burn thus even till the day. So fair and so rich should be my court that ever by day the crowns should rest on the candlesticks, and ever by night the tapers. And wit ye well that since the castle was built I have ne'er entered therein so sorrowful that I have not issued forth joyous. And therefore I go thither now, for I have greater need of joy than I have ever had before."

Thus talking the comrades rode on, and Lancelot marvelled greatly at this emprise that Galehot had recounted to him. "Ah, Lord God," said he, "how this man must hate me, who have turned him from doing all these deeds! Thus, me seemeth, I have made of the most vigorous man in the world the most sluggish. And all hath befallen him through me." And he was grieved thereat, and he wept so hard that

Lancelot expelled from the Saxon Hold

Galehot and Lancelot riding to Sorelois

[*face p. 226*

the tears fell afore him on his saddlebow, but he gave
good heed that Galehot should not perceive them.
Right so they came before the castle, and then there
befell a marvellous adventure, whereat he was more
amazed than at aught that he had e'er beheld. For
the walls of the tower split straight in the midst, and
all the crenels on one side fell to the ground.

Then Galehot stood still, and he was so confounded
that he could not speak a word. And he crossed
him for the marvel that he had seen. And anon,
before he had gone a stone's throw, all that part of
the bailey and the tower wherefrom the crenels had
fallen was overthrown to the earth, and it made such
a noise in the fall that it seemed that all the rock had
foundered.

When Galehot beheld his castle fall, there is no
need to ask if he was sorrowful, for but a little and he
had fallen from his horse to the ground. And when
he could speak, he said sighing, " Ah, God, thus
miserably my mischance beginneth! " Then he
lowered his bridle, and he turned him back towards
the left across the fields. And Lancelot pricked after
him, for he was so vexed that he knew not what to
do. And none the less he essayed to comfort Galehot,
and he said to him, " Sir, it is not seemly that so
noble a man as ye should grieve for any mischance
that befalleth him, if so be that he himself and his
friends are safe. But he who is base should fear the
loss of his goods more than of his body, for he is
worth naught save for his possessions. And ye may
well see that God hath shown His love toward you,
since we were not within ".

When Galehot heard these words, he looked at him, and he began to smile as if in disdain, and he said, "How is this, fair, sweet friend? Think ye then that I am dismayed for my castle if it is fallen? If it were worth so much that I valued it more than all the castles that are in the world, I should be no more dismayed than I am now. And I will let you know so much of my heart as to tell you that never man saw me dismayed or cast down for loss of land or goods that befell me, nor ever have I made joy or mirth for aught that I have won, save only once, and that was for your fellowship. And nevertheless my heart is dismayed, for it foretelleth me that great ill is to come".

"Sir," said Lancelot, "it oft chanceth that a heart is more at misease at one time than at another, and from misease of heart cometh that of the body. But I esteem not in a man of worship a heart that hath the forebodings of fear, for a heart should meet the forebodings boldly and surmount and overcome them."

"Fair, sweet comrade," said Galehot, "my heart foretelleth me of no fear save two, that is, for you and for me. And mischance to one would please me as much as to the other, and I have set my love in such wise that I pray God that He may never let me live a day after your death. And I fear that I may lose you within a while, and that death or other cause may part us each from other. And know well that if my lady the queen had so kind a heart towards me as I have towards her, she would ne'er take your company from me to give it to another, even if I had never done more for her than fulfil her great desire and your great joy. Howbeit she said to me that no man would make largesse of that which he could not do without, and well have I been ware thereof. And I would that ye know that the hour when I lose your fellowship, the world will lose mine."

"Certes, sir," said Lancelot, "ye have done so much for me that I could do naught that would go against your will. And I am not of the household of the king save by the will of my lady, for by my own will never a day of my life would I remain there."

Thus they talked long time together. And Lancelot, as best he might, comforted Galehot, till that he made better cheer than he was wont.

CHAPTER XXXIX

How the wise clerks of King Arthur interpreted to Galehot the signification of his dreams, and how he learned the term of his life

The knights continue their journey until they enter Sorelois. Here they are met by the master of Galehot's household, who tells him that great mischance has befallen him. Galehot at once demands if he has lost any friends, and on learning that he has not, he rides gaily on to greet his people, from whom he successfully conceals his anxiety. When he meets the master of his household again, he smilingly says, " ' Fair master, till to-day I held you wise. Wherefore supposed ye that any loss would grieve me save that of my friends ? ' ' Sir,' said the master, ' the loss is not very great, but it is so marvellous that I have ne'er heard tell of the like. For in all the realm of Sorelois there remaineth no fortress whereof the half hath not foundered, and all this befell twenty days since in one

229

night.' 'That grieveth me little,' said Galehot, 'for I myself with my own eyes saw the fortress fall that I loved moſt, and my heart suffered no misease thereby.' " He keeps up a brave countenance that evening, but on the morrow he summons his barons and knights to meet him in council at an appointed time in Sorhaut, the chief city of Sorelois, and he also despatches a letter to Arthur, begging him to send his wiseſt clerks to him, for never has he had greater need of them.

Immediately after the followers of Galehot have delivered their message at Camelot, a damsel enters the hall, accompanied by a venerable knight, Bertholai of Carmelide. She bears to Arthur a letter from her miſtress, who claims to be Guinevere, the daughter of King Leodegan of Carmelide, and therefore the wife of Arthur, united to him in lawful wedlock, anointed and crowned queen, but deprived of her rights as his consort by shameful means, of which she professes ignorance, while the present queen was basely subſtituted for her. The maiden explains to the horror-ſtricken hearers the full significance of her lady's words, and tells Arthur that early on the morning after he had brought his bride, Guinevere, the beautiful daughter of King Leodegan, from Carmelide to Logres, when he had left the chamber, she was made way with by unfaithful servants and caſt into prison, while the present queen, who ſtrongly resembled her, was treacherously conduĉted to her chamber and left there in her place. She was finally set at liberty by the efforts of Bertholai and taken to her own land. She now demands that the king either keep his plighted troth to her and punish those who were the cause of her undoing, or that he give her back the Round Table, which was a part of her dower. Arthur at once calls upon the queen to deny the charge. Gawain immediately proclaims her innocence and offers to defend her againſt any opponent. Arthur refuses to decide the matter before Candlemas, when he will hold court at Bedingran, where he bids the queen prepare to maintain her innocence.

When the messengers from Sorelois return to their own land, bringing with them the wise clerks whom Arthur has sent, Galehot and Lancelot learn of the queen's misfortune. Galehot points out to Lancelot that if the king disowns Guinevere, he shall himself present her with Sorelois, and there will be no obſtacle to Lancelot's marriage with her. But Lancelot is convinced that, if her innocence be not proved, the king will put her to death, and he entreats Galehot to aid him in saving

King Arthur and the messengers from the false Guinevere

her. Galehot is so deeply moved by his distress that he consents, even though he should lose Lancelot in consequence.

Then Galehot calls the wise clerks of Arthur into a chamber in the presence of none save Lancelot, and consults them about the malady that has overtaken him, a nameless fear, which has its seat in his heart and so oppresses him that he can neither eat nor sleep. He recounts his dreams to them, and the clerks ask for a respite of nine days, which they spend in retirement. At the end of the time they report to him the visions that they have had, and from these they together interpret the significance of the dreams. They have seen two dragons, one from the west and one from the east, fighting together until a leopard made peace between them. The dragons signify Arthur and Galehot. The leopard is a knight who surpasses all others, except one, and is the son of the king that died in grief. He is also the heart of Galehot's dream that devoured the other heart, and even as he has taken Galehot's heart from him, so he will be the cause of Galehot's death, if he is not rescued by the serpent of the dream, who is a lady in the service of Guinevere. Moreover another vision has shown them that Galehot must needs cross a deep and wide water by means of a bridge of forty-five planks, many of which were removed by the leopard and the serpent. The planks represent the limit of Galehot's life, but whether they signify years or months or days only one clerk, Helyes of Toulouse, the wisest of the number, undertakes to explain. He dismisses the other clerks and Lancelot, and remains alone with Galehot in the chapel. Lancelot departs, and going into a room by himself shuts the door and weeps, convinced that he is the leopard of the dream through whom Galehot will die.

AND Master Helyes spake to Galehot in the chapel, and he said, " Sir, I believe that ye are one of the best princes in the world, and I know that if ye have done folly, it was more through graciousness of heart than through lack of wisdom, and I would give you a little instruction to your profit. See that ye ne'er speak before man or woman that ye greatly love a word whereby the heart of either may be at misease. For each man should, so far as he may, turn affliction and disquietude away from the being whom he loveth. I say this for the sake of the knight that hath gone forth from here, for I know well that ye love him with a love as great as may be between two loyal comrades, and ye would fain have him hear your secret, but that would not be well, for he would perchance have heard words wherefrom he would have had shame enough, and he would be even more heavy because of them than ye, although his joy and his worship would be no less dear to you than to himself. But in your heart ye have more reason and discretion than he hath in his".

"Master," replied Galehot, "from your words me-seemeth that ye know him well."

"Certes," said he, "I think that I know him well, though not by any man who now liveth, save only that I have heard it said that he who made the peace between my lord King Arthur and you is the best knight that is now alive. And I know that he is the leopard that ye saw in your dream."

"Fair master," said Galehot, "then is not the lion a prouder beast and more powerful?"

"Yea," said the master, "without doubt."

"Then," said Galehot, "I aver that the knight who is better than all others should have not the semblance of the leopard but of the lion."

"Now, i' faith," said the master, "ye have spoken more wisely than many another would have done. And I will answer you truly. I know well and believe that he is the best knight who is now living, but there will be a better than he. For thus Merlin, that ever spake soothly, foretold in his prophecies."

Galehot and Master Helyes

[*face p. 232*

"Master," said Galehot, "know ye how he will be called ? "

"Of his name," said the master, "I know naught."

"How then, master," said Galehot, "can ye know who will be a better knight than he ? "

"I know well," made answer the master, "that he who will achieve the adventures of Britain will be the best knight in the world, and he will fill the last seat at the Table Round, and it is written that by the lion he is signified."

"Master," said Galehot, "know ye how he will be called ? "

And he answered, "Nay".

"Then I see not how ye can know that this knight here will not achieve the adventures of Britain."

"I know well," replied the master, "that this cannot be, for he is such an one that he cannot accomplish the adventure of the Sangreal nor attain to the Siege Perilous at the Round Table, wherein never knight sat that he met not death thereby."

"Ah, master," said Galehot, "what is this that ye tell me ?   There is no knightly virtue that is not in him.   How is it then that ye say that he is not such an one that he could attain unto this ? "

"That profiteth naught here," replied the master, "and I will tell you wherefore.   He could not win back the taches that he who may achieve the adventures of the Sangreal will have, for first of all he must needs be so utterly virgin by his nature and so wholly chaste even till his death that he shall love neither lady nor damsel.   And this he can never have, for I know a greater part of his secret than he thinketh."

When Galehot heard this, he blushed for shame, and he said to the master, " I' faith, master, think ye that he who will achieve the siege of the Round Table will be a better knight in prowess at arms ? "

" Doubt it not," said the master, " for none will be able to conquer him at arms. And wit ye well that the prowess of other valiant knights will be as nothing to his."

" Certes, master," said Galehot, " he must be a knight of great prowess to whom the prowess of this knight is as naught. And more ye know of him than I could suppose, and I see well that ye are the flower of all the clerks, even as gold is the flower of all metals. But I pray you, tell me more of the prophecies of Merlin, for willingly would I harken to them, if there be any that have to do with me."

" Verily," said the master, " Merlin said that from the isles a marvellous dragon would escape and would go flying through all lands to the right and to the left, and wheresoever he came all the lands would tremble before him. And thus he would fly to the Adventurous Kingdom, and there he would wax so great and so daring that he would have thirty heads all of gold richer and fairer than his first head, and then he would be so great that he would overshadow all the earth with his body and his wings. And when that he should come to the Adventurous Kingdom and should almost have conquered it, the marvellous leopard would hold him and would force him back, and would put him at the mercy of them that he had well nigh conquered. And thereafter they would so love each the other that they would be one and the same thing, so that one could not live without the other. And then the serpent with the head of gold would draw the leopard to her by her great subtlety and would bring death to the great dragon by parting him from the leopard. In such wise Merlin said that the great dragon would die, and I know in sooth that ye are he, and the serpent that would take him from you is my lady the queen, who loveth the knight, or will love him, so that no lady may love knight more. And this ye wit well, if ye love the knight with such a love that your heart cannot endure it."

"Certes, master," said Galehot, "I can endure it in places and at times, but for always it cannot be. For on him have I set more love than man can e'er set on a stranger. Nor see I how he can bring death to me unless I receive it by his death. And I think that after his death I could not live. But of this that ye tell me of the queen I marvel greatly, for, as I ween, he thinketh naught of lady or of maiden, and if he did, I should know it."

"I know in sooth," said the master, "that even as I have told you it must needs befall, that she will set on him all her thought and intent. And I believe that she hath even now done this rather than that she hath it still to do. And know that ye will yet see the greatest marvel that ye have ever seen in your time. For my lady is charged with the foulest blame that ever was cast upon any lady, and this, I ween, is come upon her for her sin rather than for aught else, in that she hath entered upon so great disloyalty as to dishonour the most worshipful man in the world. And therefore I bade the knight that ye love go out

235

from here. For I had liefer that ye hear me say villeiny of him than that he himself should have heard it, for I knew you for a man of such worship that all the words that I should say to you would be secret with you. And therefore I require you on your honour and on your loyalty that my lady know not through you aught that I have said, even as ye would have me conceal your secret, if ye had told it to me, for I have said that to you which would be accounted to me shame and folly. And I have thought neither one nor the other. Therefore I pray you that ye keep my worship and my honour even as ye would that I keep yours."

"Ah, gentle master," said Galehot, "there is no need to warn me of that, for there is naught that should be kept secret, that, if ye have told it me privily, I shall ever tell save only with your consent."

Galehot then entreats Helyes to reveal to him the limit of his life according to the vision of the forty-five planks. With great reluctance Helyes finally consents to use his knowledge of magic to explain the vision. He draws with charcoal on the wall four groups of forty-five lines each, the strokes in the last three groups being shorter than those in the group preceding it. These groups, he tells Galehot, in descending scale signify the years, months, weeks, and days of his life, and by a marvel which he is about to see all the lines of one of the groups, except those representing the term of his life, will be obliterated. Giving Galehot a pyx from the altar, and taking in his own hands a cross, he begins to read one of his magic books. Darkness speedily envelops the chapel, the earth quakes, an arm holding a fiery sword appears, and moving to the group of lines representing years, effaces forty-one and a quarter of them, and disappears. "When Galehot could speak, he said to Master Helyes, 'Ah, master, well have ye kept faith with me, for ye have shown me the greatest marvels that I ween were ever beheld. And ye have so wrought that I know that there still

The fiery hand with the sword

remain to me three years and more of my life. And I am more at ease thereat. And know that my life will be worth more therefor, since never did a man of my age do so much good as I shall do within these three years. And of this I assure you well, that never a day of my life shall I make sorry cheer therefor that may be seen, but I shall assay to make greater joy than I have ever made heretofore.'" Helyes replies that it is possible that Galehot may pass the appointed term of his life, if the queen will aid him by allowing Lancelot to remain with him. "Thus they ended their council, and they came out of the chapel. And Galehot made glad cheer."

CHAPTER XL

How Morgain la Fée would have the ring of the Queen from Sir Lancelot, and how her damsel brought the ring to court

When the barons of Galehot have assembled at Sorhaut in accordance with his commands, he tells Lancelot that he has gathered them together ostensibly for his own coronation, but that he has determined that Lancelot shall be crowned king of the land, and shall become its lord. Lancelot refuses to accept any signory without the consent of his lady, the queen. Galehot, therefore, announces to his barons that he intends to postpone his coronation and to make himself more worthy of the crown by sojourning for a time at the court of Arthur. He appoints King Baudemagus of Gorre, who is known to be wise and courteous and just, to administer his domain in his absence.

The land of Gorre occupies one of the strongest sites in Great Britain, for it is well protected by the marshlands and water that encircle it. When Baudemagus came to the throne, it was sparsely inhabited in consequence of the devastating wars that it had waged with the kingdom of Logres in the reign of Uterpandragon. Baudemagus determined that even as the country had been depopulated by the men of Logres so it should be repeopled by them. He therefore conftructed two bridges, which formed the only means of ingress into Gorre, each protected by a ftrong tower with armed guards; all people from the land of Logres, whether knights or ladies, who passed these bridges were compelled to swear to remain in Gorre until the coming of a knight who should be valorous enough to release them. Thus Gorre became peopled by prisoners from Logres. Baudemagus has rendered their release ftill less probable by fubftituting for the former bridges two that are even more perilous, one, the Loft Bridge, or the Bridge beneath the Waves, confifting of a single plank three feet wide, ftretched amid the waves so that there is as much water above as beneath it, and the other formed merely by a piece of fteel, one foot wide, fashioned like a sharp sword. The Sword Bridge is guarded by Meleagant, the felonious and redoubtable son of Baudemagus, who is present at the court of Galehot when his father accepts the adminiftration of Sorelois, and who at that time begins to hate Lancelot with the jealous hatred that he feels for all good knights.

When Galehot has arranged for the care of his kingdom, he and Lancelot attend the court which Arthur is holding at Camelot. On Chriftmas Day the knights of Logres and of Sorelois juft sportively together, wearing no armour and using only their lances and shields. Lancelot, who is fighting on the side of Arthur, unhorses Meleagant, who in rage attacks him with hoftile intent and wounds him. The followers of Galehot at once refuse to continue the tourney, and Baudemagus in displeasure with Meleagant sends him back to Gorre.

At the time appointed for the trial of the queen, Arthur goes to Bedingran. The maiden who has claimed her place is in reality Guinevere, the daughter of King Leodegan of Carmelide by the wife of his seneschal. She came with Queen Guinevere to Logres at the time of her marriage, planning with the counsel of Bertolai, who had a grudge againft Arthur, to commit disloyalty againft her lady. But the plan was suspected, and the false Guinevere in fear of discovery fled from Logres to a diftant land, where she has lived until her present attempt. She comes to Bedingran at Chriftmas, and in person accuses Guinevere, offering to prove the truth of her words. The queen accepts the challenge, but the false Guinevere asks for the delay of a day before the combat shall take place. Acting on the advice of Bertholai, she contrives to have Arthur decoyed into the foreſt by the prospeſt of a feigned boar hunt, seized by her knights, and taken as prisoner to Carmelide. After his disappearance she refuses to allow her case to come to judgment in his absence, and departs to Carmelide, where in order to have him more completely in her power, she gives him a love potion, which causes him to forget the queen and transfer his affeſtions entirely to her. He finally agrees to acknowledge her as his wife, and accordingly summons his knights and barons to come to Carmelide on Ascension Day. The news that he is alive causes great rejoicing at court, and the barons willingly obey the summons. Galehot accompanies the queen with a large force, determined that no harm shall befall her.

When the barons of both Logres and Carmelide are assembled, Arthur announces his own belief that the charge againſt the queen is juſt, and the barons of Carmelide, who are in the power of the false Guinevere, swear to its truth. On the advice of Galehot, however, Arthur decides to decree no punishment againſt the queen before Whitsuntide, and gives her into the keeping of Gawain till that time. When Whitsuntide comes, Arthur and the barons of Carmelide, after taking counsel together, pass sentence that the queen shall have her hair cut off, shall lose the skin of her palms and fingers, and shall be sent into exile forever. Gawain and the other knights of Logres liſten in rage and horror to the sentence. Lancelot, at a sign from Galehot, darts forward angrily, and forcing his way through the throng, ſtands before the king, with his mantle, rich in gold and ermine, slipping from his shoulders, while all the byſtanders wonder what this young knight, ſtrong, alert, and debonair, is about to say.

" ' Sire, I demand of you in my own name and that of the fellowship of these other knights here assembled if ye have passed this judgment.'

" And the king made answer that he had. ' But I did it not alone, for I had a goodly number of men of worship with me.' And he showed them to him, for they were there.

" ' Sire,' said Lancelot, ' I have been of the fellowship of the Round Table, thanks be to you that granted it to me, but now I release you of your grace in that ye made me one of your meinie, and from henceforth I would hold naught from you.'

" ' Wherefore, fair friend ? ' said the king.

" ' For that I might defend no cause againſt you,' said Lancelot, ' while I am of the fellowship of the Round Table and of your household.'

" ' And what cause would ye defend againſt me ? ' said the king.

" ' I maintain,' answered Lancelot, ' that this judgment that ye have passed on my lady is false and disloyal, and I am ready to prove it againſt you or againſt another, and if one is not enough, I will prove it againſt two or three.' "

In spite of opposition from Galehot it is arranged that on an appointed day Lancelot shall do battle with three of the knights of Carmelide in turn. When the battle takes place, he shows himself without mercy to his opponents, all of whom he overcomes. He spares the life of the third only on the intercession of the queen, whose innocence is now admitted by Arthur to be completely proved. The false Guinevere insiſts, however, that she be sent out of the country, and Arthur consequently entruſts her to the care of Galehot, who has put the kingdom of Sorelois at her disposal.

After the queen's departure Arthur falls ſtill more completely under the sway of the false Guinevere and abandons all knightly pursuits for her society. The Pope in displeasure at his treatment of the queen places Britain under an interdiċt. Soon a loathsome malady overtakes both the false Guinevere and Bertholai. Gawain points out to Arthur that this is an indication of the wrath of Heaven, and the timely admonitions of a hermit, whom Arthur encounters in the course of a hunt in the foreſt, further lead him to a sense of sin and to contrition. The hermit also persuades the false Guinevere and Bertholai to repent and to confess the truth before the king and his assembled barons. Arthur, influenced by the counsels of the hermit againſt vengeance, consigns the false Guinevere and Bertholai to a hospital, and reinſtates the queen in her rightful place. Galehot, who with Lancelot has escorted Guinevere to Logres, induces her before he leaves court to bid Lancelot return with him to Sorelois.

The king, however, is determined that Lancelot shall again join the fellowship of the Round Table, and when he and Galehot appear at court for the Eaſter feſtival, Guinevere, in spite of her knowledge of the wishes of Galehot, yielding oſtensibly to the requeſt of Arthur, but really aċting in accordance with her own desires, successfully entreats Lancelot, even on her bended knees, to take his place once more among the companions of the Round Table.

To celebrate his return the king decides to hold a great court at London at Pentecoſt. On the eve of the feaſt Gawain

Morgain giving Lancelot permission to go to the Dolorous Tower

with Lancelot and a few other knights is wandering through the foreſt, when a formidable knight, Carados of the Dolorous Tower, suddenly rides up to them, kidnaps Gawain in a trice, and dashes off before his companions can interfere. Without delay they arm themselves and ride out in different directions to rescue him.

Lancelot in the course of his queſt chances to come to the caſtle of Trahans the Gay, the knight whom he had freed from the truncheons at Arthur's court, and from whom he learns the road to the tower of Carados. Many are the adventures that he meets on his way thither before he arrives at a mistbound valley, known as the Vale without Return, or the Vale of False Lovers, which has been laid under a spell by Morgain la Fée, the malicious and powerful fairy siſter of Arthur, the determined foe of all good knights, and the implacable enemy of Guinevere ever since the day long years before, when Guinevere had separated her from a knight, Guinevere's cousin, whom Morgain had loved with an illicit love. In order to confine in the valley a faithless lover of her own, Morgain has so enchanted it that no knight or lady, if once within its encircling miſt, can issue forth until an absolutely faithful lover, who can achieve various perilous adventures that await him at the entrance, shall break the spell. Lancelot, aided by a magic ring given him by the Lady of the Lake, performs the adventures and releases the imprisoned lovers. Morgain is enraged, but dissembling her wrath induces Lancelot to accept her hospitality for the night. While he is asleep, she slips on his finger a ring that caſts him into a deeper, magic slumber, and while he is under its spell she has him carried to a prison in a remote foreſt. When he awakes, she refuses to release him unless he surrender to her a magic ring that he is wearing. It was given him by Guinevere as a love-token, and is almoſt the duplicate of one that she had given Morgain. Lancelot of course refuses to relinquish it, but swears that if Morgain will let him go to the Dolorous Tower, he will yield himself again her prisoner, when he has released Gawain. To this Morgain consents, and Lancelot, attended by one of her maidens, proceeds to the Tower, kills Carados in combat, and sets Gawain free. He returns at once to Morgain, who resumes her efforts to induce him to give her the ring.

WHEN Morgain saw that Lancelot would give her his ring neither for love nor for entreaty, she left speaking

thereon, and she made semblance that she cared naught
for it, and she said that all that she had done had
been to prove him. With all the devices that pertain
to enchantment she sought to have the ring, but
they were of no avail. Then she took an herb that
is called Drowsiness and no man when that he hath
taſted thereof e'er maketh an end of sleeping till that
he is awakened by force. This herb Morgain gave
to Lancelot to drink, and she mixed it with ſtrong
wine. That night Lancelot slept right heavily, and
then she took the ring from his finger, and she put
her own in its place, and she did it so ſtealthily as
she might, for well she knew that an he were ware
thereof, none could withhold him from killing her.
And therefore she kept him long to find out if he
perceived it. And many a time she caused him to
look at his finger. But he, that ne'er thought on
deceiving any man, discovered naught. When she saw
that he was not ware thereof, she took one of her
damsels that was discreet, and she sent her to the
court of King Arthur, and she charged her with such
a message as ye shall hear.

The damsel went ſtraight to London, where the
king ſtill tarried, and with him were Galehot and the
queen, who ever awaited the news that they longed
to hear. At the time when the damsel came to court,
the king and the queen and Sir Gawain and Galehot
were seated on one couch, and they took counsel
together about Lancelot, what they should do about
him, for they feared that he was dead. And the
damsel alighted down from her horse, and she came to
the four as they talked together all caſt down, and she

said, "Sir, I come from distant lands, and I bring you strange tidings, but I would first be assured by you and by your people that I shall receive neither shame nor ill for aught that I say, for I know not but there are some here that my news may offend".

And the king swore on his oath that she need fear naught from him or his people. "But speak, damsel, for never in my court was a messenger harmed for the news that he brought, nor may any damsel fear in the place where I am."

Forthright the damsel began to speak, and she said so on high that all, both knights and ladies, heard her clearly:—"King Arthur, I bring you tidings of Lancelot of the Lake, and know well that ye will nevermore see him in your dwelling, neither ye nor any of your fellowship, for he goeth into a place where he will not lightly be found. And nevertheless, if he were found, it would avail naught, for never again will he hang shield at his neck."

When Galehot heard these words he trembled in all his limbs, and his heart swelled within him, and he fell in a swoon among them. Then the king sprang up, and he and likewise Sir Gawain took him in their arms. But the queen was in so passing great distress that she might no longer stay among the folk, for she feared lest ill betide her therefrom, and she arose to go to her chamber. But the damsel turned her from her intent, for she cried aloud to the king, "Sire, an ye suffer the queen to leave, never shall ye hear more from me than ye have heard". And the king, that desired to hear all, swore that the queen should not move a foot. And Sir Gawain sprang forward, and held her, and he said, " Lady, if ye go, ye take everything from us ". And then the queen turned her back in sore diſtress. And Galehot, when that he came out of his swoon, lamented bitterly, and he said to the maiden, " For the love of God, tell us the truth about the beſt knight in the world, and wherefore he will ne'er again hang shield at his neck, and if he is dead or alive, for ye have killed and betrayed us, if ye say no more ".

" Before God I will say more," said she, " since ye and the king bid me speak. Lancelot in truth returned from the Dolorous Tower, where he fought with one of the beſt knights in the world, and he was wounded with a blade through the body, and he loſt so much blood by reason of his wound that he thought to die, and therefore he made confession of a vile and horrible sin againſt his lord that is here, to wit, that he had for long time betrayed the king with his lady. And thus he commanded me that I should tell it in this court, for I was in the place where he confessed him. And when he had said this word openly, he pledged him by the body of God that he would never lie more than one night in any town, and ever he would go barefoot and in sackcloth, nor would he ever hang shield at his neck or bear arms. And that this may be believed, he sendeth to Sir Gawain the words that were spoken privily between them twain the night that they went from the Dolorous Tower, for Sir Gawain asked him if he were bound for a place wherein his friends might fear for him, and he said, ' Sir, have no fear, for I go to none save a good place.' "

Lancelot spurring to the Dolorous Tower

Morgan stealing the ring from Lancelot

[face p. 244

This token Sir Gawain knew well, and he was as grieved thereby as ever he might be, and he made passing great sorrow therefor. And the damsel turned her to the queen in the sight of them all that were there, and she held out towards her the ring that Morgain had taken from the finger of Lancelot. Then she said to her, "Lady, whomsoever it may please or whomsoever it may displease, I muſt needs give my message. This irketh me, but otherwise I should perjure me, for I swore by the saints to Lancelot that I would give you this ring into your own hands, and here I give it you". Right so she gave the queen the ring, but the queen had no power to reply, for the great anguish that she had in her heart made her swoon. And many felt great pity for her, and they came forward to support her, even the nobleſt and the beſt.

When that she came out of her swoon, she lamented sore, and neither because of the king nor of any man did she cease to mourn for Lancelot with tears and sighs. And she said that he who would speak ill thereof might speak ill, but she would that all should know that she never had had tidings, save only those of the captivity at the Saxon Hold, that had so grieved her at heart.

"And let God and all the world know that I have never loved Lancelot nor he me with a base love. But he was the faireſt and the moſt worshipful and the beſt of all good knights, for he would have surpassed all them that are the moſt valiant at arms, had he been knight long time. And in sooth he had already surpassed them all, yet he had been knight no more than seven years. There is no good tache of heart or of body wherein e'er a knight surpassed Lancelot. And if he spake too boldly he did it from the nobleness of his heart, for he could not endure baseness nor disloyalty. If I ne'er did aught but recount the noble graces that were in Lancelot, my tongue would fail me sooner than my matter. But, so may God have mercy on my soul, if Lancelot would not sooner let the eyes be drawn from his head than that he should speak so great an outrage as this damsel hath recounted. And, even if it were with me and him as she hath said and narrated, never would I deny the ring nor aught else; for I gave him the ring, and I will well that all those who are here should blame me that find reason therefor, since it is blame without support."

Thus spake the queen before the king and all the others. And there were those among them that loved and honoured her the more therefor. And the king was in no wise disquieted, but he held all that the damsel had said for a lie. And he made answer to the words that the queen spake that, so help him God, he would that Lancelot had wedded her, on condition that he should be of his fellowship and should live his full term of life.

At these words the damsel took her leave, and she begged of the king that he would grant her safe convoy. And the king gave her to Sir Ewaine to conduct. And the queen went to her chamber, and she had Galehot and Lionel and the Lady of Malohaut there with her, and they made great dole together. And the queen said to Galehot, "Ah, Galehot, now hath your comrade betrayed me. I' faith, either he is dead or he is a mortal traitor. For I had thought that no one could e'er have this ring without his will. But if he is alive, he will well perceive his disloyalty, for never will my heart have joy of him ; and if he is dead, I shall pay dearer for it than he, if it is known throughout all lands ".

Long time they talked together of their great sorrow, and Galehot said that he should go after the damsel that went away, and never should he make an end of the matter till that he knew the truth about Lancelot either of his life or of his death. And Lionel said that he would go with him. And he said that he desired to have no other companion. Then they took leave of the queen, and she kissed them both weeping. And they went to the king and took leave of him.

Galehot and Lionel overtake Sir Ewaine and the damsel and entreat her to show them the road that will lead them to Lancelot. She refuses, but when they persist, she resolves to deceive them, and ostensibly consenting, she leads them out of the path to the house of a vavasour, where they lodge for the night, trusting that she will take them to Lancelot on the morrow. While they are asleep, she slips secretly away to the castle of Morgain, and reports the result of her errand to her mistress. Morgain is enraged not only because she has failed in her purpose, which was to disgrace the queen, but also because she is now convinced of the love between Lancelot and Guinevere, and is madly jealous that the queen is beloved by the most faithful of all lovers. She determines to keep Lancelot a prisoner, not from hatred of him, but in the hope that thus she will drive the queen to madness or to despair that will lead to her death.

CHAPTER XLI

How Sir Lancelot ran mad in the forest, and how Galehot
sickened for sorrow and died, and how the Lady of the
Lake healed and comforted Sir Lancelot

When on the next day the knights discover that the damsel
has tricked them, in high dudgeon they set out together, but
soon separate in order to extend their search as widely as
possible. Galehot in his wanderings comes to a castle previously delivered from enchantment by Lancelot, who has left
his shield hanging on a tree before it. Galehot at once recognises the shield and makes off with it, but his possession of it
is contested by knights of the castle, who pursue him. He
overcomes them, but is severely wounded in the combat, and
makes his way to a monastery, where he is obliged to remain for
a fortnight for the healing of his wound.

Morgain in the meantime by powerful drugs causes Lancelot
to dream that the queen is unfaithful to him. He is thus so
reduced to despair that in the early summer he is ready to accept
from Morgain an offer of freedom conditional upon his promise
not to remain before Christmas in any place where the queen
is staying. Morgain thereupon gives him fine armour and
sets him at liberty.

Lionel in his adventures encounters a damsel, who leads him
to a certain tree, from the branches of which he watches
Lancelot enter an adjacent garden, where under the guard of
ten serjeants he is in the habit of walking every evening for
diversion. Not long after Galehot has resumed his quest, Lionel
rejoins him and reports that he has seen Lancelot safe and well.
The two knights therefore return together to Sorelois, where
Galehot devotes himself to good works. Later he and Lionel
again start out in quest of Lancelot.

Gawain and Ewaine after sundry adventures meet Lancelot
in the forest. They find him weak and depressed, and entreat
him to return to court with them, but he refuses, bidding them
merely report that they have seen him sound and well. He
admits, however, to Gawain that he is in deep anguish of mind,
and believes that he has lost his knightly prowess. The knights
regretfully leave him and go back to court with their news of
him.

Lancelot, not knowing that Galehot is in quest of him, makes his way to Sorelois. Distracted at not finding Galehot there on his arrival and feeling bereft of all comfort, he loses his reason, and one night, only half clothed, he makes his escape from the castle and in his madness wanders into the forest. The circumstances of his disappearance lead the people of Sorelois to believe that he has taken his own life.

Now the story saith that when Galehot and Lionel were departed from Sorelois, they hied straight to court. And when they were come hither, they found Sir Gawain, who told them the tidings, and he said that he supposed that Lancelot was gone to Sorelois. " For I forgot to tell him that ye sought him." Forthwithal Galehot went back to Sorelois, he and Lionel with him.

But when they heard the truth about Lancelot, who had gone thence, Galehot supposed that he was dead, and that he had slain himself. And henceforth there was no comfort for Galehot. And he would have been consoled, if he had not thought that Lancelot was assuredly dead, but this cast him into despair. And he would neither eat nor drink. And such comfort as he had was in the shield of Lancelot, that he had ever before his eyes. And for the love of Lancelot he was eleven days and eleven nights without meat or drink, until the holy brethren that often came to see him, said that if he died in this manner, his soul would perforce be lost. But this availed naught, for the long fasting had wrought him too great ill. And yet another misfortune returned to him, for his wound that he had had when he won the shield festered, for it had been ill tended, and his flesh decayed. Anon there came upon him another malady, wherefrom all his body and all his members withered. And then he passed from this world, as the moſt worshipful man of his age that ever was in his time, as the ſtory doth teſtify. For the great alms that he gave would never be lightly told. And he let inveſt his nephew, Galehodin, with all his lands and receive the homage of his barons. And many other good works he did.

Now the ſtory saith that when Lancelot was departed from Sorelois and was gone forth from the land, he made dole each day, and he ate and slept little, and he was so out of his wit that he was mad. And he bided in this wise all the winter and all the summer to Chriſtmas, and he wandered mad throughout all lands. Now after Chriſtmas it befell that the Lady of the Lake, who had foſtered him, sought him far and wide, and she rode seeking news and signs of him till that she found him on the eve of Candlemas Day lying in a thicket in the foreſt of Tintagel in Cornwall. And she took him with her, and she healed him, and she kept him all the winter and throughout Lent till he returned to greater beauty and to greater ſtrength than he had ever had, for that she promised him that she would make him to have so great joy that he had never had greater. Nor knew he aught of the death of Galehot. And he bided with his Lady till fifteen days before the Ascension. Then he went to the court of King Arthur.

And the Lady made ready for him horse and arms, and she said to him, " Now the time draweth nigh when thou shalt see again that which thou haſt loſt, if so be that thou durſt. And know that it will behove thee to be at Camelot afore noon on Ascension

The Lady of the Lake healing Lancelot

[face p. 250

Day. And if thou shouldst not be there at that hour, thou wouldst love death more than life ".

" Ah, Lady," said he, " now tell me wherefore."

" For that the queen will be led away by force," said she. " And if thou art there, thou wilt rescue her from there where none hath by any means ere been rescued."

" Now, I swear to you," said he, " that I shall be there either on foot or on horse."

Therewithal the Lady showed him his arms and his horse, and she bade him set out five days afore Ascension Day. Then he forthright took leave of his Lady, and he fared forth, and he went on his way till that he came at the hour of noon on Ascension Day to Camelot to the place where Kay the seneschal was unhorsed and wounded for the queen that he led, even as the *Story of the Cart* telleth.

CHAPTER XLII

*How Meleagant came to court and demanded to do battle
for to have Queen Guinevere*

On that day King Arthur held his court at Camelot, the which was the most adventurous town that he had and one of the most delectable. But it was not a high court and marvellous of the time of Galehot, and when Lancelot of the Lake was there, for all thought that he was dead.

That day was the court full poor and disquieted,
for so soon as Lionel was come, the tidings was brought
that the noble Lady of Malohaut had died by reason
of the death of Galehot. For she had loſt in the
death of Galehot the right to be lady of thirty kingdoms, for he would have taken her to wife, if he had
lived a year.

Great was the joy that was made of Lionel, but
all was changed when he said that his cousin was loſt
and that he thought that he was dead. And the king
began to weep, and he said that it was from grief for
Galehot that Lancelot was dead. " Certes," said Sir
Gawain, " he was right, for after such a man none
should desire to live."

At these words the queen was sore troubled, for
she assented in no wise to the death of Lancelot,
and she said in answer to Sir Gawain, " What, Gawain,
then is no man of worship left on earth who is
worth aught ? "

" Lady, in sooth," said Gawain, " I know him
not."

" There is at leaſt your uncle," said she.

And he rose, and his heart swelled within him, and
the tears came to his eyes, and he turned him away,
and he said, " In sooth, Lady, he ought to be ".

Then they ceased speaking. And anon came Kay,
the seneschal, a ſtaff in his hand, and uncovered, and
he said to the king that supper was ready, and that
he should not wait for an adventure.[1] Thereupon
the king was set at meat, not that he was minded
thereto, but to do pleasure to his court. And as
many as were there ate. And Lionel was with the

queen in her chamber, and they comforted each the
other in the great sorrow and the great grief that
they had.

When the king had dined, he seated him on a couch
and he was so full of sorrow that he had no will for
merriment, but he was deep in thought. And all
his baronage stood abashed about him. And right so
as he sat in a study there entered a knight all armed
with a hauberk and greaves of iron, and he was girt
with a sword withal. And he was without a helmet,
and he was a full big knight and well fashioned in
all respects. He came down the hall at a great pace,
and according to custom he held his hand on the
pommel of his sword. And when he stood before
the king, he spake right fiercely, and he said so on high
that he was heard by all, " King Arthur, I come into
your court to make known that I am Meleagant, the
son of King Baudemagus of Gorre. And I come to
your court to prove and defend me against Lancelot
of the Lake for the wound that I dealt him the other
year at the tourney. And I have heard it said that
he maketh complaint that I wounded him in treason,
and if he sayeth so, let him come forward, for I am
all ready and prepared to defend me, for in treason
I never wounded him, but like a good knight in
honourable just ".

" Sir knight," said the king, " we have well heard
tell of your prowess, and whoe'er ye be, ye are the
son of one of the most worshipful men of the world
for his largesse ; wherefore if ye speak error, it may
well be pardoned you. And it is commonly known
in my household that Lancelot would dare defend

him againſt a better knight than ye and againſt any misdoing that had been wrought him. But the news hath so travelled in many countries that ye have assuredly heard it said that Lancelot is not here and hath not been here for long time paſt; but he is loſt, and it is great pity thereof. And if he were here and knew that ye had done him a wrong, ye would not need make haſte to prove it againſt him, for he would know well how to challenge you therefor."

"Sire," said Meleagant, "I am in all ways ready to show that I speak truth in this matter, and if he is here, in God's name, bid him come forward, for there is no knight in the world with whom I am more fain to make trial."

And the rumour spread till it came to the chamber of the queen, where Lionel was. And forthright he sprang up, and he came before the king, and he said, "Sire, here is my gage, for I am ready to prove at once againſt Meleagant that in treason he dealt Lancelot the wound whereof he speaketh". Right so the queen haſtened forward, and she seized Lionel, and she drew him aback by force, and she said to him, "Let be, Lionel, for when God shall have brought back your cousin, if he findeth this knight in any place where he hath the power to prove his right againſt him, he will dare well do it, nor if he did it not of his own might, would he count himself paid by aught that any other man wrought for him". But they might scarce withhold Lionel from the battle.

And when Meleagant saw that the matter was let pass, he went away to the entrance of the hall, and thereupon he turned him again, and he said to the king, " Sire, I came to seek chivalry in your court, but none have I found. But ere I go, I will assay to have the battle, if there are here so many good knights as men affirm. There are, in sooth, in the land of my father many folk from this country that are in servitude and exile, nor ever have ye been able to deliver them. But now they might lightly be delivered, if there were one that dared do it. For if ye dare give the queen to one of these knights to lead into the foreſt, I will do battle with him on the covenant that, if I win the queen, I lead her away to my country, and that, if he can defend himself againſt me, I release the prisoners ".

" Fair sir," said the king, " if ye hold them in prison, it irketh me sore, and I will deliver them when I may, but never shall they be set free by means of the queen."

Right so Meleagant departed. And there were none there that were wise but counted for great folly the challenge that he had made to lead away the queen into the foreſt. And he mounted on his horse, and he left Camelot, and he rode slowly toward the foreſt and often he looked back to see if no man followed him. And they of the household of the king talked thereon, and some said that Meleagant had spoken like a coward, and some there were who affirmed that all that he had said was spoken from naught save prowess.

CHAPTER XLIII

How Sir Kay demanded of King Arthur the battle with Meleagant

Sir Kay the seneschal heard well these words, and he was passing heavy for the knight that went away without battle. And he hied him to his lodgings and armed him, and then he came before the king with his ventail lowered and his gauntlets down, and he said, " Sire, I have served you well and with a true heart, and for love of you rather than for lands or treasure. And hitherto I supposed that ye loved me, but ye do not, and well am I ware thereof. And since ye love me not, I am no longer fain in any wise for your fellowship or your service. And I will go away, and I will serve a lord that will love me and hold me dear ".

Now the king loved the seneschal with a great love. And he said to him, " How now, seneschal, what aileth you ? Wherein have ye seen that I hate you or love you less than my wont ? "

" Sir," said he, " I am ware thereof, and I ask your leave to depart, for I would go away, and for no reason will I abide."

" If any man hath done you a wrong," said the king, " tell me thereof, and I will amend it so well that ye shall win honour thereby."

And he said that he made complaint of naught, but in any case he would go. The king was sore grieved thereat, and he said to him, " Seneschal,

seneschal, seeing that ye will not abide, wait here till I have come back to you ". Right so he went to the queen, and he told her that the seneschal would fain depart. "And his service pleaseth me beyond that of all others, and therefore I am grieved, and I will that ye entreat him to remain, and do ye fall at his feet sooner than he go."

" Gladly, Sire," said she.

Forthwithal the queen went to the seneschal, and she said to him, " What is this, seneschal, what will ye do, ye that would quit my lord the king ? I entreat you to abide, and if ye are vexed for aught that is denied you, if I may, I will see that ye have it, whatsoe'er it be ".

" Lady," said he, " if I were assured thereof, then I would remain."

And the queen summoned the king, and he promised to give the seneschal that which he asked.

" Sir," said he, " I will remain on this covenant. Now know ye what ye have granted me ? It is that, to set free our people, I should lead my lady the queen after the knight that is gone hence. For ye would be put to shame, if he went thus from your dwelling without battle."

When the king heard him, he was nigh out of his wits with rage, and he would liefer lose the seneschal for all his life. But the queen made sorrow beyond all others. And for another cause she had greater grief than they all, and that was for Lancelot, of whom no man might hear tidings. And she was so grieved thereby that she lost all the great beauty that she had afore and even a part of her wits. But this grieved her beyond measure that she had been given to Kay the seneschal. And she went into a chamber, and she made great dole so that but a little and she had killed her. And she and Sir Gawain had been at variance on that day, for he had said that after Galehot there remained no worshipful man in the world, and she said that in sooth there was her lord the king, and he said, " Lady, he ought to be ". Such had been the words between them. And she could not believe that Lancelot was dead, but she thought that he was imprisoned. And her heart spake thus to her.

And her palfrey was led thither, and she made passing great sorrow. And when she was about to mount on the palfrey, she looked at Sir Gawain, and she said, " Ah, fair nephew, to-day I shall learn that since the death of Galehot all prowess hath failed ". Right so she swooned, and Kay said to her, " Lady, mount up on your palfrey and have no fear, for I will bring you back, safe and sound ". And she mounted on her palfrey, and Kay rode before, and the barons and the king accompanied them till they were outside of the town. Then returned they all one and another, and none attended them further.

And Sir Gawain said to the king that he would follow the queen all the way. " And if the queen is won from the seneschal, I shall go after her as far as the entrance to Gorre." Forthwithal he armed him, and then he mounted on a good horse, and he bade two squires lead in their right hands two more horses. And in this wise he issued forth from Camelot. And on the other hand Kay led the queen till that they

came to the forest, and Meleagant, that saw them
come, was in the thickest part of the wood, and full
an hundred knights awaited him there. And he went
to them, and he told them the adventure. Then
the knights laid them in an enbushment. And
Meleagant came back and met Sir Kay.

"Knight," said he, "who are ye ? And this lady,
who is she ? "

"She is the queen."

"I am none too sure thereof," said Meleagant.
"Lady," said he, "unwimple your face, and then I
shall see if ye are the queen." And she unwimpled
her, and then he saw well that it was she.

"Sir Kay," said he, "in this forest there are many
rough places for two knights to fight, and it is too
thick. Let us go to the fairest lawn in the world,
that is hard by, where 't will be good to just."

And Kay assented thereto. "Go before," said he,
"for I know well where the lawn is." And Meleagant
went before, and Kay and the queen followed slowly
behind him till that Lancelot saw them from where
he lay in an enbushment. And he bore on his neck
the red shield bended with a white bend. He saluted
the queen so covertly as he might, and she knew him,
but she durst not believe that it was he. And she
returned his salutation somewhat more graciously than
she would have returned that of another, only for
the joy that she had at meeting him.

He said to Kay, "Sir knight, who is this lady that
ye lead here ? "

"It is my lady the queen," said Kay.

"Which queen ? " said Lancelot.

And he said, " The wife of King Arthur ".

And right so Lancelot seized his bridle. " And ye," said he, " who are ye that lead her away ? "

" I am called Kay the seneschal," said he.

" Ye will lead her no farther," said Lancelot, " for too far have ye already led her."

" Wherefore ? " said he.

" For that I take her in conduct," said he.

" Against whom take ye her in conduct ? " said he.

" Against all them that would lead her hence," said Lancelot.

And Kay said to him, " Fair sir, I lead her away at the behest of the king to defend her against a knight that awaiteth me yonder ".

" Lady," said he, " speaketh he sooth ? I would believe none save you alone."

And she said, " Yea, without doubt ".

And he thought within him that he would watch how Kay sped. For then the honour would be greater, if he won her from the knight that had won her from Kay. Therewithal Kay departed with the queen, and Lancelot followed them afar.

When Kay came to the lawn, the knight took the queen by the bridle, and he said, " Lady, ye are prisoner ".

" Ye shall not have her so lightly," said Kay, " for ye have not yet won her from me."

" As for the winning," said Meleagant, " speedily will ye come to that."

Right so each hurled him into the middle of the field and lowered his lance, and Meleagant used his own with such might that the leather of the shield of Kay was cut and his hauberk was pierced so that the blade was broken in his shoulder, and he swooned, and his horse went fleeing down the field. And Meleagant took the queen, and he led her to the knights that awaited her, and then he returned to Kay, and he so wrought for him that but a little and he had slain him.

CHAPTER XLIV

How Sir Lancelot did battle with Meleagant and his knights for the Queen

And Lancelot, that saw the queen led away, spurred his horse after her, and when he was ware that they were so many, he had such sorrow that he nigh went out of his wits, for he knew well that against such a following one man might never endure alone, if chance aided him not. And none the less he had liefer die in a quarrel for his lady than live. And he let his horse run upon the hundred knights, and he bare the first that he smote with his lance to the ground, horse and man, and he dealt him such a buffet that the sharp blade passed through him, and the lance was broken to bits. And then he laid hand to his sword and hurled upon them, and he carved their shields and helmets and hauberks, and he hewed and shivered them so that they durst not set upon him.

Then the queen knew well that this was he, and she was heavy and she was happy thereat. She was heavy, for that she might not be rescued by him, and she was happy for that she desired much to see him before she was in a land whence she thought never to issue forth. Thus one same thing pleased and displeased her.

And Lancelot travailled hard to do well for to keep his lady, and because he saw that he needs muſt. Meleagant heard the clamour, and he left Kay lying on the ground, and he came thither, and he saw the marvels that Lancelot did, and forthright his heart told him that this was Lancelot. He cried on high to his knights, and Lancelot saw him come, and he dressed him againſt him, and they dealt each other such great ſtrokes with their swords that sparks flew before their eyes, and Meleagant was ſtunned so that if he had not clung to the neck of his horse he had fallen to the ground. And the knights let run at Lancelot, and when he saw them come, he dressed him toward them, and he lashed about him to the right and to the left, and he turned him about so swiftly that it seemed to all the others that not three or eight of their knights might have dealt so many ſtrokes, and they durſt not set upon him, but they killed his horse under him. And he ran afoot upon Meleagant, that was ſtill all dazed, and he smote him such a buffet on the helm that he bore him from his horse to the ground. And he leaped on the horse, and he let run at all the others, and he cut down whosoever was in his path. And they remounted their lord on a horse, and he took a lance, and he came pricking againſt Lancelot, and he cried aloud to him that he was dead. And Lancelot turned him swiftly, and Meleagant saw him that he feared come, and he smote the horse of Lancelot through the body with his lance, and it fell dead.

Then Meleagant cried to his knights, "Away, and assay not to vanquish him, for 't would be labour loft, and much harm should we suffer ere he were slain or taken prisoner". And they fled, and they bare Kay away on a horse in such anguish that they muft needs support him on both sides. And Lancelot remained on foot, and he was so sore wounded that he could do no more, and he followed the queen as beft he might, and he was so spent that he could go but slowly. And ever he went slowly so long as he might go, for shame and grief let him not abide. And within a little space Sir Gawain o'ertook him, and he had met the horse of Kay, that went fleeing. Sir Gawain greeted the knight, but he knew him not, and he said, " Sir knight," said he, " ye have fought, as may well be seen ". And he said that howsoever he had fought, ill had he fared.

" Fair sir," said Gawain, " take one of these horses and mount upon it, for I suppose that ye know well how to aid you, and he will be of use to you in what-soever place ye may go."

And when he heard him, he leaped ftraightway upon the firft horse that he could take. And Sir Gawain asked him how he was called.

" It concerneth you not who I am," said he. " But ye have not loft your horse, for I did you a like service once upon a time,[1] and ye shall be well repaid for this."

Then was Sir Gawain sore ashamed of that which he had said to him.

CHAPTER XLV

How the horse of Sir Lancelot was slain, and how Sir Lancelot rode in a cart for to see the Queen

FORTHRIGHT Lancelot departed so faſt as ever his horse might carry him, there where he had seen the route of Meleagant go. And when he overtook them, he shouted aloud to them, and Meleagant that saw him come, said to his men, " See, here is the beſt of earthly knights ".

" Sir," said his knights, " who is he ? "

" I' faith," said he, " I know not, but none would dare undertake that which he undertaketh save one alone, and well I believe that it is he. But see that ye assay to kill only his horse, so soon as he cometh againſt you, for to seek to hold him in check would come to naught."

Then he let run upon Lancelot, but for shame he durſt not take his lance againſt him, because Lancelot had none. And they came together with their swords drawn, and they smote each the other great and heavy ſtrokes on the creſts of their helmets. And Meleagant was ſtunned so that he wiſt not whither his horse bare him. And Lancelot let run upon the others, and he gave them so hard and so cruel a battle that all were dismayed. Howbeit they slew his horse for him. And he remained on foot, and he was ware of Kay, that they bore in a litter that they had needs make, for they feared that he would die. And the queen went making such dole that but a little and

she had killed her. But now the ſtory saith no more
of her and returneth to Lancelot.

Now the ſtory saith that when Lancelot had loſt
his horse and remained on foot, he followed the road
till that a little on the right he heard a carter that was
driving a cart, and he went thither at a great pace.
And he might scarce overtake the cart. And he saw
on the shafts a dwarf, that was short and thick and
churlish, and he drave with a scourge an old horse
that was between the shafts. And Lancelot greeted
the dwarf, and he scarce returned the greeting.

" Dwarf," said he, " canſt give me news of a lady
that hath passed hereby ? "

" Ha," said the dwarf, " speakeſt thou of the
queen ? "

" In sooth I do," said Lancelot.

" Wouldſt fain hear news of her ? " said the dwarf.

" Yea," said Lancelot.

" I will let thee see her before prime on the morrow,"
said the dwarf, " if thou doeſt that which I will tell
thee."

And he said that he would do it right willingly.

" Now leap up into this cart," said the dwarf, " and
I will lead thee where thou canſt see her."

Now in those days a cart was so base a thing that
none sat therein but he who had loſt all fair fame and
honour. And when they would fain dishonour a man,
they made him mount upon a cart, and then they let
lead him throughout the town, and he abided there
till that he had been seen of all men, and he never
lay more than a single night in any town, however
large it were. And Lancelot said to the dwarf that

he would liefer follow after the cart afoot than mount thereupon. And the other said that never should he be shown the way by him, unless he mounted upon the cart.

"Wilt thou promise me," said Lancelot, "that thou wilt bring me to my lady, if I mount thereupon?"

"I promise thee," said the dwarf, "that I will show her to thee before prime on the morrow."

And Lancelot leaped forthright into the cart.

Thus the dwarf took him on his way. And so as he looked, he was ware of Sir Gawain, that came with two squires, whereof one bare his shield and the other his helmet, and he led his horse in his right hand. When he had overtaken the cart, he asked the dwarf for tidings of the queen, even as Lancelot had done. And the dwarf said to him that if he would mount upon the cart, he would show her to him either that night or in the morning. And he said that, so help him God, he would never mount upon a cart, for he that left a horse for a cart knew too little what was honour and what was shame.

"Knight," said the dwarf, "thou hatest not thyself so much as this unhappy knight here hateth himself, that hath willingly mounted thereupon for to learn that which thou askest."

"Certes," said Sir Gawain, "it is great pity thereof. Sir knight," said Sir Gawain, "leap down from the chariot before a greater shame come upon you, and mount upon this horse that is good, for I suppose that ye can better help you on a horse than on a cart."

"Now, before God," said the dwarf, "that he

266

The Knight of the Cart

[*face p.* 266

shall never do, for he promised me to-day to abide all this day on my cart."

And Lancelot bade him fear not, for he would not alight down from the cart on that day.

"Certes," said Sir Gawain, "this irketh me, for me seemeth that there is great worship in you, and 't will be a sore mishap if ye are put to shame."

"Sir," said Lancelot to Sir Gawain, "let him who should have shame thereby have it, for I charge not myself therewith."

And Sir Gawain asked him who he was. And he would not make it known to him.

"Ye said even now," said Gawain, "that ye gave me a horse,¹ and I would fain know where this was."

"Ask it not for the sake of this horse that ye have given me," said Lancelot, "for he shall surely be returned to you."

Then Sir Gawain durſt ask him no more about the horse whereof he spake, and he said no more thereof.

CHAPTER XLVI

How Sir Lancelot was lodged in a caſtle, and how he saw the Queen

The knights and the dwarf go on their way, passing a caſtle, where the people in the ſtreets make mock of the knight in the cart, while Gawain, cursing the day when the cuſtom of the cart was eſtablished, wonders who the knight can be. At length they arrive at a caſtle, where the dwarf bids Lancelot alight. The knights are admitted to the caſtle by two damsels and are conducted to a large chamber for the night. Gawain lies down in a bed at one end of the hall; at the other stand two couches, one larger and richer than the other. The damsel who has led them to the chamber and who has been treating Lancelot disdainfully, warns him against it, telling him that there is no knight of Arthur's court hardy enough to rest in it, and that great shame awaits him, if he assays to do so. "We shall soon see about that," replies Lancelot, and lies down in it. At midnight the house begins to tremble and a whirlwind accompanied by a brilliant light sweeps over it. Presently a flaming lance descends through a window and pierces the bed of Lancelot. With his sword he cuts the lance in twain and hurls it into the hall. Then he lies down again fearlessly, but in great wrath. Gawain speaks, asking him if all goes well with him. "Well, sir. Do ye sleep," replies Lancelot, who does not himself sleep till it is almost day.

AND it began to grow light, and the dwarf that had brought Lancelot thither came to the door of the chamber, and he cried on high, "Thou knight, that camest in the cart, now am I ready to keep covenant with thee". Lancelot heard his voice in his sleep, and he leaped up in his breeches and his shirt, and put his mantle about his shoulders, and he sprang forth from out the door. And the dwarf led him to a window toward the meadows, and said to him, "Look". And he looked, and he espied the queen and Meleagant near her, and Kay the seneschal, that they bore in a litter. And he looked at the queen tenderly so long as he might see her, and he leaned forward through the window, and little by little he leaned so far forward that he was wholly outside as far as his thighs. And so much he thought on that whereon he looked, that he clean forgot himself, so that but a little and he had fallen therefrom.

Then came Sir Gawain, who was arisen, and the damsels with him. And when he found Lancelot in such peril, he seized him by the arms, and he drew him back. And he said, "Ah, fair sir, in God's name, give heed to yourself". And Lancelot looked at him, and he was ashamed that he had been found thus. And the two damsels said that he might well hate naught so much as his life, for never more would he have honour. "Certes," said Sir Gawain, "never in the world will he have any, if he hath not already enough thereof." Then he took Lancelot in his arms, and he said to him, "Ah, fair, sweet sir, wherefore have ye concealed you thus from me ? "

"Wherefore ? " said Lancelot. "For that I ought to have shame to see all men of worship, for I have been at the place and at the point to win all honour, and shamefully have I fallen short thereof."

"Ah, fair sir," said Gawain, "it is not through your fault. For this," said he, "all men know, that none might achieve that which ye achieved not."

When the maidens saw that Sir Gawain thus honoured the knight, they wondered who he might be, and they asked Sir Gawain who he was. "You will not know his name through me," said he, "but this much I will tell you, that he is the best of all good knights."

Then the damsels came forward, and one of them said to Lancelot, "Pray tell us who ye are ".

"Damsel," said he, "a knight of a cart am I."

"Certes, sir," said she, "it is great pity."

Thereupon the knights called for their arms, and they armed them, and the horses were led thither, and Lancelot mounted upon one and Sir Gawain on the other. And the damsel commended them to God, and they went away together.

CHAPTER XLVII

*How Sir Lancelot raised the lid from a tomb, and how
he saw another tomb that was in flames*

The damsel, who suspects that the knight of the cart is
Lancelot, determines, if possible, to discover his name. She
therefore instructs one of her damsels to join him on his road
to Gorre, and to find out, if she can, who he is.

The knights decide to separate, Gawain electing to enter
Gorre by the Bridge beneath the Waves, and Lancelot by
the Sword Bridge. The maiden directs them to the bridges, and
later induces Lancelot to allow her to attend him on his way.

After numerous adventures they arrive at a convent, where
one of the brothers, telling Lancelot that he is recognised as the
knight who has come to the land for the sake of freeing the
prisoners from Logres, conducts him to a neighbouring cemetery
and shows him a tomb, the lid of which is sealed fast with lead
and cement. " He that lifteth this stone," says the brother,
" will accomplish the adventure that ye seek." Lancelot lays
hold of the thicker end of the stone, and raises the lid high above
his head. In the tomb lies the figure of an armed knight, and
an inscription on the lower side of the lid states that it is the
tomb of Galahad, the son of Joseph of Arimathea, who at the
time when the Grail was brought to Britain, won the land of
Hocelice, which has been called Gales after him.

A little beyond this tomb is a cave that contains another
tomb, from which a flame issues. He who can lift its lid, the
brother tells Lancelot, will achieve the adventure of the
Perilous Seat at the Round Table and will bring to an end
the quest of the Holy Grail. Lancelot at once goes to the tomb
to lift the lid, but pauses before the flames and begins to utter
loud lamentations, moaning, "Ah, God, what sorrow is mine",
when he dares not advance. Suddenly he hears a voice from the
tomb, forbidding him to approach and warning him that the
adventure is not for him.

WHEN Lancelot heard the voice that spake thus to
him, he marvelled greatly, for he saw naught. And he
asked what this was.

"Do thou tell me first who thou art," the voice made answer, "and why thou sayest, 'Ah, God, what grief and sorrow is mine!'"

"For that I am not the best knight in the world. Now I see well," said Lancelot, "that I have deceived the world, for I am not a good knight, since a good knight feareth naught."

"Now", said the voice, "thou speakest well and ill in that thou sayest, 'Ah, God, what sorrow is here', that is to say that thou art not the best knight in the world. But this is not sorrow, for he that will be the best knight will have such good taches in him that none other may equal him, for so soon as he shall put his foot within this cave and shall see the fire that burneth me, forthright he will extinguish it, for that there will never enter within him the fire of carnal sin. And none the less I hold thee not in despite, for in prowess and in knighthood thou art so richly furnished that none could surpass thee. And I know thee full well, for we are of one lineage, thou and I. And know that he that will deliver me will be my cousin, and he will be so near to thee in fleshly tie that none may be nearer, and he will be the flower of all true knights.[1] And know that thou thyself wouldst have achieved the adventures that he will bring to an end, but thou hast lost them by reason of the great carnal sin that is within thee, and for that thy body is not worthy to bring to an end the adventures of the Holy Grail because of the heinous sin wherewith thy heart is envenomed, that is, thy faithless lust. And on the other hand thou hast lost it through a sin that thy father Ban committed, for after he had wedded thy mother, who is ſtill alive, he loved a maiden, and therefrom cometh a great part of thy misfortunes. And thou wert not named Lancelot at baptism, but Galahad, for thy father let name thee after his father, who was called thus.[1] And now go thy way, fair cousin, for thou canſt never achieve this adventure by reason of this that I have told thee."

Now when Lancelot heard that his mother was ſtill alive, he had so great joy that scarce might any man tell it you.

> In answer to his queſtions Lancelot learns that he has been liſtening to the voice of Symeu, the nephew of Joseph of Ari-mathea, whose soul is saved, but whose body, in punishment for a paſt sin, muſt suffer the penalty of the burning tomb until the good knight shall come, who can extinguish the flames.[2] Lancelot insiſts upon assaying the adventure of the tomb, but he is powerless to extinguish the flames, and in grief and anger is obliged to relinquish it. "Now know I well," he says, "that he will be a knight of full great prowess that shall bring this adventure to an end." He leaves the cemetery, and the damsel, satisfied after having learned from the voice of Symeu who Lancelot is, takes leave of him. He fares on his way, achieving sundry adventures, and at length sets out for the Sword Bridge with a large escort, that a certain vavasour with whom he has lodged, insiſts that he take with him.

CHAPTER XLVIII

How Sir Lancelot crossed the Sword Bridge for to enter the land of Gorre and to rescue the Queen

So riding together they came to the highway of Gaihom. This was the greateſt city of Gorre, and Queen Guinevere was a captive there. And she was

at that hour at a window of the tower and King
Baudemagus with her. And they saw the company
of knights draw nigh, and well they had learned that
a knight was come to the land to rescue the queen,
and that he had passed all the perils.

Anon the knights came to the bridge, and thereupon
they all began to weep. And Lancelot asked them
wherefore they wept and made such dole. And they
said that it was for him, for the bridge was perilous
beyond measure. Right so Lancelot looked upon the
water on this side and on that, and he was ware that
it was black and rushing. And it befell that he
turned his face toward the city, where the queen was
at the window. And Lancelot asked what town this
was. " Sir," said they, " it is the place where the
queen is." And they named the city to him. And
he said, " Now, fear not for me, for I dread less the
passage of the bridge than ere before, and it is not so
perilous as I supposed. But that is a fair tower on
yonder side, and if they would fain lodge me there,
they shall have me to-night for a guest ".

Right so Lancelot alighted down from his horse,
and he comforted them, and he bade them be as
confident as he was. And they laced the sides of his
hauberk together and sewed them with great threads
of iron that they had brought, and his gauntlets
likewise they sewed within on his hands, and his
boots beneath and his gauntlets and they covered those
parts of his hauberk that protected his thighs with
good hot pitch, and this was done so that they might
hold better against the sword.

After that they had well and fairly equipped

Lancelot, he bade them depart, and they left him, and they swam across the water, and they led his horse with them. And he went ſtraight to the bridge and he looked toward the tower where the queen was a captive, and he bowed his head before it, and thereafter he crossed him, and he put his shield behind his back that it might not hinder him. Then he placed him aſtride of the plank, but they saw that he drew him along it armed even as he was, for he lacked neither hauberk nor shield nor greaves nor helmet. And they in the tower that saw him were all dismayed, and none there, either man or woman, knew who he was. And the threads of iron ſtayed not the blood that it gushed not forth from his hands and his feet and his knees. But not the peril of the sword, whereon he dragged him, nor the peril of the water, black and turbulent, ſtayed him that he looked not more often towards the tower than towards the water, nor recked he aught of wound or pain that he had, for if he might come to that tower, he would forthright be healed of all ills.

In such wise he dragged and drew him along till that he came to shore, and then he looked and he saw a villein that led two lions by one chain, and they made such a noise that they might be heard afar. But he had no fear save one alone, and that had taken from him all other dread. When he came to land he seated him aſtride of the bridge, and he drew his sword and he raised his shield before his face. And he called to the lions that were already unchained, and they rushed at him, and mightily they assailed him. And he gave them great ſtrokes with his sword so that

The Sword Bridge - *The fairy lions* - *The combat with Meleagant*

oft-times he buried the blade in the ground, but never could blood flow from the lions for any blow that he might deal them. And often him seemed that he had pierced each of them through the body. Then he gave somewhat aback, and he laced his two feet together beneath the plank. Then he turned back the gauntlet from his left hand, and he looked at the ring that his Lady of the Lake had given him, and therewithal he looked toward the two lions, and he saw naught. Then he wist right well that this was an enchantment.

Now when Lancelot looked upon the ring, the queen saw him well, and she knew forthright that he was Lancelot. And however great dole and sorrow she had made before, now she was at ease. And she laughed and jested and made glad cheer and showed fair countenance, so that King Baudemagus, that sat beside her, marvelled and was amazed thereat, for never since she had come had any man seen her laugh or make merry. And the king said to her covertly, " Fair lady, an it were not displeasing to you, I would say a word to you that should not offend you ".

" Sir," said she, " I have found you so worshipful and so true of your promise that naught that ye might say could displease me."

" Lady," said he, " I would ask you if ye know who that knight is yonder on the bridge ? "

" Sir," said she, " I know not."

" Lady," said he, " by the being that ye love most, know or suppose ye that he is Lancelot ? "

" Sir," said she, " I swear on the oath that ye have given me that 't will be a year on the vigil of Pentecost that I have not seen Lancelot. And many folk suppose that he is dead. And therefore I know not if this be he. But since ye have asked me both what I know and what I suppose, I will answer you without deceit. I think that it may be he rather than another, and I had liefer it were he than another, and I would trust myself to his hands rather than to those of another. For ye know well that he is a good knight. And whoe'er he be, whether Lancelot or another, for the sake of God and of your own honour, guard him well, so as ye ought, that he may dread only that which he hath reason to dread."

"Lady," said he, "I will go speak with Meleagant, for gladly would I make peace between them twain."

"Sire," said she, "go, I entreat you; for the love of God speak to him thereof. But say naught of the name of the knight, for I know not yet assuredly who he is."

"Lady," said he, "fear naught, for nothing shall be done against your will or his, for he is the knight whom I love more than aught that I possess in the world."

CHAPTER XLIX

How Sir Lancelot waged battle against Meleagant, and how the Queen denied her greeting to Sir Lancelot

Baudemagus uses every entreaty with Meleagant to induce him to give up the contest with so valiant a knight as the stranger has shown himself to be, and to surrender Guinevere to him without more ado. But Meleagant scouts the idea and insists

that the combat take place, although he grants a brief respite
for the healing of Lancelot's wounds.

AND on the morn Lancelot arose early, and he heard
mass all armed save his head and his hands. And so
soon as he had come out of the minster, he laced his
helmet, and he came to the king to ask his combat.
Then went the king to his son, and he found that he
was all ready. And then he came again to Lancelot,
and he said to him, " Fair sir, now ye shall have your
battle, and I make covenant with you that none shall
force you to make yourself known. Nor would I
force you, but I pray you of your worship and I
conjure you by that which ye love best of all earthly
things that ye take off your helmet ".

Then Lancelot took off his helmet, and the king
ran to him to kiss him. And he said, " Ah, fair,
sweet friend, ye are right welcome ". But of Galehot,
that was dead, he spake not, for he feared to grieve
Lancelot overmuch. And when he thought on the
good lord that had called him friend and companion,
he felt such sorrow therefor that his eyes filled with
tears. But the king concealed his grief so well as he
might for to hide from Lancelot his great sorrow.

And Lancelot, that desired the battle, had laced his
helm, and he was come to the field, and Meleagant
was come likewise. And the field was before the
dwelling of the king, and it was full long and broad.
And then again the king reasoned with his son and
rebuked him so much as he might, but it availed him
naught. When the king was ware of this, he said to
him and to Lancelot, " Now I pray you both not to
move one against other till ye hear me blow to the

field ". Thereupon he went up into the tower, and
he took the queen and he placed her at the window
of the hall that she might the better see the battle,
for he was fain to grant her his favours. But she
asked him naught of Lancelot, and the king marvelled
greatly thereat. And she besought the king to let
bring Kay the seneschal up thither that he might see
the battle. The king let bring him up, and he let
prepare his bed at a window. And with the queen
there were many ladies and damsels.

And the king let blow to the field. And right so
they twain that were armed lashed together. Their
horses ran swiftly, and the king had given Lancelot
the beſt horse that he might have. And the field
was fair and level, and they came together hard, and
they had lowered their lances, whereof the shafts were
short and thick and the blades were cutting, and each
dealt other sad ſtrokes on his shield. Meleagant smote
Lancelot so that his shield was cleft and the blade
ſtruck againſt the hauberk, and he buffeted him so
sore that his lance was all shivered to bits. And
Lancelot dealt Meleagant such a buffet that he bare
him from his saddle to the earth, and in his fall the
lance brake, and the truncheons thereof remained in
the shoulder.

Then Lancelot alighted down from his horse, and
he came towards him with his sword drawn and his
shield raised before his face. And in such manner he
ſtood in the field that ever he saw the queen before
his eyes. And Meleagant sprang up, and he plucked
the truncheons forth from his shoulder, and he drew
his sword, and he covered him with his shield. And

Lancelot said to him, "Meleagant, Meleagant, now have I repaid you the wound that ye gave me at the justing, but I have not dealt it to you in treason". Then they hurtled together, each upon other, and long while they fought together in such wise that if Meleagant was nimble, Lancelot was more so, till that they had both lost overmuch blood. And Meleagant was spent of his strength, and he began to lose ground, and to give way. And Lancelot led him at his pleasure by the sad strokes that he gave him with his sword.

The heat was great, and the queen unwimpled her face. And Lancelot saw her uncovered, for ever he turned his eyes toward her. And then he was so abashed that but a little and his sword had fallen from his hand. But he did naught save look at her, so that he lost thereby all his gain. And now one and now another marvelled thereat, for them seemed that he was nothing if not put to the worse, and the other gave him grievous buffets wheresoever he might, so that he was wounded in many places.

Then the queen asked King Baudemagus if this was Lancelot. "Lady," said he, "yea, without doubt."

"Certes," said Kay, "it is great pity if it be he, for greater honour would he have if he were dead, even as men supposed."

And the king said that he believed not that he was so vanquished as he seemed.

For long time was Lancelot put to the worse, and they that had ne'er seen him afore wept for the pity of it. And Kay, that was all distraught, could no longer suffer it, and not without pain he put his head out of the window, and he began to cry aloud, " Ha, Lancelot, what is become of the great prowess that made both cowards and the hardy take to flight ? And here thou art overcome by a single knight ". This word Lancelot heard, and he knew right well that it was Kay that spake.

Then he rode against Meleagant, and he held him so short that within a while he led him where he would. And they that before had been sorry were glad thereof. And Meleagant was so served that he did naught but suffer it, and well they in the field saw that he was undone. Thereupon came his father to the queen, and he said to her, " Lady, I have paid you much honour, for I have done naught that was against your will, and ye should reward me richly therefor when ye have the power ". And she said that he might be assured that she would. " But wherefore say ye so ? " said she.

" Lady," said he, " I say it because of my son, that is served worse than either he or I needed, and I am glad thereof, so help me God, if he be not slain or mishandled. So I pray you, lady, that the battle be stayed at this point by your will."

And she said, " I' faith, that liketh me well, and it irketh me that ever there was a battle. Now go and separate them, for it is my will ".

Now Lancelot had so wrought for Meleagant that, as she spake thus, they were come beneath the windows of the tower, and they heard well the words of the king and of the queen. And Lancelot thereafter touched him no more, but he put back his sword into its scabbard. And Meleagant smote him the greatest strokes that ever he might, so that he wounded him, but not that for turned Lancelot ever towards him. And the king came running down and drew his son back. And Meleagant said, " Leave me my battle, and meddle ye not therein ". " I will not," said the king, " for I see well that he would slay thee, if thou wert left to him." Then the king drew him apart, and he said so much to him that Meleagant gave over the battle with this condition that he should go to the court of King Arthur at such time as he wished, and should summon Lancelot to combat, and that Lancelot should do battle with him. And the queen swore that she would come back with him, if he could vanquish Lancelot in battle. Thus was it established between the king and the queen, and afterwards Lancelot.

When that Lancelot was unarmed and had washed his neck and his face, the king led him to see the queen, and when she saw the king she came toward him. And Lancelot, when he saw her from afar, fell upon his knee, and he bowed him low. And the king said, " Lady, here is Lancelot, who hath bought you dear, for by full many an evil passage hath he come to you ".

And she turned her head, and she said to the king, " Certes, sir, if he hath done it for me, he hath lost his labour, for I tender him no thanks therefor ".

" Ah, lady," said the king, " he hath rendered you many a great service."

" He hath wrought me so much ill on the contrary," said she, " that I shall never love him."

" Ha, lady," said Lancelot, " when have I wrought you ill ? "

But the queen to vex him the more went into another chamber. And he looked at her so long as he might. And the king said to her, " Lady, lady, this laſt service should have vanquished all the misdeeds ".

Then the king took Lancelot by the hand, and he led him there where Kay lay. And so soon as he espied Lancelot, he turned him toward him, and he said, " Welcome, lord of all knights. In sooth," said he, " he is clean out of his wit that assayeth deeds of knighthood before you ".

" Wherefore, maſter Kay ? " said he.

" For that ye have achieved," said he, " that which I assayed like a fool."

Then the king departed, and Lancelot asked Kay wherefore the queen had denied him her greeting.

" What ! " said he.   " Hath she denied it to you ? "

" Yea," said he, " before the king and before all the others."

" Certes," said Kay, " I know not the reason. But such is the reward of a woman."

" Now leave we the matter here," said Lancelot, " and be it as my lady liſt.   But how have ye fared ? "

After that they had talked long while together, Lancelot rose, and he said that he should set out in the morn to seek Sir Gawain at the Bridge beneath the Waves. Forthwithal he departed, and he went up into the hall to a great company of them that were exiled and of the folk of the land, and they did him great honour.

CHAPTER L

*How the Queen heard say that Sir Lancelot was dead,
and how she greeted him when that she beheld him alive*

In the morning Lancelot sets out for the Bridge beneath
the Waves. On his way he is taken prisoner by the people of
Gorre, who mistakenly suppose that they are acting in accordance with the king's wishes. While they are leading him back
to the king, the rumour is spread abroad that he has been killed.
" And when the queen heard it, she had such sorrow that but
a little and she had killed her. But she waited till that she
should know the truth. And then she took good counsel within
her in her heart, and thought that she would never eat again.
But she made the more sorrow for that she thought that she had
put him to death, because she deigned not to speak to him, and
she had blamed him and treated him ill. And she said that
since such a knight was dead, 't would not be fitting if she lived
longer. Thus the queen made her dole for Lancelot. And
then she went to rest, and she would that none should know or
see her grief." She remains for two days and three nights
without food and refuses all comfort.

One evening a false report of her death reaches the vavasour
with whom Lancelot and his captors happen to be lodging for
the night. "And they all, both one and another, bewailed
her sore. But Lancelot could not speak. And he longed to
be in his bed." At midnight when he thinks that his warders
are asleep, he tries to kill himself with the sword of one of the
guards, but he is discovered and foiled in his attempt. Thereafter he is more carefully guarded. The next day they go on
toward Gaihom.

AND when they were fifteen English leagues from
Gaihom, the news came that Lancelot was alive and
well. And when the queen heard it, she was so
glad that she might not be more so, and she was all
cured, and she ate and drank, for enough had she
fasted. When the king knew that Lancelot was nigh,

he mounted his horse and rode to meet him, and he made great joy of him, and he told him firſt of the dole that the queen had made for him. " And know," said he, " that, as I think, her greeting will not be denied you, when she seeth you." And when Lancelot heard that the queen was not dead, he was passing glad thereof.

Right so they entered into the city. And the queen knew well how Lancelot would have killed him. And the king let put in prison all them that had taken him, and he said that he would deſtroy them all. And when Lancelot saw the king so wroth, he fell at his feet, and he prayed him that he would pardon them their ill will, and he did so. Thereafter the king led him to see the queen. And she came to meet him, and she embraced him, and she asked him what cheer. And he said, " Good, lady ". Then they seated them all three on a couch, and the king, that was discreet, was scarce seated ere he said that he would go to see how Kay the seneschal fared, and Lancelot and the queen remained talking together. The queen asked him if he was wounded. And he made answer, " Lady, I have no ill ". And then he required her before God that she should tell him wherefore she would not speak to him the other day.

" For that," she said, " ye left the great court of London without my leave."

And he said that there he had done a misdeed.

" There is yet a greater," said she. Then she asked him for her ring.

And he said, " Lady, here it is ".

Lancelot showing his ring to Guinevere

[face p. 28

" Before God, ye have lied to me," said she. " That is not it."

But he swore so much as he might that it was. And well he thought that he told the truth. And she showed him that which she wore on her finger, and he knew that it was his, and he made great sorrow that he had worn another ring. And he drew it from his finger, and he threw it through a window the farthest that he might.

Therewithal the queen told him how the maiden had brought his ring to court, and the marvel that she had recounted, and then he bethought him of Morgain, the disloyal, and he knew that she had done this. And he told the queen all the adventure of his dream and of his ransom. And she marvelled greatly when she heard what he had dreamed. And she said, " Love, may it ne'er befall that any other knight than ye have part in me, for I should have chosen overmuch for the worse, and I believe that he is not yet born that could take your place ".

And he said, " Lady, in God's name, is my misdeed pardoned me ? "

" Fair, sweet love," said she, " I pardon you all."

That night Lancelot by agreement with Guinevere comes to talk with her at her grated window, which looks on the garden. With her consent he wrenches the iron bars of the window from their place, wounding his hands in the effort, and is received by her in her chamber, both keeping silence so that Kay, who is on guard in the room, may not wake. She tells Lancelot of the death of Galehot, " and he would have grieved thereat, but this was neither the place nor the time ". In the morning drops of blood from Lancelot's wounded hands are discovered on the queen's pillow by Meleagant, who at once accuses her of improper relations with Kay, whose wounds are not yet healed. Lancelot forthwith challenges Meleagant in order to prove the innocence of both the queen and Kay. In the combat he is victorious, but spares the life of Meleagant on the command of the queen, who intercedes at the request of Baudemagus.

CHAPTER LI

How Sir Lancelot was delivered out of prison by a lady

The next morning Lancelot again sets forth for the Bridge beneath the Waves, but he is treacherously entrapped by Meleagant, and after being taken prisoner, is given into the custody of the seneschal of Gorre, and later is placed in closer confinement in a strong tower surrounded by a marsh. Meleagant in the meantime forges a letter from Arthur to the queen, bidding her return to Logres, and telling her that Lancelot is at court. She obeys the summons, and on her arrival the disappearance of Lancelot becomes known, and the court is overwhelmed with sorrow and dismay.

One day not long afterward the king sees a cart drawn by a wretched horse and driven by a dwarf approach the palace. In the cart a knight is bound, and to its rear his horse, fully caparisoned, is tied. On catching sight of the king, the knight cries out, "Who will deliver me?" And as the knights throng about him he explains that he can be delivered from shame only if another knight will take his place in the cart. This all the knights of the court refuse to do, and the dwarf drives on through the streets amid the jeers of the people. Presently, while the king and his companions dine, the knight enters the hall and seats himself with the rest of the company. All refuse to eat with him except Gawain, who, when Arthur reproves him for thus dishonouring himself, reminds him how Lancelot had ridden in a cart.

After dinner the knight goes to the king's stable, mounts one of the best horses, and rides into the hall uttering a defiance to all those knights who have said that Gawain is dishonoured by having eaten with him. Four knights accept the challenge, and follow him into the forest, where he proceeds

286

to unhorse them in turn. He goes away with their horses, and they return crestfallen to the king.

At this moment the dwarf reappears, driving a damsel in his cart. She chides Arthur and his court for having refused to succour the knight, and then calls upon the companions of the Round Table to deliver her from the cart. Instantly Gawain for love of Lancelot springs up beside her. The maiden descends, and her own knights, who have attended her, mount her on a beautiful palfrey, that they have led with them. Then she proclaims to all that for love of Lancelot the cart should be held in high honour, and that the knight who had come to court in it is Bors, the cousin of Lancelot. Just then Bors returns and restores the five horses to their owners. The damsel departs, and Bors reveals that she is the Lady of the Lake, who has taken this means of removing the stigma of the cart from Lancelot. The king, the queen, and all the knights of the court in turn thereupon mount into the cart, which from that day forth during the lifetime of Arthur was never again used to convey criminals to the gallows.

Now a serf of Meleagant guarded the tower wherein Lancelot was put. And from the house of the serf there ran a stream as far as the tower, and they brought food to Lancelot by a little boat, and he drew it up by a cord. And the tower had no door nor window save a little window whereby he drew up his bread and water. But it was not so much as he might have eaten.

Thus was Lancelot in prison, and none knew it save Meleagant and the serf. And when Meleagant saw that he was as he wished him to be, he departed from Gorre and hied him to the court of King Arthur. And he said to him :—

" King Arthur, in sooth I won this lady from Kay the seneschal, and Lancelot came in quest of her. And so there was a battle between us twain, but such was its end that I let him lead away the queen, and he promised that within the year he would do battle with me at whatsoever time I should come to summon him therefor. And the queen likewise swore that she would return with me, if he defended her not. And I am come to summon him, but I find him not here. And if he is here, let him come forth, for such a knight as he should never draw aback."

When the king saw that he was Meleagant, he did him great honour for love of his father, and anon he said to him, " Meleagant, Lancelot is not here, nor have I seen him since that he went to seek the queen, nor for almoſt a year afore. But ye are so discreet that ye know well what ye have to do ".

. " What ? " said he.

" To wait here forty days," said the king. " And if he cometh not in the meantime, go ye back to your land, and at the end of a year, return, and if then either he or another for him fight not with you, ye shall have the queen."

And he said that thus he would do. And he tarried at the court. But here the ſtory speaketh no more of him or of the king or of his baronage, but turneth to a siſter of Meleagant.

This damsel was sore grieved for the imprisonment of Lancelot, and she hated Meleagant right bitterly for that he had taken from her the land that she should have held, for it was her heritage from her mother, save only one caſtle where she was. Nor was Meleagant her brother except by their mother. And therefore he so hated her that he had taken all her heritage from her againſt the will of King Baude-magus. When the maiden saw that the tower of the marsh was built, she thought within her that Meleagant had made it for naught else but to immure Lancelot therein. And she had nurtured the wife of the serf that guarded the tower, and she had given her in marriage and had bestowed many benefits upon her. And she thought within her that if she could deliver Lancelot from prison, he would avenge her on Meleagant better than any other man living could do. She came to the wife of the serf, and she gave her even more than ever afore. And she lodged in a dwelling that was at the end of the marsh on the road, and she gave heed that none should see her. And she watched how his food was brought to Lancelot. And then she took such pity on him that she wept tenderly, and she said within her that, an she should die therefor, she would rescue him, if she might, for 't would be a great shame if the best knight in the world should die in so base a prison.

The maiden prepared all that was needful to take Lancelot out of the tower, and that night when all the house slept, she made her ready in a chamber where her maidens lay. And she hied her to the boat, and she asked for a pick and a stout cord, and she entered into the boat, and she came to the tower, and she found the little basket wherein they sent Lancelot his food. And when she was come to the window, she heard Lancelot, that lamented and bewailed the evil prison and the misease that he endured.

Long while Lancelot made moan and raved in this wise. And anon the damsel shook the little basket, and Lancelot, that was speedily aware thereof, arose, and he came to the window, and he thrust his head forth so far as he might. And she called softly to him, and he said, " Who are ye ? "

" I am a friend ," said she, " who is passing sorry for your trouble, and I have been so heavy thereat that I have put myself in peril to set you free."

When he heard her, he was right glad thereat. And she bound the stout rope to the slender cord, and a pick withal, and he drew it up right swiftly. And he hewed the window till that he could issue therefrom. Then he tied the stout cord within, and he descended down so softly as he might, and he issued forth from the marsh. Therewithal the damsel went to rest in a chamber, and Lancelot was in a chamber near by.

And on the morn so soon as it was day Lancelot arose, and he put on the best robe that the damsel had, and he mounted on a palfrey, and the damsel led him forth in this wise in the sight of all the folk. And the damsel rode till she came to her castle in the land of her mother, and she had received none other land, for Meleagant had taken from her all her other land and had disinherited her. And when the damsel came to her castle, she gave Lancelot all that she thought would do him good, and he had great need of aid, for he had been in a passing ill prison.

In the meantime, the damsel sent to the court of King Arthur to learn tidings of Meleagant. And the messenger asked wherefore Meleagant tarried so long time at court. And they said to him that he waited forty days to have the battle of Lancelot, and they told him which day was the fortieth and when it would be. Thereupon the messenger came to his lady and told her what he had learned at court. And she told it forthright to Lancelot. And he was now sound, and he had returned to his ſtrength, and he said to the damsel that she should let him go away, for he longed to avenge him on the man whom he moſt hated in the world.

"Fair sir," said she, "I will firſt make ready for you arms and a horse, and the gear whereof ye have need, and then shall ye go. And there are yet ten days to the time when ye ought to be there."

CHAPTER LII

How Sir Lancelot fought with Meleagant and at the laſt smote off his head

THUS abided Lancelot there yet eight days. And the damsel prepared for him a horse and arms, and then he departed from there all safe and sound, and he rode till that he came to Escavalon, where the king was with a great following of knights and other people. And Meleagant was already armed, and he said that he would go away, for that there was nobody here to take the battle for Lancelot. And thereupon Bors the Exile sprang forward and said that he would forthright take it, if Meleagant liſt. And he said that he would liefer that Lancelot did it than any other.

"I' faith, Meleagant," said Sir Gawain, "if Lancelot were here, ye would not be so eager to do this

battle as ye now are. And it shall never be that ye
have not the battle because he is not here, if ye desire
it so much as ye make semblance that ye do, for I
will fight against you for love of him."

"Certes," said Meleagant, "I refuse you not. For
there is no knight in the world with whom I should
fight more willingly than with you."

Then Sir Gawain hastened to arm him. And the
king ordained that the combat should be outside of
the town in the meadows, and each assented thereto,
and they went down through the town armed at all
points. Right so it befell that Lancelot entered into
the castle, and he was well armed. He met Sir
Gawain, that knew him well, and he him, and they
made such joy each of other that neither could make
greater. The news of Lancelot speedily came to
court, and great was the joy thereat. And the king
came to kiss him, and so also the queen and all the
baronage. And when Meleagant knew the truth, he
was sore abashed.

And Lancelot came to him, and he said to him,
"Meleagant, Meleagant, ye have made such a hue
and cry that now ye shall have the battle. For I am
out of the tower of the marsh wherein ye put me by
treason, thanks be to God and to her that took me
thence".

Forthright they came to the field, and the guards
were set. Then they let their horses run, and they
dealt each the other great strokes on their shields,
and they brast their hauberks on their arms and on
their shoulders, and each harmed other to his power,
and they held together ever at one point till midday.

Lancelot escaping from the tower

Lancelot and Meleagant doing combat

[*face p. 292*

Then Meleagant began to grow weary, as one that could no longer suffer blows. And he had endured so much that his blood poured forth from more than thirty places. And Lancelot raised his sword on high and assayed to smite him a great ſtroke, and he, that had great fear, drew aback so quickly as he might. And when Lancelot saw that he had not reached him with his ſtroke, he hurtled againſt him with his shield so hard that he made him fall to the ground all up so down. Then forthright he leaped upon him and raced the helmet off his head and threw it into the field so far as he might, and then he lowered his ventail. And Meleagant, when he saw that he was in peril of death, cried him mercy. But Lancelot would by no means hearken to him. Then the king came before Lancelot and prayed him that he slay him not, and the queen made a sign to him that he cut off his head, so that Lancelot saw it full well. Then said Lancelot to the king, " Sire, I will do so much for you that I will let him rise and put his helmet on his head, and if another time I have the upper hand of him, know that he shall have no surety that he will not die ".

Forthright Lancelot raised himself from above Meleagant, and suffered him to lace his helmet and to take his sword and his shield. Then Lancelot ran upon him, and in a little while he had wrought so for him that there was none in the field so base but felt pity for him. And Lancelot took him by the helmet and raced it off his head. And Meleagant sprang up with his head uncovered, and he had fear of losing his head, and he drew aback so speedily

as he might. And Lancelot smote him such a ſtroke
with his sword that he made his head fly into the
midſt of the field, and the body lay ſtretched out on
the ground. And Lancelot put his sword back into
the scabbard. And then Kay the seneschal sprang
forward, and he took his shield from his shoulder,
and he said to him, " Ah, sir, beyond all other knights
in the world are ye welcome as the flower of all earthly
knighthood, and well have ye given proof thereof
here and elsewhere ".

After Kay the seneschal came King Arthur and
embraced Lancelot all armed as he was, and he himself
took his helmet from his head, and he gave it to Sir
Ewaine, who kissed him on the mouth and said to
him, " Fair, sweet friend, ye are right welcome ".
Anon came Sir Gawain, and he sprang toward Lancelot
with arms outſtretched, and the queen likewise came
to him as glad as any lady there. And then thereafter came all the barons, and they made joy of him
as great as e'er a man might devise, and they led him
with joy and mirth up into the palace.

Then the king ordained that the tables should be
placed, and they were. And then the knights seated
them there at hand, and it was yet but the hour
between noon and evensong. Then the king did that
which turned to great honour for Lancelot, and he
had never done it afore for any man. For he made
him sit at his high table right before him where he
ate, and never afore had knight sat there save at high
feſtivals at supper, when it chanced that some ſtranger
knight who had won the tournament or the quin-
tain sat there, albeit not close to the king but somewhat

removed from him, and the king made him sit there for that all the others might see him and might henceforth know him. But on that day Lancelot sat there by the prayer of the king and by the command of the queen, his lady. And he was sorry and much abashed thereat, and he sat there much againſt his will, but to do the will of the king and at the command of his lady he assented thereto.

Great was the joy and the cheer that the king made of Lancelot, for long time it had been that he had not seen him, and he queſtioned him and asked him how he had sped. And he said, well, and thanks be to God that he was safe and sound. And the king durſt not tell him the tidings of the death of Galehot, for he supposed that he knew not a word thereof.

CHAPTER LIII

How Sir Lancelot came to the tomb of Galehot, and how he let bear his body to the Dolorous Gard and buried him there

After spending a week at court in the full favour of the queen, Lancelot sets out on further adventures. In the course of a series of exploits, early one evening he seeks lodging for the night at a convent on the border of the foreſt of Sarpenic.

When Lancelot was come to the house of religion he found at the door four brethren that had sung complines, and they were come out into the evening air, and they rose up to meet him and to dismount

him, and they bade him welcome. And they made him
enter within, and they asked him if he had eaten that
day. And he said, "Nay." And they forthright bade
their servitors place the table, and the cloth and the
bread thereupon. But he said that he would not
eat till that he had gone to the church and made his
orisons, for he had not been in a church that day.

Anon he entered into the church to pray. And
when he kneeled down, he looked toward the right
hand, and he saw a grill of silver cunningly wrought
with flowers of gold and with birds of divers kinds
and with beasts, and behind it there were five knights
armed at all points with helms on their heads and with
swords in their hands, and as ready to defend them
as if a foe would assail them.

And Lancelot marvelled greatly thereat, and he
turned him speedily, and he went thither, and he
saluted the knights. And they bade him welcome.
And he entered within the grill that was so rich that,
as he thought, a king might not buy it. And hard
by the knights he was ware of a tomb, the richest that
ever man saw, for it was all of fine gold with precious
stones that were worth more than a mighty kingdom.
And if the beauty of the tomb was great, it was as
nothing to the richness thereof. And it was the
largest tomb withal that Lancelot had ever seen.
And he marvelled who the prince might be that had
been laid therein. And he asked the knights what
they did there.

"Sir," said they, "we guard him that lieth here
in this tomb that he be not carried hence. And we
are five to guard it every day, and at night there are

other five, who do the same service that we do by day."

"And why are ye in fear", said Lancelot, "that he will be carried away?"

"Sir," said they, "for that one of the brethren here, who is a worshipful man of holy life, told us short while since that a knight would come here, who by force would take it hence and would let carry it out of this country. And our people of this land would liefer die than that it should be removed from among us. And therefore we guard it even as ye see, for the good man told us that the knight would not tarry in his coming."

"Now tell me," said Lancelot, "was not he for whom this tomb was made a prince of high lineage?"

"Sir," said they, "he was of high lineage and rich, and he was the moﬅ worshipful man of his time withal."

"Ah, God," said Lancelot, "who was he?"

"Sir," said they, "if ye know aught of letters, ye may see who he was, for his name is writ on the head of this tomb."

Therewithal Lancelot went thither, and he found writing that said, "HERE LIETH GALEHOT, THE SON OF THE FAIR GIANTESS, WHO DIED FOR LOVE OF LANCELOT". And when he saw this, he fell to the earth in a swoon, and he lay long time without saying a word. And the knights ran to him to raise him up, for they marvelled greatly what ailed him and who he might be. And when he was come out of his swoon, he cried on high and said, "Alas, what sorrow and what loss!" Thereupon he beat one fiﬅ upon the other,

and he tore his hair and gave himself great buffets
with his fists on his brow and on his breasts, and he
wept so sore that there was none there but had pity
on him. And he reviled himself, and he cursed the
hour when he was born, and he said, "Ah God, what
pity and what loss is this that one of the most worshipful
men on earth hath died for the sake of the basest and
foulest knight that ever was!"

So great dole and outcry made Lancelot that they
who stood by looked at him wondering, and they
asked who he was. And he could answer them not
a word, but ever he wept and beat his breast and tore
his hair. And when he had long while made his
dole, he looked at the writing that said that Galehot
had died for him. And right so he said that he would
be a caitiff, if he died not likewise for him. And he
sprang out from the grill and he said that he would
go to fetch his sword, and that he would kill him,
for thus had Galehot done. And anon when he was
outside of the church, he met one of the damsels
of the Lady of the Lake. And she knew him well,
and she took him by the skirt of his tunic, and she
checked him.

"What is this?" said she. "Whither are ye bound
in this wise?"

"Ah, damsel," said he, "let me fulfil my sorrow,
for never in this world shall I have joy or repose."

"Tell it me," said she.

And he answered not a word, but he sprang forward
beyond her in such wise that he escaped her hands.
And when she saw him go thus, she cried out, "I
forbid you," said she, "by the being that ye love

beſt of all earthly things to go further ere ye have
spoken to me ". And he ſtayed him, and he looked
at her, and when he knew her, he bade her welcome.

" Now sir, before God," said she, " ye should make
me better cheer than ye do, at leaſt because I am a
messenger from your Lady of the Lake."

" Damsel," said he, " now let it neither grieve you
nor enter into your thought that I shall ever have
joy for whatever fortune may betide me."

" In God's name, ye shall," said she. " Now
harken what word my Lady sendeth you. She biddeth
you take the body of Galehot hence and let carry it
to the Dolorous Gard, and there let it be put in the
same tomb whereon ye found your name written.
And she would have it thus, for she knoweth well
that in that same place your body will be buried."

And when he heard this he was right glad and he
said that these tidings were pleasant to him, and that
he would do all even as she said. Then he asked
how his Lady sped.

" I' faith," she said, " my Lady hath been passing
sick for a se'nnight, for she had learned by lot, as she
hath since told me, that so soon as ye should find the
tomb of Galehot, ye would slay you from sorrow,
if ye were turned not therefrom. And therefore she
sent me in great haſte hither. And she biddeth you
leave your grieving, for it can work you naught but
harm. And she beggeth you by the being that ye
love moſt in all the world that ye take comfort with
the beſt cheer that ye may. And if ye do not thus,
wit ye well that then when ye firſt have need of
her, she will fail you."

And he said that he would take comfort, since she would have it so.

"Now I command you that ye arm you," said she, "for I know well that the knights will not let you carry away the body so long as they can defend it."

And he said that they should all die sooner than he should fail to carry it hence. And he went to arm him.

And the damsel went to the knights that guarded the tomb, and she said to them, "Sirs," said she, "will ye turn you from that which needs muſt be done by force? And I say this to you for the body that ye guard, and know ye well that it will be taken away from here".

"It will not," said they, "so long as we can do aught."

"Now perdy it shall be," said she, "for he is come that will take it out of the tomb. And if ye gainsay him, ye will all die therefor. And for this reason it will be better for you that ye let take it away than that ye let you be slain."

And they said that never while they lived should it be carried away. "And let the knight that is come know well," said they, "that if he were more worshipful even than Lancelot, he should in no wise take it away."

"Now ye shall see," said she, "what will betide you."

At these words Lancelot came thither all armed. And when the knights were ware of him, they asked him what he would.

"I would have the body that is yonder," said he.

The damsel bidding Lancelot fight for the body of Galehot

[*face p.* 300

"I' faith," they made answer, "ye shall by no means have it. We will die sooner than that ye carry it away."

"To dying are ye all come," said he, "since ye will not at leaſt keep away from it."

And he sprang within the grill, and they ran upon him, for they thought to make him flee aback from fear of death. And they smote him wheresoever they could reach him. And he had in his hand his sword all naked, and he ran at them wrathfully, and dealt them great buffets with his sword so that he made them all give way before him.

> In the ferocious ſtruggle that follows Lancelot severely
> wounds three of the knights, ſtrikes the fourth to the ground,
> puts the fifth to flight, and then proceeds to deal further with
> the fourth.

And Lancelot returned to the other, who had raised him from the ground. And Lancelot gave him such a buffet that he made his helmet fly into the field. And when he felt that his head was uncovered, he cried for mercy and said that Lancelot muſt not kill him, for he was ready to do his will.

"Then," said Lancelot, "it behooveth thee to swear that thou wilt take the body of Sir Galehot to the Dolorous Gard and let keep it there till I come. And if any man ask thee who sent thee, say it was he who wore the white armour the day that the caſtle was taken."

And he pledged Lancelot his troth that thus he would do. Then Lancelot took the cover of the tomb by the thicker end, and he raised it with such might that but a little and he had torn all his muscles asunder, and the blood gushed forth from his nose and his mouth, and his body sweated from the travail. Yet not for the pain did he give over till that he had raised the ſtone on high. But no misease that he had e'er had was in any wise so great as the sorrow that he felt when he saw the body of Galehot all armed even as he was. And he found his sword beside him that was fair and good, and without fail he would have slain himself therewith, if the damsel had not forbidden him.

Therewithal Lancelot let make a bier of wood, and he let cover it with the richeſt pall that was there, and when he had prepared it so richly as he might, the knight that was his prisoner said to him, " Sir," said he, " it would be well, if we should leave by night ".

" Wherefore ? " said Lancelot.

" For that if the knights of this country", said he, " knew that it was to be carried hence, they would set ambushes at the passes, so that it should be ſtayed in some place. And therefore I advise that it go forthwith, for it would be twenty English leagues diſtant before day."

And he accorded well thereto, and he put a litter on two ambling palfreys. And thus they bore Galehot out of the house. And the brethren made great dole and sorrow that he was borne away. And Lancelot accompanied him a great part of the night, weeping and lamenting and bewailing his prowess and his valour. And if it had not been for the maiden that was with him, he would have done even more than he did, but she turned him therefrom. And he commanded the knight that Galehot should not be interred ere he came to him.

Forthwithal Lancelot departed, and he returned to the abbey and went to reſt. And that night he would neither eat nor drink for aught that they said to him, but ever he wept and lamented. And he was weary for the day that tarried so long. And on the morn, so soon as the day appeared, he arose and he heard mass, he and the damsel with him. And he armed him, and he took leave of the brethren, and he fared on his way, he and the damsel with him. And then she told him tidings of Bors. And she said to him, "Sir, ever he goeth seeking you, and he will never reſt till that he hath found you".

"Ah, damsel," said Lancelot, "if ye think to find him afore I do, I would pray you to carry to him this sword which belonged to Sir Galehot. And bid him wear it from me, for it is right good."

And she said that she would find him within a while, and she would give him well the message. And so she parted from Lancelot.

And Lancelot journeyed till that he came to the caſtle of the Dolorous Gard. And nevertheless they of the country called it the Joyous Gard, but in other lands it never changed its name. And when Lancelot was come thither and saw the body of Galehot, there is no need to ask if he made dole, for all they that saw him thought that he would die on the spot. But they of the caſtle entreated him and comforted him as beſt they might, for they were sore grieved at his sorrow. And anon he bade them make one of the richeſt tombs that they could devise.

" Sir," they said, "wherefore ? "

" For that I would that this body be laid there,"
said he.

" Now i' faith, sir," said an ancient dame, " in
this caſtle is the richeſt tomb that there is in all the
world, but we know not in what place. And if ye
would find it, let summon all the old men from here,
and ye will learn true tidings thereof, as I believe."

Even as the lady counselled him Lancelot did, for
he summoned the moſt ancient men of the place and
made them assemble together to take counsel, and
when they had advised together they came before
him, and they said that it was in the chief chapel
near an altar. " And know that it is the richeſt tomb
in the world. And it was made for King Marbaduc,
who afterward created the laws that the Saracens
keep. And this caſtle was theirs, and before Joseph
of Arimathea came¹ they buried the king there, and
they laid him within the tomb and accounted it
holy. But so soon as the Chriſtians came, it was taken
out and thrown into a ditch of the town, and the
tomb remained in its place, that thereafter was
diſturbed by no man."

Of this adventure was Lancelot right glad. And
he let dig the tomb out from there where it had been
placed. And when he saw it, he prized it much.
And that was no marvel, for it was not made of gold
or of silver, but it was all of precious ſtones, joined
so subtly one to other that it seemed that a mortal
man could not have made such a work. When the
tomb was borne there where Lancelot had found the
name written, they placed it before an ambry, and

Lancelot in the tower of Gorre

A scribe of King Arthur

[face p. 305

then they laid there the body of Galehot. And he was armed at all points, even as it was the custom at that time. And Lancelot himself laid him within the tomb. And when he had laid him there, he kissed him three times on the mouth with so great anguish in his heart that but a little and it had burst. Thereupon he laid over him a rich samite wrought with gold and precious stones, and he put the cover thereon. And thereafter he departed thence, and he commended the folk of the castle to God.

And then he went on his way, and he rode till that he came to the court of King Arthur, who sojourned then at Camelot. When the king knew that he was there, he came down from the hall and all his baronage with him, and the queen and her maidens withal, and they received him with as great joy as if he had been God Himself. And when they had unarmed him, they went to meat. And when they had eaten, the king bade his clerks come before him that put into writing the adventures of the knights, and they put into writing the adventures of Lancelot even as he recounted them.

CHAPTER LIV

*How Sir Lancelot helped a dolorous lady from her pain
and how he fought with a serpent*

A year later Lancelot again leaves court and enters upon a protracted series of adventures. After having won great renown at a certain tourney, he consents to accept hospitality for the night from the lady of a certain castle, who allures him

by promising to show him the most beautiful object in the
world on the morrow. She and her husband entertain Lancelot
with the utmost honour. In the morning when he is ready to
leave, the lady sets out with him, announcing to her husband
that she intends to conduct him to Corbenic.[1]

AND so the lady and Lancelot rode till afternoon,
when they entered into a valley. And then they
espied before them at the end of the valley a little
castle that was well set, for it was encircled all around
by a deep water and by good embattled walls. When
they drew nigh, they met a damsel that said to the
lady, " Lady, whither lead you this knight ? " And
she said, " To Corbenic ".

" In sooth, lady," said the maiden, " then ye love
him little, for ye lead him to a place whence he shall
never depart without shame and ill."

Then they rode on till they came to the castle,
and they found the bridge and crossed it, and when
they came into the chief street the people of the place
began to say, " Sir knight, the cart awaiteth you."
And he answered low that if he must needs mount
thereupon, 't would not be the first time that he had
been there. And ever they rode till that they came
to the chief tower. And Lancelot praised it greatly,
for it was the fairest and the richest that ever he saw
to his knowledge.

He looked to the right, and him seemed that he
heard the voice of a woman near him. And he went
there, and he saw that this was the maiden that Sir
Gawain would fain draw forth from the vat, but he
might not.[2] And she cried, " Ah, Holy Mary, who
will deliver me hence ? " And when she espied
Lancelot come, she said to him, " Ah, sir, draw me

306

forth from this water that burneth me". And
Lancelot went to the vat, and he took her by the arms,
and he drew her forth. And when she saw that she
was set free, she fell at his feet, and she kissed his
ankles and his feet, and she said to him, "Ah, Sir,
blessed be the hour when ye were born, for ye have
delivered me out of the greatest pains wherein ever
woman was".

And now the hall began to fill with ladies and with
knights, and all they of the town gathered about to
behold the maiden, and they led her into a chapel
to give thanks to our Lord. And forthwithal they
led Lancelot to a cemetery beneath the tower, and
they showed him a tomb that was passing rich, where
there were letters written that said, " THIS TOMB SHALL
NOT BE RAISED TILL THAT THE LEOPARD FROM WHOM
THE GREAT LION SHALL ISSUE FORTH SHALL LAY HAND
THEREON. AND THEN THE GREAT LION SHALL BE
ENGENDERED IN THE FAIR DAUGHTER OF THE KING OF
THE FOREIGN COUNTRY ".[1]

When Lancelot had read the letters, he understood
not what they would say. And the folk that were
about him said to him, " Sir, we suppose that it is
ye whereof the writing speaketh, for we know well by
the damsel that ye have holpen that ye are the best
knight of all them that now are ".

" What will ye that I do ? I am ready to do all
your will."

" We will," said they, " that ye raise this stone to
see what there is beneath."

And he put his hand on the thick end of the stone,
and he lifted it up lightly, and he saw within it the

most horrible serpent and the most venemous to behold whereof ever he had heard tell. And when it saw Lancelot it spat forth at him burning fire, so that it burned all his hauberk and his armour on him. And then it darted out of the tomb into the midst of the cemetery so that the shrubs that were in the cemetery began to burn for the heat of the fire. And the people that were there turned them in flight, and they went up to the windows to see how Lancelot would fare, and they threw down his shield and his lance to him and he took them, and he raised his shield before his face. Then he dressed him there where he saw the serpent, as he that feared no adventure that might befall him. And the serpent spat poisoned fire upon him so that it burned all his shield before him. And Lancelot smote him in the breast with his lance in such wise that he thrust it into his body, blade and shaft. And the serpent began to beat the earth with his wings like a creature wounded unto death. And Lancelot put his hand on his sword, and he smote him such a stroke there where he could reach him that he made his head fall from him.

Then the knights that had already been armed came forward to succour Lancelot. And when they saw that he had slain the serpent, they received him with great joy, and the bells began to ring. And so many knights and ladies and maidens came there that it was naught but a marvel. And they said that he was welcome beyond all knights in the world, and they led him into the chief palace, and they unarmed him.

Lancelot and the serpent of Corbenic

[*face p. 308*

CHAPTER LV

How Sir Lancelot came to King Pelles, and of the Holy Grail, and of the daughter of King Pelles

AND so as they were speaking there issued forth from a chamber a big knight, and he led with him a great following. And he was one of the nobleſt men that Lancelot had seen since he was departed from Camelot, and well he seemed of gentle birth. And when the people of the caſtle saw him come, they rose to meet him, and they said to Lancelot, " Sir, this is the king that cometh ". Then Lancelot came toward him and gave him greeting. And the king greeted him in return, and he threw his arms about his neck, and he said to him, " Sir, greatly have we longed to see and to have you, and now, thanks be to God, we possess you. And wit you well we have great need of you, for our land hath been so waſte and desert that the poor have loſt all that they had gained, and it will be full juſtice, if it be the will of our Lord, that their losses be made good to them and their possessions, which they have long lacked, reſtored to them ".¹

Then they sat them down together, and the king asked Lancelot whence he was and how he was called. And he said, Lancelot of the Lake.

" Now tell me," said the king, "was not King Ban, that died of grief, your father ? "

" Sir," said Lancelot, " yea."

" I' faith," said the king, " then am I well assured that by you, or by that which shall issue from you, this land shall be delivered from the strange adventures that befall here day and night."

Forthwithal there came before them a lady so old that she might well have been an hundred years of age, and she called the king, and she said to him, "Sire, I would fain speak with you". The king left Lancelot, and he bade his knights bear him company. And they said that they would. Then he went with the lady into a chamber, and when they were seated, she said, "Sire, what can we do with this knight that God hath brought to us ?"

"I know not," said the king, "what we should do with him, save that he shall have my daughter."

"I' faith," said the lady, "I wit well that he will never desire to take her when she is offered to him, for he so loveth the queen, the wife of King Arthur, that he will have no other. And therefore one must needs deal with him so wisely that he shall know naught thereof."

"Do ye deal," said the king, "for it must needs be done."

"Meddle no more therewith," said the lady, "for I shall bring it to a good end."

Then the king went back to the hall, and he came to Lancelot to bear him company. And they spake of many things, and they held the goodliest language together that they might. And Lancelot asked the king how he was named. And he said that men called him Pelles of the Foreign Country.

And anon as they thus talked Lancelot looked and he saw come in at a window the dove that Sir Gawain had seen, and in her mouth she carried a censer of gold that was passing rich. And so soon as she was entered therein, the palace was filled with all the sweet odours that the heart of man could devise. And then all they that were there were silent, so that there was not one that spake a word, but they all kneeled when they saw the dove come. And it went into a chamber. Forthright the servitors came forward speedily, and they laid the cloths on the tables, and they all sat down, and no man spake a word, and none summoned them to meat. And Lancelot marvelled greatly thereat. And he did even as the others, and he sat down before the king, and he saw that all the others knelt in prayer and in orisons, and he did even as they.

After that the king was seated, within a while they saw a damsel come forth from a chamber, and she was so fair and so goodly in all respects that Lancelot himself said that he had never seen so great beauty in woman save only in his lady the queen. And he said that she who led him thither had spoken sooth. And he looked upon the vessel that the damsel bare betwixt her hands that was to his knowledge the richest that had e'er been beheld by mortal man. And it was fashioned in semblance of a chalice. And him seemed and well he believed that this was an holy thing and worthy of honour. And then he joined his hands together and bowed his head devoutly before it. And so as the lady passed among the tables, all they at each table kneeled before the holy vessel. And Lancelot did likewise. And therewithal the tables were filled with all manner of fair meats that one could think upon, and the place was filled with

good savours, as if all the spicery of the world had
been spread abroad there.

After that the damsel had passed once before the
tables, she returned ſtraight to the chamber whence
she had come. And when she was gone, King Pelles
said to Lancelot, " Certes, sir," said he, " I fear
greatly leſt the grace of our Lord fail you suddenly
even as it did Sir Gawain the other day when he was
here ".

" Fair sir," said Lancelot, " it need not be that our
Lord, Who is so gracious, should be angry with His
sinners every day."

CHAPTER LVI

*How Sir Lancelot was deceived by Dame Brisane, and
how Galahad was engendered*

AND when the king had eaten at his leisure, the cloths
were removed, and he asked Lancelot what he thought
of this rich vessel that the damsel had borne.

" It seemeth to me," said he, " that I have never
seen a maiden so fair. Of a lady I speak not."

When the king heard this word, he thought forthright on that which he had heard said of Queen
Guinevere. And well he believed that it was true.
And he went to Brisane, who was miſtress of his
daughter, she that had spoken to him afore. And
he told her that which he had said and Lancelot had
replied about his daughter. " Sire," said she, " I said

so to you. Now wait for me a little, and I will go
to speak with him." And she went to Lancelot, and
she began to ask him for tidings of the king, and he
gave her such tidings as he knew.

"Of the queen, sir," said she, "I ask you not, for
but short while since I saw her sound and happy."

And he trembled for joy when he heard her speak.
And he asked her where she saw the queen.

"Sir," said she, "I saw her but two leagues hence,
where she will lie to-night."

"Lady," said he, "ye mock me."

"So help me God, sir," said she, "I do not. And
for that ye may believe me better, come with me,
and I will show her to you."

"Certes, lady," said he, "I will well."

Then she sent to fetch his arms, and she went
ſtraightway to the king that awaited her in the chamber,
and he asked her how she had wrought. "Now make
your daughter to mount speedily," said she, "and
send her to the Casse, the sooneſt that ye may, and I
will ride, Lancelot and I, after her. And when we
shall be there, I will make him to think that she is
Queen Guinevere. And I have prepared a draught
that I will give him. And so soon as he shall have
drunk it, and its force shall have mounted to his
brain, I doubt not that he will do all my will. And
thus may befall that which we seek."

Then the king bade his daughter make her ready,
and he gave her twenty knights to attend her to the
caſtle of the Casse. And when they were come there
and were alighted down from their horses, they let
make in a hall the richeſt bed that they might. And

there the maiden was laid to rest, since they that had
led her thither would have it so.

And Lancelot had taken his arms and was mounted
on his horse, and he departed, and he left the lady
that had led him thither. And they rode, he and
Brisane, till that they came to the castle of the Casse.
And when they were come, it was dark night, and the
moon was not yet risen. Therewithal they alighted
down from their horses, and Brisane led Lancelot
into a chamber where the knights were. And when
they saw him come, they turned them towards him,
and they said that he was welcome. And they unarmed
him. And there was a bright light there, for there
were more than twenty tapers lighted. And Brisane,
who had acquainted one of her maidens with that which
she would fain do and had given her the philter, said
to her, " And when thou shalt hear me call for a
drink, then bring a full goblet of this potion, and give
it, and no other drink, to Lancelot, and bring it not
to him till that he is thirsty." And she said that she
would well.

When Lancelot was unarmed, he had a great desire
to drink, for that he had been heated in coming.
And he asked for his lady the queen. " Sir," said
Brisane, " she is here in this chamber. And she is
already asleep, as I think." And he called for the
wine, and the maiden that had been bidden brought
the drink, the which was clearer than a fountain and
was of the colour of wine. And the cup was not large
and it was full, and he had desire to drink. And the
lady said to him, " Sir, drink all, for it will do you
naught but good, and I suppose that ye have never

314

tasted such ". And he took the cup and he drank
it all, and he found the poison good and sweet, and he
asked for still more, and she brought it, and he drank
it all.

Then he was more merry and more talkative than
was his wont. And he asked Brisane how he might
see his lady the queen. And she looked at him, and
she saw that he was already distraught, so that he knew
not where he was or how he came thither, but he
thought that he was in the city of Camelot. And him
seemed that he spoke to a lady that ever bore the queen
company after the Lady of Malohaut was dead. And
when she saw him so assotted and knew well that he
might lightly be deceived, she said to him, " Sir,
my lady may well fall asleep. Why delay ye to go
to her ? "

" For that she hath not sent for me," said he.
" But if she sendeth for me, I am fain to go."

" Lord love me," said she, " ye shall have a message
speedily."

Then she went into a chamber, and she made
semblance that she had spoken with the queen. Then
she returned to Lancelot, and she said to him, " Sir,
my lady awaiteth you, and she biddeth you come speak
with her ". And he went ; and he came to the
maiden as he who wend that she was the queen.
And she that desired naught save to meet him whereby
the knighthood of the world was illumined, received
him gladly and merrily.

In such wise were brought together the best knight
and the fairest, and the fairest and most nobly born
maiden of their time. And each desired other for

diverse reasons. For she desired him not so much for his comeliness or for carnal affection as that she might receive the seed whereby all the country was to return to its former beauty, which by the dolorous stroke of the sword with the strange girdles had been made waste and desert, even as the story telleth openly in the *History of the Grail*.[1] And he desired her in another manner, for he coveted her not for her beauty, but he supposed that she was his lady the queen. And therefore he was inflamed, and he knew her, but even as Adam knew his wife faithfully and by the commandment of our Lord, so he knew this maiden in sin and in adultery, contrary to the law of God and of Holy Church.

And none the less our Lord, in Whom all pity dwelleth, and Who judgeth not always according to the misdeeds of sinners, looked upon this union according to the merits of the people of the land, not desiring that they should ever be in exile, and He gave them twain to engender and conceive such fruit that for the flower of virginity that was there despoiled and violated, there was created another flower, from the virtue and sweetness whereof many lands were replenished and restored, even as the *History of the Holy Grail* setteth forth to us. For in place of this lost flower was created Galahad, the virgin, the good knight, he who brought the adventures of the Holy Grail to an end, and he sat in the Siege Perilous of the Round Table, wherein never knight sat but he died. And even as the name of Galahad was lost to Lancelot by carnal sin, so was it recovered by this Galahad through abstinence of the flesh. For he was virgin in will and in deed even to his death, as the story saith. And thus was recovered flower for flower, for in his birth the flower of maidenhood was crushed and bruised, and he who thereafter was the flower and mirror of all knighthood was created by the common union. And if virginity was corrupted when he was conceived, well was the misdeed amended in his life by his own virginity, the which he rendered pure and whole to his Saviour, when he passed from this world. And for the good deeds that he did in this life the sin of his conception was blotted out. And now the story leaveth speaking of him and returneth to speak of Lancelot.

In the morning when Lancelot awakes, he discovers the deception that has been practised upon him. In a frenzy of rage he seizes his sword and is about to kill the damsel, but when he sees her beauty and hears her cries for mercy, he lays the sword aside and begs her to pardon him for his violence. He forthwith leaves her and rides aimlessly away in unspeakable grief and anger.

CHAPTER LVII

How the Queen knew that for love of her Sir Lancelot might not achieve the Holy Grail

After many misfortunes and exploits Lancelot at length arrives at Camelot. Arthur summons the knights who have been absent from court, Lancelot first among them, to narrate their adventures, which he bids his clerks record. Lancelot recounts all his experiences except his intercourse with the daughter of King Pelles. Gawain comes next in turn, and in the course of his narrative relates that in a deserted chapel he had

317

found a burning tomb, upon which was an inscription ſtating
that the fire would never be quenched till the knight should
come there, who by his carnal sin had loſt the adventure of the
Holy Grail; and in another inscription he was called the son
of the Queen of many Sorrows.

Now on that day there was great merrymaking and
great joy, and there was much talk on many matters.
And at length it chanced that the queen was at a
window of the palace, and Lancelot was there beside
her, and they were alone, they two together, and
they were so far apart from the other folk that none
but they heard that which they said.

Then said the queen to Lancelot, " Ah, Lancelot,
heard ye to-day Sir Gawain tell how he found the
adventure of the tombs in the Waſte Chapel and the
words that said that no man might bring this adventure to an end till the unhappy knight should come
there, who by his carnal sin had loſt the power to
achieve the adventure of the Holy Grail ? And in
another place the knight was called the son of the
Queen of Sorrows. Tell me if ye know who this
knight is ".

" Lady, nay," said he.

" On my life," said she, " it is ye whereof the
letters spake, for ye were son of the Queen of Sorrows.
And it irketh me sore that through luſt of the flesh
ye have loſt the power to bring to an end that for
which all the chivalry of the world travaileth. In
sooth, well may ye say that ye have bought my love
dear, since through me ye have loſt that which ye
shall ne'er be able to recover. And wit ye well that
I grieve no less therefor than ye, but perchance even

more. For this is a great sin, inasmuch as God had made you the best and the fairest and the most gracious of all men, and He had moreover given you such favour that ye saw openly the marvels of the Holy Grail. And now ye have lost it for that we twain have met together. Better were it for me, I ween, had I ne'er been born than that through me such great good should remain undone as will now remain."

"Lady," said Lancelot, "ye speak ill. Know in sooth that never should I have come to so great renomee as I have but for you, for of myself I should not have been minded at the beginning of my chivalry to undertake the feats that others let be through lack of prowess. But my desire for you and your great beauty filled my heart with such pride that I might find no adventure that I brought it not to an end. For well I knew that if I might not achieve adventures by prowess, I should be worth naught in your eyes. And I must needs achieve them or die. Wherefore I tell you soothly that this it was that most increased my prowess."

"Then it should not irk me that ye have loved me, since ye are come to such worship, but it irketh me that thereby ye have failed to achieve the adventures of the Holy Grail, wherefor the Round Table was established."

"Ye speak in error," said Lancelot, "and I will tell you wherefore. Never, I ween, would I have come to the great worship wherein I am held save by you. For I was young and simple, and I was away from mine own country, and without great prowess I might never bring to an end this exploit whereof ye speak, nor might I have done aught, if I had not stood so well with you as I stand."

And then the queen asked him of Morgain, the sister of Arthur, that had threatened him. And he told her all, and she was sore dismayed thereat, for she wist well that Morgain hated him only because of her, and she said, " If Morgain hateth you, I warn you to beware of her, for she is greatly to be dreaded, for she knoweth so many enchantments that she could bring to shame the most worshipful man in the world. And I know not how to counsel you save to bid you that ye wear on your finger a gold ring that your Lady of the Lake gave me, when you were a young knight, that revealeth all enchantments and maketh them known. And of this ye will have great need against her ". Therewithal Lancelot took the ring and he put it on his finger.

That night the king let spread the bed of Lancelot in the best chamber of the palace, and he let remove his own therefrom. Wherefore all that were ware thereof said that the king did more honour to Lancelot than to any other knight of the court.

CHAPTER LVIII

How Sir Lancelot was taken prisoner by Morgain la Fée, and how he painted the walls of his prison for love of the Queen

Lancelot soon sets out in search of Lionel and Hector,[1] who had gone in quest of him during his previous absence from court. One day in his wanderings he meets a damsel of Morgain,

A maiden decoying Lancelot to a castle of Morgain

[*face p. 321*

who by promising to lead him to a certain perilous adventure decoys him to a castle that Morgain has built in the forest with the intention of imprisoning him there. Morgain, rejoiced that he is at last in her power, by magic drugs succeeds in beclouding his brain and reducing him to utter weakness. In this condition she has him carried to a large chamber with grated windows that look into a garden. Here she plans to keep him confined for the rest of his life.

Thus bided Lancelot a full month, and he knew not that he was in prison till that he was cured of his ills. And thus he bided there from the month of September even to Christmas. When the cold was past, it befell on a day that he came to a grated window to lean against it, and through this window one might look into the palace. He opened the window, and he espied there a man that painted an ancient history, and above each image there was writing. And he knew that it was the story of Aeneas, how he departed from Troy. Then Lancelot thought within him that, an the chamber wherein he lay were thus painted with his exploits and his sayings, right well would it please him to see the fair face of his lady, and 't would be a great solace for his ills. Then he prayed the good man that painted there to give him of his colours that he might make an image in the chamber where he lay. And he said that he would do so gladly. And right so he gave Lancelot the instruments that he needed therefor. And Lancelot took that which was given him, and he closed the window so that no man might see what he did. And then he began to paint first how his Lady of the Lake took him to court to be knighted, and how he came to Camelot, and how he was abashed at the great beauty of his

lady when that he first saw her. And that was the
first day's work of Lancelot. And the images were
as well and as subtly portrayed as if he had plied this
craft all the days of his life.

At midnight Morgain came there, for she was
wont to come there every night so soon as he slept.
For she loved him for his great comeliness so much
as woman may love man, and it grieved her sore that
he would not love her, for she kept him not in prison
from hatred, but she thought to conquer him by his
misease; and she had many a time prayed him for
his love, but he would hear naught thereof. And
when she espied the images, she wist well their significance, for she had oft heard tell how he came to court
and in what guise.

And Morgain said to the damsel that had led
Lancelot thither, " I' faith," said she, " ye may
behold marvels in this knight, that is so clever in his
chivalry and in all respects ". Then she shewed her
the images that Lancelot had made, and she explained
to her the significance of each. And she said to her,
" See, here is Lancelot, and here is the queen, and
here is King Arthur ", till that the damsel knew well
that which each one signified. " Now," said Morgain,
" I shall by no means fail to keep this painter prisoner
till that the entire chamber be painted. For I wit
well that he will portray there all his acts and all
his words and all his deeds with the queen. And if
he should have painted it all, I would bring it to pass
that my brother, King Arthur, should come here,
and then I would make known to him the deeds of
Lancelot and the queen, and the truth concerning

them." Forthwithal they came away, and they shut
the door after them.

On the morn when Lancelot was arisen and had
opened the windows and doors toward the garden,
he saw in the painting the image of his lady, and he
bowed him before it and gave it greeting, and then he
drew nigh to it, and he embraced it and kissed
it on the mouth, and he took pleasure therein as he
did in no woman save his lady. Then he began to
paint how he came to the Dolorous Gard, and how
he won the castle by his prowess. On the next day
thereafter he portrayed all that he did to the time of
the tourney when he wore the red armour, the day
when the King of the Hundred Knights wounded him.
And thereafter from day to day he painted the history
not of his own deeds alone, but also of those of the
other knights, even as the story hath already told.
And ever he set him thereto through all the season
till that Easter was past.

CHAPTER LIX

*How Sir Lancelot plucked a rose in the garden of Morgain,
and how he escaped from her prison*

Now the story saith that Lancelot bided in the prison
of Morgain till that he had been there two winters
and one summer, and thus it had passed on until after
Easter. And he saw that the garden hard by his
chamber began to grow green again, and the trees
were in leaf and laden with flowers, and the rose put

forth shoots each day before his window. For Morgain had let plant there a passing fair garden, so that Lancelot might be more at ease all through the summer, for he had been at misease all the winter, since that the prison irked him sore, where he had been for so long time. And it would have irked him even more but for the images that he had painted in the chamber, whereon he delighted to look, and much they embellished it, for he had done no deed of knighthood, great or small, that it was not portrayed there, each after its own manner, so that it was a marvel to see. And every morn when he was arisen, he came to each image that was there in the place of the queen, and he kissed its eyes and its mouth so as if it were his lady the queen, and he wept and made sorrow out of measure. And when he had long time lamented and bewailed his mischance, he came back to her images and kissed them, and he did them the greateſt honour that he might. And thus he comforted him by his own devices, and 't was this wherein he took the moſt delight.

And when it passed on from Eaſter to the beginning of May, Lancelot saw the trees full of leaves and of flowers, and he saw the verdure that made his heart rejoice, and the rose that each day blossomed fresh and red. And he thought on his lady the queen, and on her face that was so fair and rosy that the rose put him in remembrance of her. For whenever he looked at the rose, him seemed that it was his lady, and he knew not which was the more rosy in hue, the rose or his lady. And this it was that nigh drove him out of his wits.

Lancelot and the rose

[*face p. 325*

How Lancelot plucked a Rose

On a Sunday in the morning Lancelot arose so
soon as he heard the birds begin to sing, and he came
to the window that had bars of iron, and he sat him
down to look at the verdure, and he bided there
till that the sun shone throughout the garden. And
then Lancelot looked at the rose tree, and he espied
a rose new blown that was twofold fairer than the
others. And then he said, "Thus saw I my lady
fairer than all the other ladies at the tournament at
Camelot. And for that I cannot have her, it is meet
that I should have this rose, which putteth me in
remembrance of her". Then he thruſt his hand
through the window to pluck the rose, but in no manner
might he come at it, for it was too far from him. And
he drew back his hand, and he looked at the bars of
iron of the window, and he saw that they were wonderly
ſtrong.

"How now," said Lancelot, "shall a fortress be
able to hinder me that I should not do my will?
Certes, nay." Then he took two of the bars of iron
in his two hands, and he pulled them to him with
such a might that he rent them out of the walls,
and he threw them into the midſt of the chamber.
But he so wrought that he tore the skin of his fingers,
so that the blood leaped to the ground, yet he recked
little thereof. Then he issued forth out of the
chamber, and he went there where he had espied
the rose, and he kissed it for love of his lady that it
was like, and he pressed it unto his eyes and his
lips, and he put it into his bosom next his flesh.

Then he turned him to the court, and he found
the door open, and he entered therein, and he found

helms and hauberks and armour in great plenty. And
he armed him so well as he might, and then he took
a sword that he found in a coffer. Then he went
down from the tower so well armed that he dreaded
no man that might assail him. And he went on from
chamber to chamber till that he found two horses
that were ſtrong and swift, and he put a saddle on
him that he thought was the better, and then the
bridle, and he mounted up on him. And it was ſtill
so early in the morning that no man was yet arisen
save he that guarded the gate. And when Lancelot
came to the gate, he found him. And when he saw
Lancelot come he marvelled greatly, for he had not
supposed that a knight had been there. Lancelot
asked him who was the lord of the caſtle.

"Sir," said he, "there is no lord here, but there
is a lady, who is miſtress of the dwelling."

"And how is she hight?" said Lancelot.

"Sir, they call her Morgain la Fée, and she is
siſter to King Arthur."

And when Lancelot heard him, he was minded to
turn back to slay her, but he let her be for love of
King Arthur, and for that she was a woman. And he
said to the squire, "Fair friend, say to thy lady that
Lancelot of the Lake greeteth her as the moſt disloyal
woman in the world. And well may she know that
but for the love of King Arthur I had done to her
that which it behoveth to do to a disloyal woman.
And do thou give her all the message that I send her".

And he said that he would bear the message. Then
he came to his lady, who ſtill slept, and he woke her,
and he told her the words that Lancelot had sent

her. And when she heard him, she was sorrowful
out of measure, and she said, "Alas, ill have we
guarded that which we should have guarded". Then
she began to make the greateſt dole in the world,
and she looked at the bars of the window that Lancelot
had burſt and rent asunder, and she showed them
to the people of the caſtle, and she said to them,
"Now saw ye e'er such a marvel as this demon hath
wrought? For he hath broken these irons, that were
so ſtrong, by the might of his hands. I' faith, never
hath man done such deviltry".

CHAPTER LX

How Sir Bors saw Galahad at the caſtle of Corbenic

In the midſt of the series of exploits, upon which Lancelot
at once enters, he learns that the news has come to court that he
who shall fulfil the adventures of the Holy Grail has been born,
and that he is the son of the beſt knight in the world and the
daughter of King Pelles. Lancelot is deeply moved, knowing
that the child muſt be his. Somewhat later he and Bors meet
and are riding on their way to Camelot, when adventure
separates them. Bors in his journeyings comes to the caſtle of
Corbenic, which he has already visited without, however, seeing
its marvels. He is welcomed with great honour by King Pelles
and his daughter, who are rejoiced to hear of the welfare o
Lancelot.

RIGHT so as they talked together there entered an
old knight, and he carried in his arms a child so young
that he might not be a full year old, but he lacked
two months thereof. And the child was as beautiful
as a child may be, and he was wrapped in silk. And

the knight showed him to Bors, and he said to him,
"Sir, ye have ne'er seen this your little kinsman.
Know in sooth that he is issued from the highest
lineage of Christendom ; know in sooth that he is
your cousin ". Now so soon as Bors looked on the
child him seemed that he was Lancelot, and in truth
he resembled Lancelot as much as one being may
resemble another, and Bors asked who he was. " Sir,"
said the knight, " know ye a man in your lineage to
whom he is like ? Now look him well in the visage,
and I shall marvel much if ye know him not." And
Bors durst not say that which he thought, for well
he believed that this was a child of Lancelot, and for
that he knew how matters were with Lancelot and
the queen, he durst not declare or make known that
which he thought. But for that it behoved him
to make answer to that which the knight asked of
him, he said, " Certes, sir, me seemeth that he resem-
bleth more Sir Lancelot of the Lake than another ".

" I' faith," said the knight, " he should resemble
him, for he issued from him as truly as ye issued
from your father."

When Bors hearkened to these words, he had more
joy than at aught that he had e'er heard, and he
asked how the child was called. And the knight said
that he was called Galahad. And Bors took him in
his arms and kissed him more gladly than he had e'er
kissed any earthly being, and he wept over him for
pity, and he said to him, " Sir, in a happy hour were
ye born, for I trow that ye will be the support of our
lineage. And blessed be God, Who led me here, and
now may God love me, if I were so glad had He given

Bors and the infant Galahad

[*face p. 328*

me the finest castle in the world as I am at these tidings ".

And even as they talked there entered the dove that carried a censer of gold in her mouth, and she hied her into the chamber where she was wont to repair, and forthwith the palace was filled with all the spicery of the world. And anon the servitors spread the tables there, and they seated them at meat with no man summoning them, for there was not a man there who spake a word, but together they all made their prayers and orisons, both old and young. And not long after they were all seated, there issued forth from the chamber the maiden that bore in her arms the Holy Grail, and so soon as she entered into the palace, they all kneeled down before her, and they said softly, " Blessed be the Son of God, amen, Who of His grace feedeth us ". And even as the damsel passed before the high table, forthright they saw the tables filled with all manner of goodly meats, and when she had gone about the tables even as they were placed, she went back to the chamber whence she had issued forth, and entered thereinto. Then all they that had been silent began to speak throughout the hall, and when they had eaten, the cloths were removed.

And anon the king went to lean against one of the windows of the palace, and he had led Bors with him, and they spake of him whereon they most thought, till that Bors asked the king the truth about the child. And the king told him all that which had befallen Lancelot and his daughter, and how he had been deceived. " Blessed be God," said Bors, " Who

hath turned this craft to His purpose, for never
from craft came such good as will come from this, for
without doubt from my lineage shall issue the true knight
by whom the adventure of the Holy Grail will
be brought to an end, and who will sit at the Round
Table in the Siege Perilous, where no man ever sat
but he died. And if he is not this child, I know not
who he may be."

CHAPTER LXI

How Sir Lancelot came mad to Corbenic, and how he was healed by the Holy Grail

At Pentecost Lancelot returns to court. In his first interview
with the queen after his arrival she tells him that during his
absence Claudas of the Desert Land has taken prisoner one of
her maidens, whom he intercepted as she was carrying a letter
from her mistress to the Lady of the Lake, and that he has
replied with an insolent message to Guinevere's demand for her
release. Lancelot declares that now is the time for him to take
vengeance upon Claudas for a long series of wrongs beginning
with the death of King Ban. He proclaims to his companion
knights that he intends to declare war upon Claudas as a
usurper, and immediately receives support from them and
from Arthur, who announces that he purposes to conquer
Gaul, and then and there invests Lancelot with it. Claudas
offers a vigorous resistance, but the war with varying fortunes is
carried on to a successful termination by the hosts of Arthur,
and Claudas is driven from his territory. Queen Elaine, the
mother of Lancelot, leaves her convent and comes to Gannes
to greet her son, when he enters the town in triumph, but after
a few days she returns to her abbey and a week later dies there.
Lancelot, who has no wish to abandon chivalry for the sake of
becoming a king, refuses the crown of Claudas that he has won,
but proposes to invest Hector with Benoich, Lionel with Gaul,

King Arthur investing Lancelot with Gaul

[face p. 330

and Bors with Gannes. Bors, however, declines the honour, since he also desires to continue the life of a knight.

Arthur after his return to Camelot announces a great court to be held at Whitsuntide. The daughter of King Pelles, hearing of the victory of Lancelot over Claudas, attends the court with Galahad, longing to see Lancelot, whom her presence throws into the utmost embarrassment. Brisane, who has accompanied her, once again deceives Lancelot as she did at the castle of the Casse. Guinevere discovers that, as she supposes, he is being untrue to her with the daughter of King Pelles, and banishes him from her sight. Lancelot in anguish retreats to the forest, where he speedily loses his reason and becomes a dangerous maniac. The daughter of King Pelles leaves court at once, first telling Bors of all that has taken place. He vows that he will go immediately in search of Lancelot, and sets out accompanied by Hector and Lionel. Before he takes his leave, however, he reduces the queen to repentance for her conduct and obtains from her permission to bring Lancelot again to court.

Lancelot wanders in the forest deprived of reason and memory. He is befriended first by a kindly knight and later by a hermit, but he stays with neither for long, and finally in the course of his mad roaming in the woods he comes to Corbenic. Here he finds food and shelter in a stable and remains during many months, unrecognised, though King Pelles and the barons see him often and make merry over his folly. One day, as he lies sleeping by a fountain in the garden, the daughter of King Pelles and one of her maidens come upon him.

AND the daughter of King Pelles that looked long at Lancelot regarded him till that she knew that it was he. Then was she so glad and sorrowful thereat that none might be more so, glad because she had found him, and sorrowful because he was out of his wits, for she knew well that it was he that had oft appeared at the court of her father in the guise of a fool. And when she came to the palace, she asked where her father was, and they told her. And she came to him, and she drew him apart, and she said to him, " Sir, I can tell you a marvel ".

"What is it ? " said the king. "Tell me."

"Sir," said she, "Sir Lancelot of the Lake is here, and we knew it not."

"Hush, daughter dear ; Lancelot died erewhile, as they of the Round Table affirm."

"Now before God, sir," said she, "he did not, for I have seen him all sound in his limbs. Now come with me and I will show him to you."

"Yea, then, let us go," said he.

And therewithal they went into the garden together with no other company, and they came to the fountain where Lancelot lay sleeping. When the king was come there, he knew that this was he that had oft-times repaired to his court in the guise of a fool. "Sir," said his daughter, "what think ye ? Is not he Sir Lancelot of the Lake ? " And he answered naught, but he regarded him more and more till he knew that this was Lancelot. And then he could no longer keep silence, but he began to sigh heavily, and the tears fell down his cheeks, and when he spake, he said, "Ah, God, what pity is here ! " Thereupon he said to his daughter, "In truth it is he whom ye say. Now let us go from here that he wake not, and I will give the best thought thereto that ever I may". Then the king turned him back and he came to his palace, and he said to his daughter that she should tell no man that this was Lancelot. And she said that she would not, whate'er should betide.

And the king summoned six big and strong squires, and he said to them that they should take the fool and that they should bind his hands and feet, without wounding him, and then that they should do his pleasure. And they feared that he might let kill them. And none the less since they durſt not refuse the command of the king, they took him even as he slept, and he would fain escape from them, but that might not be, for they were valiant and ſtrong. And they took him by force, and they carried him ſtraight-way into the chamber beneath the tower. In the evening when all there had gone to reſt, the king let bear him into the Adventurous Palace, and they left him there all alone without the company of other folk, for well they thought that by the virtue of the Holy Grail, so soon as it came into the palace, he would be healed and would return to his memory. And it happened even as they thought, for when the Holy Grail came to the palace as it was wont, Lancelot was at once healed, and he abided there till morning.

CHAPTER LXII

How Sir Perceval and Sir Lancelot fought together in the Joyous Isle, and of their great courtesy

When Lancelot is reſtored to reason, he begs King Pelles to allow him to remain with him and his daughter in secrecy, since he cannot go back to court. King Pelles proposes that Lancelot take up his abode at Caſtle Bliaut on an island near Corbenic, called the Joyous Isle, where he may live in retirement with only a few knights and the daughter of Pelles to bear him company. Lancelot agrees, and after he is eſtablished in the isle, he hangs his shield on a pine tree and by a squire issues a challenge to all the knights of the country to come to the Joyous Isle to do battle with the Knight that Hath Trespassed; for thus he ſtyles himself, and in token of his name he has had painted in argent in the centre of his black shield the device of a queen before whom a knight kneels with his hands clasped in entreaty. Many knights answer the challenge, but all leave the Joyous Isle defeated, and the renown of the Knight that Hath Trespassed so increases that he is called the beſt knight in the world.

Heƈtor and Perceval are in queſt of Lancelot. They chance to come to the shore opposite the Joyous Isle, and here learn of the knight and his challenge. They decide to cross the water to the island, but since only one knight is allowed to enter there at a time, Heƈtor gives the battle to Perceval and waits upon the shore, while Perceval is ferried over the water by a boatman.

AND when Perceval issued out of the vessel, he went away under a tree, and he looked at his harness to see that he lacked naught. Then he mounted on his horse, and he waited till that the knight was come forth from the tower well accoutred and richly in black armour. And he was mounted on a black horse, and he held his shield by the ſtraps. And so soon as he espied the knight, he dressed his horse againſt him, and he likewise againſt him that feared him no whit. When they had begun the battle there was none that looked not willingly upon them, for they were both knights of great prowess, so that their peers might not likely be found. And in short while they hewed their shields and their helms and their hauberks so that they were all covered with blood. Then they began to show them the more orgulous one toward other. And the battle laſted till the hour of noon was paſt. And then they were both so spent and so foredone that they muſt needs reſt them to gain their breath.

And when they had reſted them a little, Perceval spake, and he said to the knight, "Sir, I would ask your name, for certes I never met a knight that I

A damsel directing Hector and Percival to the Joyous Isle

would so fain know as you. And I pray you of your
courtesy that ye tell me how ye are called, an it
please you ".

" In sooth, sir knight," said the other, " ye are so
worshipful a knight that I will not conceal it from
you. Now know that he who would rightly name me
calleth me the Knight that Hath Trespassed, and of
this name I bear the token. Now have I told you
how I am called, and I pray you, an it pleaseth you,
tell me likewise your name, and who ye are."

And he said that he was of the household of King
Arthur and of the company of the Round Table.
" And I am called Perceval de Gales, the brother of
Agloval."

When the knight heard this, forthright he threw his
shield to the ground, and he took his sword, and he
kneeled down upon his knees afore Perceval, and he
said to him, " Sir knight, I hold me vanquished, nor
will I do battle more with you, seeing that ye are of
that household, for from henceforth I could no more
have force or virtue against you for love of the hostel
wherein all sweetness dwelleth ".

And when Perceval saw the knight on his knees
before him, he suffered him not, but he raised him
up, and he said to him, " Ah, sir, in God's name,
what say ye ? "

And therewithal the knight took off his helmet,
and he held his sword out toward him, and he said,
" Sir, take all my weapons ".

And Perceval looked at him, and he saw that he
wept right piteously, and he marvelled why this was
so. And he said to him, " Sir, by the faith that ye

owe the being that ye love best of earthly things, I
require you, tell me how ye are called ".

And he replied weeping, " Sir, since ye have so
required me, I will tell you. Men call me Lancelot
of the Lake ".

" Ah, sir," said Perceval, " ye are in sooth welcome,
for I sought none save you. For more than two years
I have ne'er made an end of seeking you, but thanks
be to God, now is my quest finished, since that I have
found you. And know ye who the knight is that
awaiteth me yonder ? "

" Nay," said Lancelot.

" I' faith, sir," said Perceval, " he is Sir Hector des
Mares, your brother."

And when Lancelot heard this word, he began to
make greater dole than before, and he said, " Ah,
fair brother, I ne'er thought to see you again ". Then
he bade the boatmen go fetch the knight that was on
the shore. And they did so. And when Hector was
passed over to the island and he saw his brother, he
began to weep for joy, and he embraced and kissed
him.

Then issued forth the knights of the tower to the
number of seven, old men and hoary, and in their
company was the fair damsel, the daughter of King
Pelles. And when she saw Hector, she made great
joy of him. And then she led them to the castle,
and she let unarm them. And then there began mirth
and glad cheer among them all. When Hector saw
that the fair damsel was the daughter of King Pelles,
he asked her for tidings of Galahad, her son and the
son of Lancelot, and his nephew. And she said,

" Galahad is the fairest child in the world, and he is already as large as a child of ten years ".

" I' faith," said Hector, " I would fain see him."

" Sir," said she, " he dwelleth with my father, King Pelles, yonder, where he hath ever been nurtured. And ye may see him in time, for I know full well that he will accompany his father when he leaveth this country."

" And how came Lancelot to this land ? " said Hector.

" Sir," said she, " he came clean out of his wit and all naked, and in such sorry plight that scarce might he be known for Lancelot. But so soon as he drew nigh the Holy Grail he was healed. And he came into this isle for that he would not be known. And he hath abided here since then, so well concealed that none know him save the lord of this castle and my father only."

Long time talked they together of this matter.

CHAPTER LXIII

*How Sir Lancelot went with Sir Perceval and Sir Hector
to court, and how Galahad abided in an abbey*

AND when the morrow was come, Hector said to Lancelot, " Sir, my lady the queen summoneth you, and it is meet that ye should go to court ".

" It may never be ", said Lancelot, "that I should go thither, for she forbade me."

"I tell you truly," said Hector, "that she hath sent for you."

And he said that then he would go with a good will. Thereupon he made it known to King Pelles that he would go hence on the third day. And when the king heard this, he was heavy thereat, and he said to Galahad, "Fair grandson, your father would go away".

"Say ye so, sir?" said the child. "He will do as he list, but to whatsoever place he goeth, I would fain be so near him that I may see him often."

When the king heard the desire of the child and saw that he might not keep him, he took counsel as to what he should do. "Sir," said a knight, "in the forest of Camelot there is an abbey whereof your sister is abbess. Send the child thither and two knights with him to guard him withal, and when he is there, he may go often to see his father." And the king assented thereto, and he equipped the child and gave him to four knights to conduct him, and to six squires to serve him, and he gave them so much of his goods that they might sustain them well into whatsoever place they might go.

On the third day Lancelot came to Corbenic with a great company of knights. Then Hector asked to see Galahad. And the child came to him. And when Hector saw him, he loved him so that he could love no child better. And when his mother knew that Galahad must go, she made great sorrow, and naught would have withheld her from going with him but that her father, King Pelles, forbade her. And therefore she stayed.

On the morn when they were all ready for the mounting on their horses, the king led Galahad before Lancelot, and he said to him, " Sir, in whatsoever place ye find this child, hold him for your son, for wit ye well that ye engendered him in my fair daughter ". And Lancelot said that of this he was right glad. And forthwith he departed, and when they had accompanied him for long Lancelot bade them return. And he went on his way, he and Hector and Perceval. And they rode till that they came to Caerlion, where they found King Arthur and Bors and Lionel. When they knew that the knights were come, they went to meet Lancelot, and they received him with great joy, and they served him to their power. Howbeit there was none that greeted him so fair as the queen, for she made him such glad cheer as the heart of man might devise.

Galahad, when he had departed from his grandsire, rode till that he came to an abbey of nuns. And here he abided till that he was a strong damoiseau of fifteen years. Then he was so fair and so valiant and so nimble that men might not find his match in the world. And fast by the abbey dwelt a holy man that oft-times came to see Galahad, and by the grace of our Lord he knew the worthiness of the child. And after Easter on a day he said to him, " Fair son, ye are now come to the age to receive the order of knighthood. Therefore will ye be made knight at this Pentecost ? "

" Yea, sir," said the lad, " if it please God, for thus my masters instruct me."

" Now," said the holy man, " see that ye enter

thereinto having so confessed you that ye shall be clean and purged from all ſtain."

And he said that he would do so, an it pleased God. And so they twain talked long together that day.

On the morrow at the hour of prime, it befell that King Arthur, who hunted in the foreſt, came there to hear mass. And when mass was said, the holy man summoned the king, and he said to him, "King Arthur I tell thee soothly as in confession that on the day of Pentecoſt, that draweth nigh, he that shall bring to an end the adventures of the Holy Grail shall be a new knight. And on that day he will come to thy court and he will without fail accomplish the adventures of the Siege Perilous. Now look to it that thou summon all thy barons on the eve of Pentecoſt to be on that day at Camelot to see the marvels that will there befall".

"Sir," said the king, "speak ye soothly?"

"I say it to thee", said he, "as a prieſt."

The king was right glad of these tidings, and anon he went his way, and he ſtayed in the foreſt till even. And when he was come to Camelot, he sent through all the realm of Logres, and he bade all his barons that they should be at court on the day of Pentecoſt, for he would hold there the greateſt and the richeſt court that he had e'er held. And so many of them were assembled there on the vigil of Pentecoſt that there was none that saw it but held it for a marvel.

Here finisheth Maſter Walter Map his book and beginneth the *Grail*.

Joseph of Arimathea with the Grail at the foot of the Cross

[*face p. 341*
(*frontispiece to Book II*)

BOOK II

THE QUEST OF THE HOLY GRAIL

The damsel demanding Lancelot of King Arthur

CHAPTER LXIV

How a damsel desired Sir Lancelot for to come and dub a knight, and how he went with her

At the vigil of Pentecoft when all the fellowship of the Round Table have assembled at Camelot, a damsel comes riding in hafte into the hall, and after saluting the king demands in the name of King Pelles that Lancelot follow her into the neighbouring foreft, but promises that he shall return to court on the morrow. He goes with her through the foreft to an abbey of nuns, where he is received with acclaim and where, to his surprise, he finds Lionel and Bors, to whom he admits that he is in ignorance of the purpose for which he has been brought there.

AND while that they talked thus there entered three nuns that brought with them Galahad, the which was so fair a lad and so well made in all his members that scarce in the world might his match be found. And she that was the lady of higheft degree led him by the hand, and she wept full tenderly. And when she came before Lancelot, she said, " Sir, I bring you here this child that we have nurtured, and he is all our joy, our comfort, and our hope, to the end that ye may make him knight, for of a worthier man than ye, as we think, he may not receive the order of knighthood ".

Lancelot looked on the lad and saw him so wonderly adorned with all manner of beauties that he wend never in his life to see so fair a form in man. And since that he saw him so demure, he hoped for so

343

much good in him that it pleased him well to make
him knight. And he said to the ladies that he would
ne'er gainsay them their request and that gladly he
would make him knight, since they desired it.

" Sir," said she that led him, " we would that it
be to-night or on the morrow."

" Please God," said he, " it shall be even as you
wish."

That night Lancelot bided there, and he bade the
young squire keep vigil all night in the minster, and
on the morrow at the hour of prime he made him
knight, and he did on one of his spurs, and Bors did
on the other. And thereafter Lancelot girt on his
sword and gave him the accolade, and he prayed that
God would make him a man of worship, for in beauty
He had not stinted him.

And when Lancelot had done for him all that it
was meet to do for a young knight, he said to him,
" Fair sir, will ye come with me unto the court of
my lord the king ? "

" Nay, sir," said he, " I will not go with you."

And then Lancelot said to the abbess, " Lady,
suffer that our new knight come with us unto the
court of my lord the king. For 't will profit him
more to be there than to tarry here with you ".

" Sir," said she, " he will not go now, but so soon
as we believe that it is time and that there is need
thereof, we will send him."

Right so Lancelot departed from there, both he
and his fellowship, and they rode till that they came
to Camelot.

CHAPTER LXV

How all the knights were replenished with the Holy Grail, and how they avowed the Quest thereof

That day, after Lancelot and his cousins have returned to court, they observe that above each seat at the Round Table the name of the knight who should occupy it is inscribed, but above the Siege Perilous they find newly written letters that say, " Four hundred and fifty-four years are accomplished after the Passion of Jesus Christ. And on the day of Pentecost this siege shall find its master ". Lancelot recognises that the predicted day of Pentecost has come, and in order that none may see the writing before the master of the siege appears, the knights hang a silken cloth over the letters.

A little later in the day there comes floating down the river to the palace steps a great stone into which a rich sword is set, bearing in its pommel a jewel inscribed with letters of gold saying, " Never man shall take me hence save only he by whose side I am to hang, and he shall be the best knight in the world ". The king and all the knights hasten to the riverside to see the marvel, and the king on reading the letters bids Lancelot draw the sword, for by right it belongs to him as the best knight in the world. But Lancelot soberly answers that he is not worthy to assay it, for it has been predicted that on that day the adventures of the Grail must begin. Other knights in vain try to draw the sword, and they all return to the palace to dine, leaving the stone floating in the river.

While the knights sit at meat at the Round Table, only the Siege Perilous being vacant, a young knight in red arms, but having neither sword nor shield is led into the hall by an aged man, who presents him to Arthur as the Desired Knight, who shall bring to an end the adventures of the land. Then bidding the young knight follow him, he leads him to the seat beside Lancelot, the Siege Perilous, and lifting up the silken cloth that covers the letters, he reveals another inscription newly made, " This is the siege of Galahad ". " Sir knight," he says aloud to his charge so that all may hear, " sit ye here, for this place is yours." The young knight seats himself with assurance, and dismisses the old man, telling him that his mission is accomplished. The knights all regard him with amazement,

345

and hasten to do him honour, for they recognise that he must be the long looked for knight, by whom the quest of the Grail will be achieved. But Lancelot, knowing that he is the young squire whom he has himself knighted that morning, and Lionel and Bors, being well aware that he is the son of Lancelot, rejoice in him more than all the rest.

Then Arthur declaring that God has sent this young knight to court that he may accomplish that wherein other knights have failed, leads him to the stone in the river, and tells him that the most worshipful knights of the court have failed to draw the sword. "That is no marvel," says Galahad, "for the adventure is not theirs, but mine. And for the surety that I had of having this sword I brought none to court, so as ye may see." Then laying his hand on the sword, he draws it lightly from the stone and girds it to his side.

At this moment a damsel mounted on a white palfrey comes riding toward them at full speed, and saluting the king demands if Lancelot is there. "Ah, Lancelot," she says to him mournfully, when he comes before her, "how hath your estate changed since yestermorn. Ye were then the best knight in the world, and he that called you Lancelot, the best knight of all, said sooth, for then were ye it. But he that should say so now, should be accounted a liar, for there is a better than ye, and well is it proved by the change and the removal of your name, whereof I have put you in remembrance, for that ye shall not suppose from henceforth that ye are the best knight in the world." And Lancelot replies that he will never suppose it, for this adventure has put it out of his thought. Then turning to the king, the damsel announces to him that on that day the Holy Grail shall appear in his dwelling and shall feed the fellowship of the Round Table. So saying, and refusing all entreaties that she abide, she goes away whence she came.

Since the knights are so soon to be scattered in the quest of the Holy Grail, Arthur in order to bring them all together once more, but especially to test Galahad, lets cry a tourney in the meadow at Camelot. In the justing Galahad gives proof of surpassing prowess and is led back in triumph through the main street of Camelot without his helmet, so that all may see his face. His resemblance to his father at once convinces the queen, when she sees him, that he is the son of Lancelot.

AND for that it was a high festival anon the ladies came down from the palace to hear evensong, and

Galahad drawing the sword.   The damsel reproaching Lancelot

[face p. 346

when the king was come forth from the minſter, he went up into the upper hall of the palace, and he commanded that the tables be set. And thereafter the knights went to sit each in his own place, even as they had done in the morning. And when they were all seated there and were all silent, then anon they heard a blaſt of thunder so great and so marvellous that them seemed the palace would all founder. And right so there entered a sunbeam that made the palace sevenfold brighter than it had been afore, and all they that were there were as if illumined by the grace of the Holy Spirit, and they began to look one upon other, for they wiſt not whence this brightness might have come. And none the less there was no one there that might speak or utter a word, and they were all dumb, both great and small.

And when they had bided thus a great while so that none among them had power to speak, but they looked each on other as they had been dumb cattle, then there entered into the hall the Holy Grail, covered with white samite, but there was none that might see who bore it. And it entered by the great door of the hall. And so soon as it was entered thereinto, the hall was filled with good odours, so as if all the spicery of the world were spread therein. And it went through the hall all about the tables on one hand and on the other, and so soon as it passed before the tables forthright they were all filled before each seat with such viands as each knight moſt desired. And when they all were served, then suddenly the Holy Grail departed, so that they wiſt not what might have become of it, nor saw into what part it went.

And then they all had power to speak that afore might not utter a word. And the greater part of them gave thanks to our Lord for His great honour that He had done them when He had replenished them with the grace of the Holy Vessel. But of all them that were there King Arthur was the most happy and glad, for that our Lord had shown him higher favour than to any king that had been afore him.

Now of this grace all, both those of the king's household and those from abroad, were passing glad, for them seemed in truth that our Lord had not forgotten them, since He had showed them such high favour. And they talked thereon so long as they sat at meat. And the king himself began to speak to them that were the nearest to him, and he said, " Certes, my lords, we should rejoice and be glad, in that our Lord hath showed us so great sign of His love that He of His grace was fain to feed us at so high a feast as is the day of Pentecost ".

" Sire," said Sir Gawain, " there is yet another grace that ye know not. For there is no man here but he hath been served with that whereon he thought with desire, but they were beguiled that they might not see the Holy Grail openly, but its true semblance was covered for them. Wherefore I here make avow that on the morn without longer abiding I will enter upon the quest in such wise that I shall hold me out a year and a day and yet more, if need be, and never shall I return to court for aught that betide, till that I have seen it more openly than it hath here been showed me, if so be that I can and may behold it. And if that may not be, I shall return again."

348

The manifestation of the Grail at the Round Table

When they of the Round Table heard these words, they all arose from their places, and they made such avows as Sir Gawain had made, and they said that they would never give over the quest till they should sit at the high table, where such sweet viands were ever prepared as those that they had had there. And when the king saw that they had made such an avow, then he was sore troubled, for he wist well that he might not turn them from this emprise. And he said to Sir Gawain, " Gawain, Gawain, ye have set me in great sorrow of heart, that I may never cast from me till I know truly to what end this quest may lead. For I have great doubt that my friends in the flesh shall never more return hither ".

" Ah, Sire," said Lancelot, "what words are these ? Such an one as ye should not give place in his heart to fear, but to justice and hardihood and good hope. And ye should take comfort, for, certes, an we all should die in this quest, it would be to us a greater honour than if we died in any other wise."

" Lancelot," said the king, " the great love that I have ever had for them maketh me speak such words, and it is no marvel if I am displeased at this their departure. For never Christian king had so many good and worthy knights at his table as I have had here this day, nor ever will have when these are departed hence, and they will ne'er be reassembled at my table so as they have been here. And this it is that most grieveth me."

To these words Gawain wist not what to answer, for he knew well that the king spake soothly. And he would fain have repented him of the avow that he

had made, had he durſt, but that might not be, for
now the hall was too full of folk, and already the word
had gone abroad that the queſt of the Holy Grail
was undertaken, and that they who would be of its
fellowſhip would set out from court on the morrow.
And many were there that were more sorrowful than
joyful thereat, for by the prowess of the companions
of the Round Table was the hoſtelry of King Arthur
renowned above all others. And the queen began
to weep tenderly, and so likewise did all the ladies
and the damsels that were with her. Thus was all
the court troubled by the news of those that were
to go.

CHAPTER LXVI

How the Queen asked Galahad the name of his father

AND the queen came to Galahad, and she seated
her beside him, and she began to ask him whence he
was and of what country and of what lineage. And
he answered her in great part as one that knew enough
thereof, but of how that he was son to Lancelot he
said naught. And none the less by the words that
the queen heard from him she knew in truth that he
was the son of Lancelot, and that he had been engendered in the daughter of King Pelles, of whom she
had many times heard tell. And for that she would
fain hear and know from his own mouth if this were
so, she asked him the truth about his father. And he

made answer that he knew not of a surety whose son he was.

" Ah, sir," said she " ye hide it from me. Wherefore do ye thus ? So help me God, ye need never shame you to name your father. For he is the comeliest knight in the world, and he is come on all sides of the stock of kings and of queens, and of the most noble lineage that is known, and hitherto he hath been renowned as the best knight in the world. Wherefore ye ought of right to surpass all the knights of the world. And certes, ye resemble him so wonderly that there is no man so simple but he would be ware of it, if he gave heed thereto."

When Galahad heard these words, he was abashed for the shame that he had had. And he answered, " Lady," said he, " since ye know him so certainly, ye may name him to me. And if this is he that I believe to be my father, I shall deem that ye speak truth, and if it is not he, I could not accord thereto for aught that ye said ".

" Now, before God," said she, " since ye will not say it, I will tell it you. He that engendered you is called Sir Lancelot of the Lake, the goodliest knight and the best and the most gracious, and the most desired by the eyes of all men, and the best loved that ever was born in our time. Wherefore, me seemeth, that ye need not conceal him either from me or from another, for from a more worshipful man or a better knight ye might not be born."

" Lady," said he, " since ye know it so well, wherefore should I tell it you ? It will be known openly enough in time."

Long while talked the queen and Galahad together
till that it drew toward even. And when it was
time to sleep, the king took Galahad and he led him
into his chamber, and in honour of the highness of
Galahad he made him reſt in his own bed, wherein
he was wont to lie. And thereafter the king went
to reſt, and Lancelot and the other barons of the
court. And that night the king had no ease, and he
was full of thought for love of the barons of the court,
that he had loved well, that on the morrow would
depart from him and go there where he supposed
that they would long time ſtay.

CHAPTER LXVII

*How the Queen commended Sir Lancelot to God's keeping,
and of the departing of the knights*

AND when the queen was ware that the knights had
made them all ready to go, and that they could tarry
no longer, she began to sorrow heavily so as if she saw
before her all her friends dead. And that no man
should perceive her sorrow, she departed into her
chamber, and she fell on her bed, and she began to
make so great moan that no man, howe'er hard-
hearted he might be, an he saw her, would not have
had pity on her.

And when Lancelot was ready dight to mount up
on his horse, he that had as great grief of the sorrows
of his lady, the queen, as ever man might have, went

to the chamber whereinto he had seen her enter, and he likewise entered. And when the queen saw him come in all accoutred, she began to cry aloud, " Ah, Lancelot, ye have betrayed me and put me to death, for that ye leave the hostel of my lord, the king, to go into strange lands, whence ye will ne'er return, if our Lord lead you not back therefrom ".

" Lady," said he, " I shall return, please God. I shall come again more speedily than ye think."

" In sooth," said she, " my heart sayeth it not, for it setteth me in all the misease and in all the fears that ever gentle lady suffered for man."

" Lady," said he, " I will go with your leave, when it pleaseth you."

" Never would ye go by my will," said she, " but since ye must needs depart, go in the keeping of Him that suffered travail upon the True and Holy Cross to save mankind from eternal death, and may He guide you to safety, wheresoever ye go."

" Lady," said he, " God grant it of His tender mercy."

Right so departed Lancelot from the queen, and he went down to the court, and he saw that all his fellowship was mounted, and they awaited none save him. And he went to his horse and he mounted up thereon.

And then all the barons and the knights mounted, and they departed from the court both one and another, and they rode down through the city till they were issued forth therefrom. And ye ne'er beheld so great grief as they of the city made when they saw the fellowship go forth in the quest of the

Holy Grail, nor was there a baron nor a poor man nor a rich of all them that muſt needs remain but wept piteously, for they made great sorrow of this departing. But in no wise it seemed that they who were to go counted it for aught, but ye would have thought, an ye had seen them, that they were passing glad thereof. And so in sooth they were.

CHAPTER LXVIII

How Sir Lancelot half sleeping and half waking saw a sick man borne in a litter, and how he was healed of the Holy Grail

Lancelot and Perceval, riding through the foreſt in their queſt, encounter Galahad, with whose arms they are too unfamiliar to recognise him from them. Lancelot breaks spears with him, and is unhorsed. Galahad next turns upon Perceval, unhorses him, and rides away at such a pace that the older knights, sadly discomfited, do not attempt to overtake him. Lancelot, however, determines that he will ride after him, but Perceval decides to poſtpone the pursuit till the morrow.

It is night, and Lancelot with difficulty finds his way. At a crossroads he comes to a ſtone cross before a deserted chapel, within which he sees an altar with a silken cloth and rich vessels upon it, while before it ſtands a silver candleſtick bearing lighted tapers. He tries to enter, but finds that an iron grill bars the way. Disappointed, he loosens his horse and lets him graze; then taking off his helmet and sword, he lies down on his shield before the cross, and in his weariness would soon have fallen asleep, but for the recollection of the white knight who unhorsed him.

AND after that he had lain awake a long time, he saw come in a litter, the which two palfreys bare, a sick knight that bemoaned him piteously. And when he was nigh to Lancelot, he paused and he looked on him, but he spake not a word, for he supposed that

Lancelot slept. And Lancelot said not a word, for he was like to a man that neither slept verily nor woke verily, but he was heavy with sleep. And the knight of the litter, that abode by the cross, began to make great moan, and he said, "O Lord, shall this pain ne'er leave me ? O Lord, when shall the Holy Vessel come, whereby this mighty pain shall be ſtayed ? O Lord, suffered e'er a man such ill as I suffer for a small trespass ! " A full great while the knight complained thus, and made lament before God for his ills and his sorrows. And Lancelot neither moved nor said a word, for he was as it were in a trance, albeit he saw the other well and heard all his words.

And when the knight had long time bided thus, Lancelot looked and he saw come toward the cross the candleſtick of silver with the tapers that he had seen within the chapel, and he looked at the candleſtick as it came toward the cross, but he saw not who brought it, and he marvelled thereat. And thereafter he beheld come on a table of silver the Holy Vessel that he had seen aforetime in the house of the Fisher King, the same that men called the Holy Grail. And so soon as the sick knight beheld it come, right so he sank down to the earth even from where he was, and he clasped his hands and held them up toward it, and he said, "Fair Lord God, Thou Who by this Holy Vessel that I behold come hither haſt wrought many a fair miracle in this land and elsewhere, Heavenly Father, look upon me in Thy pity in such wise that this pain wherefrom I am in travail be assuaged for me in short while, so that I may enter into the queſt, wherein other men of

355

worship are entered ". And therewith he went dragging him by the ſtrength of his arms to the ſtone whereon the table of silver ſtood with the holy Vessel thereupon. And he took it in his two hands and he raised him up so far that he kissed the table of silver, and he touched it with his eyes. And when he had so done, he felt him as it were lightened of all his ills, and he uttered a great cry, and he said, " Ah, God, I am whole ! " And right so he fell asleep.

And when the Vessel had tarried there a while, anon the candleſtick went into the chapel and the Vessel with it in such wise that Lancelot knew not either at the going or at the coming by whom it might be borne. And none the less thus it befell him, either for that he was too heavy from toil, or for the sin wherewith he was overtaken, that he moved not for the coming of the Holy Grail, nor made semblance that he counted it for aught. Wherefore he found thereafter in the queſt that men said much shame of him and that misadventure came to him in many a place.

CHAPTER LXIX

How a voice spake to Sir Lancelot, and how thereafter he was shriven, and what sorrow he made, and of the counsel that was given him

The knight of the litter, when the Grail has departed, kisses the cross and thanks God that he is healed. He marvels at the indifference of Lancelot to the Grail, and concludes that he muſt have sinned too deeply to have a share in the vision. His squire equips him with the horse and the arms of Lancelot, telling him

Lancelot sleeping and the sick knight praying before the Grail

[*face p. 356*

that they will be better employed by him than by the sleeping
knight to whom they belong. Thus accoutred the knight takes
a solemn oath to pursue the Grail and rides off on his quest.

And when the knight was well nigh a half a league or
more distant, it chanced that Lancelot sat up where
he was like a man that has just wholly awakened, and
he bethought him if what he had seen were a dream
or the truth, for he knew not if he had seen the Holy
Grail, or if he had dreamed it.[1] And then he turned
him and he espied the candlestick before the altar,
but he saw naught of that which it would have liked
him best to see, to wit the Holy Grail, whereof an he
might, he would fain have had true tidings.

When Lancelot had looked long while within the
grill, if so be that he might see aught of that whereof
he had the greatest desire, anon he heard a voice that
said to him, " Lancelot, harder than stone, more
bitter than wood, more naked and barren than the
fig-tree, how wert thou so bold that thou durst enter
into the place whereto the Holy Grail repaired ?
Get thee gone from here, for the place is polluted
by thy presence ". And when Lancelot heard this
word, he was so heavy that he wist not what to do.
And forthright he departed thence, groaning heavily
and weeping sore, and he cursed the hour wherein
he was born, for well he deemed that never would
he have worship more, inasmuch as he had failed to
learn the truth about the Holy Grail. But the three
words whereby he had been called he had not forgotten, nor would he ever forget them so long as he
lived, nor could he be at full great ease till that he
knew wherefore he was so called.

And when he was come to the cross, and found there neither his sword nor his helm nor his horse, then he was ware that what he had seen was the truth. And then he began to make great and marvellous dole, and he called himself an unhappy wretch, and he said, " Ah, God, now appeareth my sin and my evil life. Now see I full well that my wickedness more than aught else hath confounded me. For when I ought to have amended me, then the enemy deſtroyed me, for he hath taken from me the power to see aught that is of God. And 't is no marvel if I may not see clearly, for from the time when I was firſt made knight, never was there an hour that I was not wrapped in the darkness of mortal sin, for more than any other man I have hitherto lived in wantonness and in the base desires of this world ".

Thus Lancelot contemned and blamed him right ſternly, and he made sorrow all night. And when the day came fair and bright, and the small fowls began to make melody through the foreſt, and the sun began to shine through the trees, and he saw the fair weather, and he heard the song of the birds wherein he had many a time rejoiced, then he was ware that he was shent of all things, of his arms and of his horse, and he wiſt well that our Lord was displeased with him, and he supposed that he would ne'er find aught in the world that might give him back his joy. For where he had thought to find joy and all worldly honours, there he had failed, to wit, in the adventures of the Holy Grail, and this it was that made him disconsolate.

And when he had long time bewailed and lamented

and bemoaned his mischance, he departed from the
cross and he went through the forest on foot without
helmet or sword or shield. And he went not back to
the chapel where he had heard the three marvellous
words, but he turned him into a path and he followed
it till by prime he came to a hill where he found a
hermitage and the hermit, that would fain begin mass,
and he was already clothed with the arms of Holy
Church.[1] And Lancelot entered into the chapel as
sad and as full of thought and as sorrowful as ever man
might be. And he kneeled him down in the chapel,
and he beat his breast, and he cried on our Lord for
mercy for the ill deeds that he had done in this world.
And he heard the mass that the good man and his
clerk said, and when it was said and the good man had
laid off the arms of our Lord, Lancelot called him and
drew him apart, and prayed him in God's name that
he would give him counsel. And the good man asked
him whence he came, and he said that he was of the
household of King Arthur and of the fellowship of
the Round Table. And the good man asked him,
" Wherein would ye have counsel ? Would ye make
confession ? "

" Yea, sir," said Lancelot.

" Come in the name of our Lord," said the good
man.

And right so he led him before the altar, and they
sat them down together. And the hermit asked him
how he was called. And he said that his name was
Lancelot of the Lake, and he was son of King Ban of
Benoich. And when the good man heard that this
was Lancelot of the Lake, whereof the most good in

the world was said, he marvelled for that he saw him
so sorrowful. And he said to him, " Sir, ye ought
to render hearty thanks unto God, for that He hath
made you so goodly and so valiant that in all the world
we know none that is your peer in beauty and in
prowess. He hath lent you the wit and the memory
that ye have. And ye should render unto Him such
a return that His love be so preserved in you that the
devil may ne'er be profited by the rich gift that He
hath given you. Serve Him then with all your might,
and keep His commandments, and with the gifts that
He hath given you ne'er serve His foe, to wit the
devil. For if God hath been more bounteous unto
you than unto another, and should now lose you,
justly should ye be blamed therefore. And if by this
rich gift that He hath given you ye become His
enemy, wit ye well that it will advantage you naught
in a little space, if ye at once cry not mercy of Him in
true confession and in repentance of heart and amendment of life ".

" Sir," said Lancelot, " I wit well that when I was
a child Jesus Christ garnished me with all the good
gifts that man may have, and for His great largesse
unto me and for that I have thus ill repaid that
wherewith He entrusted me, I know well that I shall
be judged even as the wicked servant that buried
his talent in the earth. For I have all my days
served His enemy, and by my sin have I warred
against Him. And thus have I destroyed me upon
the road that at the beginning is found broad and
sweet as honey, to wit, the beginning of sin. The
devil showed me the sweetness and the honey thereof,

Lancelot at the hermitage

[*face p.* 360

but he showed me not the eternal pains wherein he will be set that walketh in this way."

And when the hermit heard these words he began to weep, and he said to Lancelot, " Sir, in this way, whereof ye speak, I know well that none walketh that shall not be brought to eternal death. But even as ye see that a man at times misseth his path when he is heavy with sleep, and he returneth thereto when he hath awaked, so is it with the sinner that sleepeth in mortal sin. He wandereth from the right way and afterward he returneth into his path, that is, to his Creator, and he turneth him toward the Lord Most High, Who ever proclaimeth, ' I am the Way, the Truth, and the Life ' ".

And anon he looked about him, and he espied a cross whereon the image of the True Cross was painted, and he showed it to Lancelot, and he said, " Sir, ye see this Cross ? " " Yea," said he. " Now know in truth ", said the good man, " that this Figure hath stretched out His arms as if to receive each one of us. Even in such wise hath our Lord stretched out His arms to receive every sinner, both you and all them that turn unto Him, and ever He crieth, ' Come unto Me, come unto Me.' And since that He is so gracious that He is ever ready to receive all, both men and women, that turn unto Him, know that He will ne'er refuse you, if ye offer you unto Him even as I have said, with true confession from your mouth and with repentance of heart and amendment of life. Now tell unto Him your estate and your need in confession before me, and I will give you succour according to my power, and counsel you as best I may."

And Lancelot thought a little while, as one that never had disclosed how it was between him and the queen, and that would never have spoken thereon, had not good counsel led him to do so. And he gave a great sigh from the depths of his heart, and he was so ſtirred within him that he could not utter a word with his mouth. And none the less he would fain have spoken, but he durſt not, like a man that is more cowardly than bold. And ever the good man admonished him to renounce his sin and utterly leave it be, for otherwise would he have shame, if he followed not his counsel; and he assured him of eternal life, if he confessed it, and of perdition, if he concealed it. And by his good words and good examples he so wrought for him that Lancelot began to speak.

"Sir," said Lancelot, "I am dead in sin for a lady that I have loved all my life, to wit, Queen Guinevere, the wife of King Arthur. She it is that hath given me gold and silver in abundance, and the rich gifts that I have aforetime given to poor knights. She it is that hath set me in full great ease and in the high eſtate wherein I now am. She it is for love of whom I have done the mighty deeds of arms whereof all the world speaketh. She it is that hath brought me from poverty to riches and from want to all earthly good. But I wit well that for this sin because of her our Lord is so wroth againſt me that He plainly manifeſted it to me yeſtereven."

And he told the good man how he had seen the Holy Grail, yet he had not moved to meet it, neither from reverence of it nor yet for love of our Lord. And when he had told him all his estate and all his life, he prayed him before God to give him counsel.

"Forsooth, sir," said he, "no counsel would avail you aught, if ye promise not God that ye will not again fail into this sin. But if ye will wholly forsake it, and cry unto God for mercy, and repent you with your whole heart, I believe that our Lord will number you with His servants and will open to you the gate of Heaven, where eternal life is prepared for all them that enter therein."

"Sir," said Lancelot, "ye will tell me naught that I shall not do it, if God granteth me life."

"Then I require you", said the good man, "that ye promise me that ye will never offend your Creator in committing mortal sin with the queen nor any other lady, nor in any other way whereby ye would anger Him."

And he promised it him as a loyal knight.

CHAPTER LXX

How Sir Lancelot learned the significance of the three words that he had heard

"Now tell me of the Holy Grail," said the good man, "and what befell you therewith."

And Lancelot told and repeated to him the three words that the voice had spoken to him in the chapel when he was called stone and wood and a fig-tree. "Now for the love of God," said he, "tell me the significance of these three things, for I have ne'er heard words that I would so fain know as these. And therefore, I pray you, make them plain to me, for I wit well that ye know their true meaning."

Then began the hermit to think for a great space, and when he spoke, he said, " Certes, Lancelot, I marvel not that these three words were spoken to you, for ye have ever been the most marvellous man in the world, and therefore it is no marvel if more marvellous words have been spoken to you than to others. Now, since ye would fain know the true meaning thereof, I will gladly tell it you. Now hearken. Wherein the voice called you harder than stone there is a marvel to be understood. For every stone is hard by nature, but one more than another, and by the stone wherein hardness is found may be understood the sinner that is so asleep and hardened in his sin that his heart is hardened so that it may not be made soft either by fire or by water. By fire it may not be made soft, inasmuch as the fire of the Holy Spirit may not enter nor find place therein for the defilement of the vessel and by the sins of folly that have been increased and heaped up therein day by day. And it may not be softened by water, for the word of the Holy Spirit, the which is sweet water and sweet rain, may not be received into the heart. For our Lord will not dwell there where His enemy is, but He desireth that the hostel wherein He lodgeth be clean and purged of all vices and all defilement. And therefore the sinner is called a stone for the great hardness that our Lord findeth within him. But it behoveth thee rightly to understand how thou art harder than stone, that is to say, how thou art a sinner beyond all other sinners ".

And when he had spoken thus, he fell into thought, and then he said unto him, " I will tell thee how thou art a sinner beyond other sinners. Thou hast heard tell of the three servants to whom the rich man gave the talents to increase and to multiply.[1] The two that had received the most were good and faithful servants, discreet and provident, and the other, he that had received least, was a wicked and unfaithful servant. Now bethink thee if thou mightest be among those servants whereunto our Lord gave the five talents to multiply. Me seemeth that He gave thee much more, for he that would seek among the knights in all the world would not find a single man, I ween, to whom our Lord gave so much grace as He hath lent to thee. And thou hast been the wicked servant, and so unfaithful that thou hast left Him and hast served His enemy, that ever warreth against Him. Thou hast been the wicked hireling, the which so soon as he hath received his hire leaveth his lord and goeth to help his enemy. Thus hast thou done unto our Lord, for so soon as He had paid thee well and richly, thou leftest Him to go to serve him that every day warreth against Him. So, to my knowledge, no man e'er did, whom He had so well paid as He had paid thee. And therefore canst thou see well that thou art harder than stone and more a sinner than any other sinners ".

" Sir," said Lancelot, " now tell me wherefore the voice said that I was more bitter than wood."

" I will tell thee," said the good man. " Now

hearken unto me. I have shown thee that in thee is all hardness, and there where so great hardness dwelleth no sweetness can abide, nor ought we to suppose that there remaineth aught save bitterness, and therefore as great bitterness is found within thee as there should be sweetness. Wherefore thou art likened unto dead and rotten wood, wherein no sweetness abideth but only bitterness. Now have I showed thee how thou art harder than ſtone and more bitter than wood.

" Now in the third place it remaineth to show thee wherefore thou art more naked and more barren than a fig-tree. Of the fig-tree whereof we speak the Gospel¹ maketh mention there where it telleth of Palm Sunday, the day whereon our Lord entered into the city of Jerusalem riding on an ass, the day whereon the Hebrew children went to meet Him singing the sweet songs whereof Holy Church maketh mention every year, the day that we call the Day of the Palms. On that day the Lord Moſt High, our Maſter and our Prophet, preached in the city of Jerusalem among them that harboured all hardness within them. And after that He had toiled all day, when He had left speaking, He found in all the town none that would harbour Him ; wherefore He went without the town. And when He was issued forth, He saw in the way a fig-tree that was right fair and well garnished with leaves and with branches, but of fruit there was none. And our Lord came to the tree, and when He saw it so barren of fruit, He spake as in wrath and cursed the tree that bare no fruit. Thus it befell the fig-tree that was before Jerusalem.

Now bethink thee if thou mightest be like unto it, and more naked and barren than it was. When the Lord Most High came unto the fig-tree, He found there leaves that He might pluck if He would. But when the Holy Grail came before thee, it found thee so barren that within thee was neither good thought nor good will, but thou wert base and befouled and laden with lechery, and all barren of leaves and of flowers, to wit, of good works. Wherefore there were spoken to thee the words whereof thou hast told me, 'Lancelot, harder than stone, more bitter than wood, more naked and barren than a fig-tree, get thee gone from hence.'"

"Certes, sir," said Lancelot, "ye have taught and shown me plainly that I am rightly said to be stone and wood and a fig-tree, for all those sins whereof ye have told me are harboured within me. But since ye have said to me that I have not gone so far that I cannot turn me back, if I would fain keep me from falling again into mortal sin, I promise first to God and thereafter to you that never will I return to the life that I have led for so long, but I will preserve my chastity and keep my body as pure as ever I may. But from following knighthood and doing deeds of arms I may not keep me so long as I am sound and whole as I am."

And when the good man heard these words, he was passing glad, and he said to Lancelot, "Certes, sir, if ye should leave your sin with the queen, I ensure you that our Lord would love you again, and would send you succour, and would look upon you with pity, and would give you power to achieve many adventures that ye could ne'er accomplish because of your sin ".

" Sir," said Lancelot, " I leave her in such wise that never again will I sin with her or with another."

And when the hermit had heard him say this, he enjoined him such penance as he thought that he might do, and he assoiled him and blessed him, and he prayed Lancelot to abide with him that day. And he replied that he muſt needs do so, for he had no horse whereon he might mount, or shield, or lance, or sword.

"As for that, I will help you ", said the good man, " before the morrow at even, for hereby dwelleth my brother that is a knight, the which will send me horse and arms and all whereof ye have need, so soon as I shall ask him."

And Lancelot replied that then he would well abide, and the hermit was glad and rejoiced thereat. And he gave Lancelot such good counsel that he repented him deeply of the life that he had led so long, for well he was ware that, an he died, he would lose his soul and perchance ill would befall his body, if he were brought to juſtice therefor. And so he repented him that he had e'er loved the queen wantonly, for he had misspent his time therein. And much he blamed and despised him therefor, and well he purposed in his heart that never again would he fall into this sin.

Lancelot receiving admonitions from a hermit

Lancelot by the river Marcoise

[face p. 36°

CHAPTER LXXI

How a knight brought unto Sir Galahad a horse, and bade him come away from his father, Sir Lancelot

After three days Lancelot leaves the hermit and rides through the forest. In a few hours he comes to another hermitage, where the hermit recognises him and begins to rebuke him for his sins, urging him to renounce them with the assurance of the forgiveness of God. Never can he hope to see the Grail, if he does not with a true heart cry for mercy unto God. Then he requires Lancelot in penance to put on the hair shirt that had belonged to a hermit, who had been slain that day by enemies before the hermitage. Lancelot willingly consents to suffer discipline and puts on the hair shirt, promising to make confession every week.

After sundry adventures, in the course of which Lancelot has learned that the white knight with whom he had done combat and whom he is seeking, is Galahad, he meets with misfortunes that finally leave him without horse or food on the banks of the river Marcoise, in a valley where he is surrounded by the water, a dense forest, and precipitous rocks. He decides to lie down there and sleep, trusting in God. A voice in his dreams counsels him to take the first ship that he sees. In the morning a rudderless boat without sails comes to the shore of the river, and he goes aboard. It is a ship built by King Solomon and designed for his descendant, Galahad. On this ship Lancelot dwells for more than a month, miraculously fed from Heaven with food that he finds daily prepared for him. Here he is joined by Galahad, and together the father and son sail in the marvellous ship for more than a year and a half performing many adventures and surrounded by many marvels.

AFTER Easter in the fresh springtime, when all the earth groweth green, and the birds sing their divers sweet songs throughout the woods for that the sweet season beginneth, when all things turn them towards joy more than at other times, it befell on a day that

24

at the hour of noon the two knights arrived at the edge of a forest before a cross. And then they saw issue forth from the forest a knight armed with white arms, and he was mounted full richly, and he led by the right hand a white horse. And when he saw the ship that was come to shore, he went thereto so speedily as he might, and he greeted the two knights in the name of the Most High, and he said to Galahad, " Sir knight, ye have been long enough with your father. Come out from the ship, and mount upon this horse that is fair and white, and go there where chance shall lead you, seeking the adventures of the kingdom of Logres and bringing them to an end ".

When Galahad heard this word, forthright he ran to his father, and he kissed him full tenderly, and he said to him weeping, " Fair, sweet sir, I know not if I shall ever see you more. I commend you to the true Body of Jesus Christ, that He may keep you in His service ". And then both one and the other began to weep.

And when Galahad was gone out of the ship and had mounted on his horse, they heard a voice that said to them, " Now let each one of you think to do well, for one will not see other till the great and dreadful day when our Lord will render to each man according to his deserts. And that will be the great Day of Judgment ".

When Lancelot heard this word, he said to Galahad weeping, " Son, since it is thus that I part from thee forever, pray the Most High for me that He hold me in His service, and that He so preserve me that I may be His servant both in this world and in heaven."

The parting between Lancelot and Galahad

[*face p.* 370

And Galahad made answer, " Sir, no prayer availeth so much as your own, and therefore give heed to yourself ".

And then they departed one from other. And Galahad entered into the forest, and a great and marvellous wind smote against the ship that speedily bore Lancelot away from the shore.

CHAPTER LXXII

How Sir Lancelot came afore the door of the chamber wherein was the Holy Grail

And Lancelot was driven for well a month throughout the sea in such wise that he slept little, but he kept vigil oft, and he prayed our Lord weeping full tenderly that He would bring him to a place where he might see some sign of the Holy Grail.

So it befell on an even toward midnight that he arrived before a castle that was rich and fair and well set. And at the back of the castle there was a postern gate that opened toward the sea, and it was ever open by day and by night. And the people of the castle kept no watch there, for two lions were there that guarded the entrance one before the other, so that no man might enter there save betwixt them, if so be that he desired to enter by this gate. At the hour when the ship came there, the moon shone so clear that one might see far and nigh. And thereupon Lancelot heard a voice that said to him, " Lancelot,

371

go out of this ship and enter into this castle, where thou shalt find great part of that thou seekest and hast so greatly desired to see ".

And when he heard this, right so he ran to his arms, and he did them on, and he left naught there that he had brought with him. And when he was issued forth, he came to the gate, and he found two lions, and he supposed that he might not depart thence without a combat. Then he set his hand to his sword and made ready to defend him. And when he had drawn the sword, he looked up, and he saw come a hand all afire that smote him so sore on the arm that the sword fell out of his hand. And then he heard a voice that said to him, " O man of little faith and of evil belief, wherefore trustest thou more in thy hand than in thy Creator ? Caitiff art thou, that supposest not that He into Whose service thou hast entered can avail thee more than thy harness ".

By this word and by the hand that had smitten him Lancelot was so abashed that he fell to the ground all stunned and in such case that he knew not if it were day or night. But after a time he lifted him up and he said, " Ah, fair Father Jesus Christ, I thank Thee and I praise Thee in that Thou deignest to reprove me of my misdeeds. Now see I well that Thou holdest me for Thy servant since Thou hast shown me a sign of my unbelief ".

Then Lancelot took again his sword and he put it back into the sheath, and he said that never by him on that day would it again be drawn, but that he would put himself at the mercy of our Lord. " And if it please Him that I die, that will be to the salvation of my soul. And if it be that I escape, I shall win great honour thereby." Then he made the sign of the cross on his forehead, and he commended him to our Lord, and he came to the lions. And when they saw him come, they sat them down nor made semblance that they designed to do him harm. And he passed betwixt them, so that they touched him not. And he came into the chief street, and he went up along the side of the castle till he came to the chief fortress thereof.

Now throughout the castle they were all at rest, for it was full midnight. And he came to the stairs, and he went up till he entered into the great hall, so armed as he was. And when he was there, he looked far and nigh, but he saw neither man nor woman, whereat he marvelled greatly, for he had ne'er conceived that so fair a palace with such fair halls as he saw could be without folk. And he passed on, and he thought that he would go forward till he had found some folk that would tell him where he was arrived, for he wist not in what country he was.

And at last Lancelot came to a chamber whereof the door was closed and fast locked. And he set his hand thereto and thought to undo it, but he might not, and he enforced him, but naught availed him that he might enter therein. Then he listened and he heard a voice that sang so sweetly that it seemed no earthly voice, but a heavenly. And him thought that it said, " Glory and praise and honour be unto Thee, Father of Heaven ". When Lancelot heard the words that the voice spake, his heart was melted within him, and he kneeled down before the chamber, for he thought that the Holy Grail was therein. And he said weeping, " Fair, sweet Father, Jesus Chriſt, if ever in this life I did aught that pleased Thee, fair Lord, of Thy pity hold me not in despite that Thou grant me not some sight of that which I seek ".

When Lancelot had said this, he looked afore him and he saw the door of the chamber open, and at the opening thereof a great clearness came forth, as if the sun himself made his dwelling therein. And with this great clearness that came forth was all the house as bright as if all the torches of the world had been lighted there. And when he saw this he had such joy and so great desire to see whence this great clearness came that he forgot all else. And he went to the door of the chamber, and he would fain enter therein, when a voice said to him, " Flee, Lancelot, enter not, for thou oughteſt not to do it. And if after this command thou entereſt, thou shalt repent thee thereof ". When Lancelot heard this word, he withdrew him aback, right sorrowful, as he that would fain have entered, but nevertheless he refrained him for the command that he had heard.

And he looked within the chamber, and he saw on a table of silver the Holy Vessel covered with red samite. And he saw thereabout many angels that guarded the Holy Vessel in such wise that some held censers of silver and burning torches, and others held a cross and the ornaments of an altar, and there was not one but served it in some office. And afore the Holy Vessel there sat an old man clothed as a prieſt, and it seemed that he was at the sacrament of the mass. And when he was about to elevate *Corpus Domini*, it seemed to Lancelot that above the hands of the good man there were Three Men, whereof Two put the Youngeſt between the hands of the prieſt, and he raised Him up on high, and he seemed to show Him to the people.

And Lancelot that beheld this marvelled not a little, for he saw that the prieſt was so charged with the Figure that he held that well he seemed as if he would fall to the ground. And when Lancelot saw this he was fain to help him, for it seemed that none of them about him were minded to succour him. Then he had so great desire to go there that he remembered not the command that had been given him that he set not foot therein. And he came to the door at a great pace, and he said, " O fair Father, Jesus Chriſt, be it not accounted unto me for sin that will damn me, if I go to help this good man that hath need thereof ".

And then he entered thereinto and he turned him toward the table of silver. And when he came nigh he felt a breath of wind so hot, him seemed as if it were mingled with fire that smote him in the face so that he thought that it burned his visage. Then he had no power to go forward, as he that hath loſt the power of his body and of hearing and of seeing, nor hath a member whereby he may help him. Therewithal he felt many hands that laid hold of him and that carried him away, and when they had borne him up and down, they flung him out of the chamber, and they left him there.

375

CHAPTER LXXIII

How Sir Lancelot lay four-and-twenty days and nights in a trance, and how he knew that he might see no more of the Holy Grail, and how he returned towards Logres

ON the morrow morn, when the day broke fair and clear, and they of the castle were arisen, they found Lancelot lying before the door of the chamber, and they marvelled greatly that this could be. And they bade him rise up, but he seemed not to hear them nor stirred him. And when they saw this, they said that he was dead, and right so they unarmed him speedily, and they looked upon him up and down to know if he were alive. And they found that he was not dead but full of life, but he had no power to speak nor to utter a word, for he was like a clod of earth. And they took him by every part of the body, and they bare him in their arms into one of the chambers there, and they laid him in a rich bed far from all folk for the noise that might do him ill. And they took care of him so far as they might and stayed all day ever beside him. And they questioned him many times to know whether he might speak, but he answered never a word nor seemed ever to have spoken. And they looked at his pulse and his veins, and they said that it was a marvel of this knight that was alive and yet might not speak to them ; and others said that they understood not how this might befall, if it were not a vengeance or a manifestation of our Lord.

376

In such wise lay Lancelot four-and-twenty days that they looked for naught save his death. And on the four-and-twentieth day it befell about noon that he opened his eyes. And when he saw the folk he began to make great sorrow, and he said, " Ah, God, why haſt Thou so soon awakened me ? I was e'en now so much more at ease than I shall be henceforth. Ah, fair Father, Jesus Chriſt, what man might be so blessed and so worshipful that he might see openly the great marvels of Thy secrets there where my sinful gaze and my sight defiled by the corruption of the world was blinded ? " When they that were about Lancelot heard these words, they had passing great joy, and they asked him what he had seen.

" I have seen ", said he, " so great marvels and so great blessedness that my tongue could ne'er reveal it nor even my heart conceive thereof, so great a matter is this, for it hath been not earthly but spirit-ual.[1] And had it not been for my great sin and my great mischance, I had seen yet more, if I had not loſt the sight of mine eyes and the power of my body for the great disloyalty that God had seen within me."

Then Lancelot said to them that were there, " Fair lords, I marvel greatly how I chance to find me here in this wise, for I remember not how I was laid here, nor in what manner ". And they told him all that they had seen of him, and how he had dwelt among them four-and-twenty days in such eſtate that they wiſt not if he were dead or alive. And when he had heard this word, he began to consider within him by what significance he had remained thus for so long. And at length he bethought him that for a term of four-and-twenty years he had served the devil, wherefore our Lord had put him in penance so that he lost the power of his body and his members for four-and-twenty days. Then looked Lancelot before him, and he saw the hair that he had worn for more than half a year, whereof he had been freed. And it irked him sore, for him seemed that thus he had broken his vow. And they asked him how it was with him. And he said that thanks be to God, he was sound and whole. " But for the love of God," said he, " tell me where I am." And they told him that he was in the castle of Corbenic.

Thereupon there came before Lancelot a damsel that brought him a shirt of fresh and new linen, but he would not put it on, but he took the hair. When they that were about him saw this, they said, " Sir knight, well may you leave the hair, for your quest is achieved. For naught will ye travail further in the quest of the Holy Grail, for wit ye well that ye will see no more thereof than ye have seen. Now may God lead to us them that are to see more thereof ". But Lancelot would not let the matter be for this word, and he took the hair and he put it on, and he did on the shirt of linen over it, and thereafter the robe of scarlet even as they brought it to him. And when he was clothed and arrayed, all they of the castle came to behold him, and they counted it a great marvel that God had thus wrought for him. And they had scarce beheld him when they knew him, and they said, " Ah, Sir Lancelot, is it ye ? " And he said that it was he. Then they began to make great and marvellous joy of him, and the tidings went from

378

one to other till that King Pelles heard tell thereof.

And a knight said to him, " Sir, I can tell you a marvel ".

" What is that ? " said the king.

" I' faith, the knight that hath lain as dead so long is now risen up sound and whole, and know that he is Sir Lancelot of the Lake."

When the king heard this, he was right glad, and he went to see him. And when Lancelot saw him come, he turned him toward him and said that he was welcome, and made great joy of him. And the king gave him tidings of his fair daughter, that had died, her in whom Galahad was engendered. And Lancelot was heavy thereat, for that she was so gentle a lady and sprung of such high lineage.

Four days abided Lancelot there, whereof the king made great joy, for long he had desired to have him with him. But on the fifth day, as they sat at dinner, it befell that the Holy Grail so filled the tables that no man might think on greater plenty. And when they had eaten, Lancelot asked of the king that he would let bring his armour, for he would go to the realm of Logres, where he had not been for a year past. Then the king commanded that the armour be brought, and they brought it to him, and he did it on. And when he was accoutred so that there remained naught but the mounting, the king let lead into the court a horse that was strong and swift, and he bade Lancelot mount thereon, and he did so. And when he was mounted, he took leave of all them of the castle, and he departed, and he rode long journeys through strange realms.

And he rode till that he came to the court of King Arthur, where all both one and another made great joy of him so soon as they saw him, for much they desired his coming and that of the other knights, whereof few had yet returned. And they that were come back had achieved naught in the quest, and they had great shame thereof.

King Arthur at the castle of Morgain

[*face p. 381*
(*frontispiece for Book III*)

BOOK III

THE DEATH OF KING ARTHUR

CHAPTER LXXIV

*How Sir Lancelot brought the Queen to King Arthur,
and how King Arthur required of him that he leave the
kingdom of Logres*

In spite of his vows to the hermit and his renunciation
of Guinevere, within less than a month after his return to court
Lancelot falls again into sin with her.   But, whereas previously
they have been cautious left their love be discovered, now
by their indiscretions they arouse the suspicions of Agravain,
the brother of Gawain, who in common with other knights
has become jealous of the favour that Arthur has shown
Lancelot.   He is not reluctant, therefore, to reveal to Arthur
the relations between Lancelot and the queen.   Arthur
refuses to believe him.   Chance, however, brings him a further
warning.   One day he happens to lose his way in the forest,
and wanders to the castle where Morgain la Fée once held
Lancelot a prisoner.   He is welcomed by Morgain, who takes
care that he shall see the paintings with which Lancelot had
decorated the walls of his chamber, and when Arthur demands
an explanation of them, she relates with satisfaction the history
of Lancelot's love for Guinevere and tells Arthur of his sojourn
in her castle.   Arthur is only half convinced of the truth of her
words, and departs declaring that, provided he have proof
of the guilt of Lancelot and the queen, he will exact the utter-
most penalty.

As time passes the ardour of the lovers increases, and aban-
doning all prudence they unwittingly betray themselves to
Gawain and his four brothers, Agravain, Gaheriet, Guerres,
and Mordred.   One day as the brothers are talking of the
matter together, the king overhears them and insists that they
tell him what they are discussing.   In order to convince him
that they have ground for their suspicion, Agravain suggests
that while Arthur is at the hunt the next day, when Lancelot
will surely visit the queen, he, Guerres, and Mordred shall go

to her chamber with some followers and surprise her with Lancelot. The plan is put into effect, and the brothers discover the lovers together. In the fray that ensues Lancelot kills one of Agravain's party and puts the rest to flight. He then takes counsel with Bors and Hector as to what is to be done, and the three knights decide that their wisest plan will be to leave court at once and take refuge with an armed force of their followers in the forest, where they will remain in hiding till the queen is brought to judgment, as she certainly will be; then they will return and rescue her, and later can take her away with them to their own kingdoms of Benoich and Gannes. They immediately carry out their decision and go to the forest, Lancelot leaving a young squire in Camelot with instructions to bring him word how the queen fares.

Arthur, since Lancelot has thus eluded him, decides to wreak his vengeance upon Guinevere. He decrees that she shall be burned at the stake at once, and that Agravain with a strong force of knights shall guard the fire, so that Lancelot will be unable to approach to rescue her. The squire of Lancelot hastens to his master with the tidings. Lancelot and his companions ride at full speed to the field where the fire is to be kindled. Lancelot, who is riding before the others, rushes upon Agravain and kills him, and then unwittingly slays Gaheriet. Hector kills Guerres, and of the remaining force that guard the stake only two knights beside Mordred escape alive. Lancelot comes to the queen and asks her will. She begs to be conducted to a place over which Arthur has no power, and the knights accordingly, on the suggestion of Lancelot, escort her to Joyous Gard.

Arthur resolves to lay siege to Joyous Gard, and Gawain, who has vowed vengeance upon Lancelot for the death of his brothers, swears with the other barons to support him in the expedition. Lancelot prepares for the assault of Arthur and gathers large forces from Benoich and Gannes to aid him. He is thus able to withstand Arthur, when he appears before the castle, and to endure a protracted siege from the royal forces. The Pope, learning of the situation, but not of the guilt of Guinevere, threatens to lay Arthur and his realm under an interdict, if he does not take back the queen. Arthur is willing to receive her again as his wife, but refuses to abandon his war against Lancelot. The queen, after having been urged by Lancelot to accept the king's pardon, consents to return to him when he has agreed to allow Lancelot with his kinsmen and

The rescue of Guinevere

their followers to leave the country and go unmolested to Gannes.

The next day Lancelot, after exchanging rings with Guinevere, attended by his followers in their richest array conducts her to the king, who has gone to meet them.

AND when Lancelot saw the king draw nigh, he alighted down from his horse, and he took the queen by her bridle, and he said to the king, " Sire," said Lancelot, " here is my lady the queen, that I give back to you, and that erewhile would have been put to death by the disloyalty of them of your household, if I had not set me in jeopardy to rescue her. And I did it not for bounty that she had e'er given me, but only for that I knew her to be the noblest lady in the world. Wherefore it would have been a passing great wrong and a passing sad loss, if the liars of your household that had passed judgment of death upon her had done that which they fain would do. And, so help me God, it is, as I think, better that they be slain in their disloyalty than that she alone should be put to death ".

Thus Lancelot gave the queen back to the king, and he received her, sad and full of thought on the words that Lancelot had spoken to him.

And Lancelot said to the king, " Sire, now know in truth that if I loved my lady the queen basely, even as the liars of your court made you believe, I should not give her back to you for many months, for ye see well that by force ye would not have had her, for our castle is so strong that it feareth but little either your siege or that of any other man, and it was so well garnished with victuals that they could have sufficed us for two years longer ".

385

"Lancelot," said the king, "ye have wrought so well for me that I am much beholden to you. And this that ye have done may still avail you much at some time."

Then Sir Gawain came forward, and he said to Lancelot, "Lancelot, Lancelot, ye have wrought so well for my lord the king that he is much beholden to you, but he requireth of you yet one thing more".

"What is that ?" said Lancelot. "Tell it me, and I will do it, if I can."

"He requireth of you", said Sir Gawain, "that ye leave his land in such wise that from henceforth ye shall not be found therein so long as he liveth."

"Sire," said Lancelot, "doth it please you that I should do thus ? Is it your command ?"

"Since it is the will of Gawain," said the king, "it pleaseth me. Leave me my land on this side of the sea, and go ye yonder into your own country beyond the sea, for it is fair and rich enough."

"Fair sir," said Lancelot, "when that I shall be in my own land, shall I be assured against you ? And which shall I expect from you, peace or war ?"

"Ye may be assured", said Gawain, "that ye shall ne'er lack war so long as my lord the king hath so great power as he now hath, nor ever, because ye are in your own country, shall ye have respite from war, a greater and mightier war than ye have had hitherto. And it will endure till that my brother Gaheriet, the best knight of our lineage, whom ye basely slew, shall be avenged on your own body, nor would I take the whole world in exchange for your life and your head."

And the king assured Lancelot that so soon as he should be in his own country he would find the war fiercer than he could believe.

Then said Lancelot to the king, " Sire, I will go on the morrow from your land in such wise that for all the services that I have rendered you, I will take with me of your possessions not the value of a spur ".

And thus the parley ended, and the king went to his tent and Queen Guinevere with him. And Lancelot commanded his meinie to make ready their gear, for he would depart on the morrow.

That day Lancelot summoned a squire, and he said to him, " Take my shield that is in this chamber and go straight to Camelot, and carry it to the great church of St. Stephen, and leave it there in such place that it may abide where it may be seen, so that they who henceforth behold it may have in remembrance the marvels that I have wrought in this land. And know ye ", said he, " wherefore I do such honour to this place ? For that I first received there the order of knighthood, and I love the place and the town more than any other. And therefore I would that my shield should remain there in place of me, for I know not if adventure will e'er bring me thither, since that I shall be gone from out this land ".

And the squire forthright took the shield, and therewithal Lancelot gave him four pack animals laden with treasure, for that he would that they of the church might ever pray for him ; whereby they increased thereafter and prospered. And when they saw the shield of Lancelot they were not less rejoiced than by the other gift. And right so they let hang the shield by a chain of silver so richly as if it had been the body of a saint. And when the folk of the country knew it, they came to see it in a great press and as to a feaſt, and the greater part of them wept when they beheld the shield, for that Lancelot was gone out of the kingdom.

CHAPTER LXXV

How Sir Lancelot departed from Joyous Gard, and how he passed over the sea

Now the ſtory saith that the day after the queen was given back to King Arthur, Lancelot departed from Joyous Gard, both he and his following, and sooth to say, by the command of the king he gave the caſtle to one of his knights that had served him long time, in such wise that in whatsoever place the knight might be he should receive the profits from the caſtle throughout his life. And when Lancelot was issued forth with all his company they saw that they were full four hundred knights without the squires.

And when that Lancelot was come to the sea, he began to look at the land and the realm wherein he had had such worship and such honour that never single knight had had so much, and he began to change colour and to heave great and marvellous sighs, and his eyes began to weep full piteously. And when he had been for long time thus, he said so low that no man that was on the ship heard him save Bors

Lancelot leaving Joyous Gard

The letter of Mordred

[face p. 388

alone, " Ah, sweet realm, pleasant and delectable, joyous and beauteous, and full of all blessings, wherein all my spirit and all my life ever abide, be thou blessed by the mouth of Jesus Christ, and blessed be all they that after me remain within thee, be they my friends or my foes! May they have peace! May they have rest! God grant them greater joy than is mine! God send them honour and victory over all those that would work them ill! And in sooth He will, for none might bide in so sweet a land as this that he were not more highly favoured than all other men. From mine own knowledge I say it, for I have proved it, for so long as I dwelt therein all happiness came to me more abundantly than had I been in any other realm ".

Thus spake Lancelot when he was departed from Logres, and so long as he could see the land he looked upon it. And when he had lost the sight of it, he went to rest in his bed, and then he began to make so great sorrow that none might see it but he had great pity thereon, and his sorrow lasted until he came to shore.

CHAPTER LXXVI

How Sir Lancelot came to the hermitage where the Archbishop of Canterbury was, and how he took the habit on him

After his arrival in his own country Lancelot gives the kingdom of Benoich to Bors and that of Gannes to Lionel, keeping Gaul, which Arthur had given him, for himself. A few months later Arthur, urged by Gawain, decides to set out on his expedition against Lancelot. On his departure he entrusts the care of Guinevere and the kingdom to Mordred, the brother of Gawain. Mordred speedily carries out plans of his own. By his munificence he gains the affection of all classes in Logres and seeks unsuccessfully to win that of Guinevere, of whom he is deeply enamoured. He accordingly forges a letter purporting to come from Arthur, addressed to the barons of the land, in which he announces that his army has been decimated and he himself mortally wounded by Lancelot. He bids the barons give both the kingdom and the hand of Guinevere to Mordred as his successor, for he knows that when he is dead, Lancelot will come to Logres and take possession of Guinevere by force. The barons at once prepare to fulfil the king's supposed request, but Guinevere refuses to listen to it, and takes refuge in the Tower of London, where with a body of armed men she defends herself against Mordred, who besieges her with the support of the barons of the land. Guinevere also sends a squire to Gaul to learn whether Arthur is dead or alive, and in case he is dead to ask the protection of Lancelot.

While these events are taking place, Arthur is encamped before Gannes and is laying siege to it. When it becomes evident that he is making no headway, Gawain decides that the war had best be settled by a single combat between himself and Lancelot. He challenges Lancelot, charging him with having killed Gaheriet in treason. Lancelot is reluctant to accept the challenge because of his old comradeship with Gawain, whom he still loves with a deep love ; but since he is summoned for treason, he would be forever disgraced if he refused. He stipulates, however, that if he is victor, the war with Arthur shall be ended. The knights meet outside the walls of Gannes and begin a combat that lasts with fearful intensity all day, but towards vespers Gawain, whose strength waxes and wanes with the course of the sun, shows signs of weakness, and Lancelot, perceiving that he cannot endure much longer, reminds him that according to custom any knight who summons another on a charge of treason must lose his quarrel, unless he prove it before vespers. He begs him, therefore, since he has fought beyond the required time to call the battle ended. But Gawain refuses and declares that one of them must die on the field. Lancelot at once appeals to Arthur :—" ' Ah, Sire, I begged Sir Gawain to leave this battle, for certes, if we fight longer, one of us muſt needs receive harm.' And when the king, that was well aware that Sir Gawain had the worſt of the battle, heard the graciousness of Lancelot, he made answer, ' Lancelot, Gawain will never leave the battle be, if it pleaseth him not, but ye may leave it, if ye will, for the hour is now paſt, and ye have acquitted you well in that which ye had to do '. ' Sire,' said Lancelot, ' if I feared not that ye would account me a recreant, I should go away, and I should leave Sir Gawain in the field.' ' Certes,' said the king, ' ye have never done aught wherefor I should be more beholden to you than for this.' ' Then will I go,' said Lancelot, ' with your leave.' ' God be with you', said the king, ' and lead you to safety as the beſt knight that hath ever lived and the moſt courteous.' And Lancelot went away to the men of Gannes.''

After Lancelot and his following have retired into the city of Gannes, Arthur goes to Meaux, where Gawain is treated for the wounds that he has received from Lancelot. As he is beginning to recover, Arthur hears that the Emperor of Rome, who desires to exact tribute from him, is advancing againſt him with a large hoſt through Burgundy. He goes to meet the imperial forces and wins a complete victory over them, but in the course of the fighting Gawain's wound opens again, and it becomes evident that he cannot recover. On the day when the Romans are finally routed, the messenger sent by Guinevere reaches the camp and brings the king the news of Mordred's treachery. He at once haſtens with his forces and the wounded Gawain to the coaſt, and prepares to embark for Logres. Gawain, knowing that he is dying, weeps with sorrow because he shall never see Lancelot again. " ' More I grieve that I may not see Lancelot ere I die than for my death. For if I might see him that I know for the beſt knight in the world and the moſt courteous, and if I might cry him mercy for that I have been so base toward him at the end, me seemeth that my soul would be more at ease after my death.' " He entreats the king to send for Lancelot to aid him againſt Mordred, but Arthur fears that he has done Lancelot too great ill to hope for his forgiveness. They embark for Logres, Gawain growing visibly weaker as they sail toward Britain.

The Tower of London holds out bravely againſt Mordred, but when he learns that Arthur has returned to Logres, he raises the siege and collecting a large force advances to meet him.

Guinevere is left in sore perplexity and diſtress. If Mordred wins the approaching war, he will accept no ransom for her, and will surely kill her; if Arthur is victorious, he will put her to death, believing that she has betrayed his honour with Mordred. The next day she goes to a convent not far from London, and prays the abbess to allow her to take the vows of religion. The abbess, fearing the king's displeasure if he should defeat Mordred, consents to harbour her and, if Mordred has the victory, to receive her into the order; but if Arthur is successful, she undertakes to obtain his forgiveness, so that Guinevere may return to him without fear.

Very shortly after Arthur and his hoſt have landed at Dover, Gawain dies. The king is inconsolable and feels that now he is deprived of all his friends. He advances to meet Mordred on Salisbury Plain, where Merlin had predicted that his final battle would be fought. In the battle his forces are greatly outnumbered by those of Mordred, and by the end of the day only he himself, the knight Gifflet, and Lucan, the king's cup-bearer, remain alive. Arthur and Mordred join in a hand to hand conflict, in which each wounds the other mortally. Lucan and Gifflet mount Arthur on a horse and take him for refuge to a neighbouring chapel. Here on the following day Lucan dies, and Arthur, beside himself with grief, bids Gifflet ride away with him to the sea.

When they have reached the shore, Arthur ungirds his sword. "Excalibur," he cries, "my good rich sword, the beſt in the world save only that with the ſtrange girdles, now wilt thou lose thy maſter and thy lord. Never wilt thou find another with whom thou wilt be so well employed as thou haſt been with me. So help me God, thou wilt not find him, if thou comeſt not into the hands of Lancelot of the Lake, the moſt worshipful man in the world, and the beſt knight and the moſt courteous that I have ever seen. Would to Jesus Chriſt that thou heldeſt it, Lancelot, and that I knew it! Before God, my soul would ever be more at ease." Then he turns to Gifflet, and giving him Excalibur bids him go to a neighbouring hill, where there is a lake, and caſt the sword into it, that it may never fall into unworthy hands. Gifflet with reluctance and many hesitations obeys. No sooner has he flung the sword into the lake than a hand emerges from the water, seizes it, waves it three times, and disappears with it beneath the waves. Speedily Gifflet returns to Arthur,

Guinevere entering the convent

⎣ *face p. 392*

who dismisses him, saying that he is going elsewhere, though he will not tell Gifflet where.

Gifflet turns away, but when he has reached a hill not far distant, he looks back. "And he saw come over the sea a boat that was full of ladies, and when they came to the shore of the sea, the lady among them that held Morgain, the sister of the king, by the hand began to pray the king that he would enter the boat. And so soon as the king saw that she was Morgain, his sister, he rose up from the ground where he sat, and he entered into the boat, and he took his horse with him and his armour. And when Gifflet, who was on the hill, had seen that the king entered into the boat with the ladies, he turned him back so fast as ever his horse might run till he came to the shore. And the boat was in short while gone more than two bowshots hence. And when Gifflet saw that he had thus lost the king, he alighted down on the shore, and he began to make the greatest dole in the world."

Three days later Gifflet returns to the chapel, where Lucan died. There he finds beside the tomb of Lucan another, bearing the name of King Arthur. The hermit of the chapel tells him that ladies brought the body of the king there, but who they were he knows not. Gifflet decides to remain in the hermitage, but in a fortnight he dies.

The sons of Mordred, as soon as they learn that the battle has been fatal to both their father and to Arthur, take possession of the kingdom of Logres without difficulty, since all the good knights of the realm have been slain. Guinevere, when she hears of the death of the king, fearing the sons of Mordred, becomes a nun in the convent where she had taken refuge. In the meantime a messenger goes to Lancelot, who is in Gannes, and tells him of the death of Arthur and the usurpation of the throne by the sons of Mordred. With Bors, Lionel, and Hector, Lancelot at once leads a force to Logres to attack them. The two opposing hosts encounter each other outside of Winchester. "On that day whereon the battle was to take place, tidings had come to Lancelot that the queen his lady had died and had passed from this world three days since. And thus it had befallen even as was told him, for the queen in sooth had recently passed from this world. But never lady of high degree made a better end or a more full repentance, or more sweetly cried mercy of our Lord than she." Lancelot, in sorrow and wrath at her death, rides furiously against the enemy. He and his companions rout

them completely, but Lionel is killed in the battle. Lancelot
leaves the field in sore grief.

AND ever Lancelot rode through the forest, and ever
he made the greatest dole in the world, and he said
that now naught remained to him on earth, since
that he had lost his lady and his cousin. In such
bitterness and in such grief he rode all the night as
fortune led him, for he ne'er followed the path.

In the morning it chanced that he found on a
mountain, full of rocks, a hermitage that was far from
all men. He turned his horse thither, and him thought
that he would go to see the place, that he might learn
who abided there. And he went up a path till that
he was come to the hermitage, the which was poor
enough, and there was a little ancient chapel there.
He alighted down from his horse at the entrance and
he did off his helm, and when he was entered thereinto, he found two good men clothed in white robes,
and well they seemed to be priests, and so they were.
He gave them greeting and when they heard him
speak, they returned his greeting. And when they
had looked him well in the face, they both ran to him,
their arms outstretched, and they made great joy of
him.

And then Lancelot asked them who they were, and
they made answer, "Ah, sir, know ye not us?" And
when he heard this, he looked upon them again, and
he was ware that one was the Archbishop of Canterbury, he that had for long time sought to make peace
between the queen and King Arthur. And the other
was Bliobleris, the cousin of Lancelot. Then was
Lancelot passing glad that he had found them, and

he asked them, "Fair sirs, when came ye here? Now wit ye well that I am right glad to have found you". And they said that they had been there since the dolorous day when the battle was fought on Salisbury Plain.

"And we tell you for a truth that, so far as we know, of all our fellowship none remained save King Arthur and Gifflet and Lucan the Botteler, but we know not what became of them. And chance brought us hither, and we found here a hermit, a good man, that welcomed us to his company. And since then he hath died, and we have bided here after him, and if it pleaseth God, we shall spend the reſt of our lives in serving our Lord Jesus Chriſt and praying Him that He pardon our sins. And you, sir, what will ye do, ye that have hitherto been the beſt knight in the world?"

"I will tell you", said he, "what I will do. Ye have been my companions in the pleasures of the world. Now, an it pleaseth you, I will bear you company here, nor ever, so long as I live, shall I leave this place, but I shall remain here all my life. And if it be that ye receive me not into your dwelling, then will I go elsewhere."

And when they heard him, they were passing glad, and they thanked God with a full heart, and they raised their hands towards heaven. And in such wise abided Lancelot there with the holy men.

CHAPTER LXXVII

*How Sir Lancelot sickened and died, and how his body
was carried to Joyous Gard for to be buried*

Bors after the battle with the sons of Mordred has gone to
Winchester to care for the burial of Lionel in the minster
there. Then he fares forth to seek Lancelot far and wide,
but after three months of fruitless effort he gives up the quest
as idle, and returns to his own kingdom. Hector, however,
is not willing to leave Logres or to abandon all hope of finding
Lancelot. Chance at length leads him to the hermitage where
Lancelot is dwelling. He has been so influenced by the
counsel of the archbishop that he has become a priest, and
practises the strictest abstinence. The two brothers rejoice
in their meeting, and Hector resolves to remain in the hermitage
with Lancelot. Thus the brothers dwell together, giving
themselves to the service of Jesus Christ, for four years, when
Hector dies.

FIFTEEN days before May Lancelot laid him in his bed
with a grievous malady, and he ne'er again rose therefrom. And when he knew that he must pass from
this life, he prayed the archbishop and Bliobleris that
so soon as he should die, they would carry his body
to Joyous Gard and lay it within the tomb wherein
the body of Galehot, the lord of the Far Away Isles,
was laid. And they promised him as brothers that
they would do it. Four days thereafter Lancelot
lived and no more, and he passed from this world
on the fifth day.

And at the time when his soul parted from his body,
neither the archbishop nor Bliobleris was there, but

The meeting of Lancelot and Hector

they slept without beneath a tree. And it chanced that at that hour Bliobleris awoke first, and he saw the archbishop that slept near him, and in his sleep he made the greatest joy in the world, and he said, " Ah, Lord, blessed be Thou, for now I see that which I was fain to see ". When Bliobleris saw that the archbishop lay sleeping and saw what he did, he marvelled not a little, for he feared that a devil had entered into him. And anon he waked him so softly as he might. And when the archbishop had opened his eyes and saw Bliobleris, he said to him, " Ah, brother, why have ye taken me from the great joy wherein I was ? " And he asked him in what joy he had been.

" I was," said he, " in so great joy and in so great a company of angels that I never saw so many folk assembled in any place where I have e'er been, and they bore up to heaven the soul of our brother Lancelot."

And when Bliobleris heard this, he marvelled much at this vision, and he said, " Brother, now let us go see if he be yet alive ".

" Forsooth," said the archbishop, " gladly will I go."

Forthright they rose and they went there where Lancelot lay, and when they were come, they found that his soul had already gone.

And then the archbishop said, " Now blessed be God, now know I of a truth that erewhile the angels made great joy for his soul, even as I saw them. Now know I well that penitance availeth above all else. Never shall I cease from penitance so long as I live. But it behoveth us to carry his body to

Joyous Gard, for we promised it him while he lived ".

" Yea, sir, that is sooth," said Bliobleris.

Then they prepared a bier, and when it was ready, they laid the body of Lancelot thereon, and then one took it on one side and the other on the other, and with great toil and travail they journeyed till they came to Joyous Gard. When the folk of the castle were ware that this was the body of Lancelot, they came to meet them, and they received them with weeping and wailing, and then ye might hearken to such noise of lamenting that scarce might a man have heard God thunder. And they went down into the great church of the castle, and they did to the body such great honour as they might and as they ought to do to so worshipful a man as he had been.

On that day when the body of Lancelot was brought to Joyous Gard, King Bors alighted down at the castle with so small a following as only a single knight and a single squire. And when he knew that the body was in the church, he went thither, and he let uncover it. And when he beheld the body, he fell down on it in a swoon, and he began such doleful complaint that no man might make greater, and he began to lament bitterly.

All that day was there dole out of measure in the castle, and that night they let open the tomb of Galehot, that was the richest that ever might be, and on the morrow they let lay the body of Lancelot thereinto. And they let put writing upon it that said, " HERE LIETH GALEHOT, THE LORD OF THE FAR AWAY ISLES, AND WITH HIM RESTETH LANCELOT OF THE LAKE,

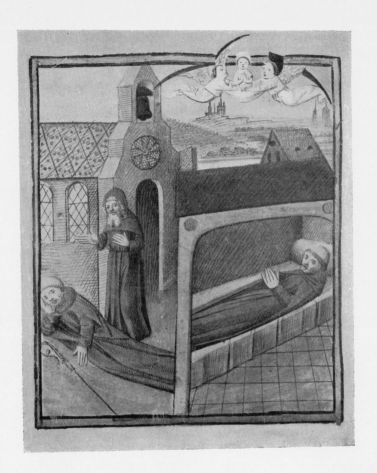

The death of Lancelot

THAT WAS THE BEST KNIGHT OF THE KINGDOM OF LOGRES,
SAVE ONLY GALAHAD, HIS SON ". And when the body
was buried, then might you see the folk of the castle
kiss the tomb.

And then the people of the town asked King Bors
how it chanced that he had come in time for the
interment of Lancelot.

" In sooth," said Bors, " a hermit that dwelleth in
the kingdom of Gannes told me that if I were on this
day in this castle, I should find my lord either alive
or dead. Therefore I came, and I see well that he
spake sooth. But, for the love of God, tell me where
he hath been, for I would fain know."

And when the archbishop heard him, he told him
all the life of Lancelot and his end, even as he himself
had seen it and known it. When King Bors had
hearkened unto him, he made answer, "Sir, since he
hath abided with you even to his end, I will bear you
company in his stead so long as I live, for I love well
the place for love of him. And I will go hence with
you, if it pleaseth you, and I will pass the rest of my
life in the hermitage and in the service of our Lord ".
And the archbishop gave glory and thanks to our
Lord Jesus Christ.

On the morrow King Bors departed from Joyous
Gard, and he sent his knight and his squire into his
country, and he bade his people make king whomsoever they would and whom they judged good for them,
for they would never see him more. Thus King Bors
went all alone with the archbishop into the hermitage,
and he passed the rest of his life there for love of
our Lord.

And now Master Walter Map leaveth speaking of the history of Lancelot, for he hath brought it to a good end according to all that befell, and he so endeth here his book that no man can recount aught further therein that would not lie.

Here endeth *The Death of King Arthur*

LIST OF BOOKS

Manuals of literature are not included in this list

JAKOB BÄCHTOLD, *Der* Lanzelet *des Ulrich von Zatzikhoven*, Frauenfeld, 1870.

MYRRHA BORODINE, *La femme et l'amour au XIIe siècle d'après les poèmes de Chrétien de Troyes*, Paris, 1909.

JACQUES BOULENGER, *Les romans de la Table Ronde nouvellement rédigés*, Paris, 1922-23. 4 vols. :—(1) *L'histoire de Merlin l'enchanteur ; Les enfances de Lancelot.*—(2) *Les amours de Lancelot du Lac ; Galehaut, sire des Iles Lointaines.*—(3) *Le chevalier à la charrette ; Le château aventureux.*—(4) *Le saint graal ; La mort d'Artus.*

ARTHUR C. L. BROWN, " The Grail and the English *Sir Perceval* " (with a discussion of the *Lanzelet* of Ulrich von Zatzikhoven), *Modern Philology*, XVII (1919), 361ff.

JAMES DOUGLAS BRUCE, " The Composition of the Old French prose *Lancelot*," *Romanic Review*, IX (1918), 241ff., 353ff. ; X (1919), 48ff., 97ff.

—— *The Evolution of Arthurian Romance*, Göttingen and Baltimore, 1923-24. 2 vols.

—— (editor), *Mort Artu*, Halle, 1910.

—— Review of F. Lot, *Etude sur le* Lancelot *en prose*, *Romanic Review*, X (1919), 377ff.

CHRESTIEN DE TROYES, *Le conte de la charrette.*—Edited W. Foerster, *Der Karrenritter und das Wilhelmsleben*, Halle, 1899.—Translated, W. W. Comfort, *Erec and Enid*, London and New York, 1913 (Everyman's Library), pp. 270ff.

WILLIAM WISTAR COMFORT. See above, Chrestien de Troyes.

—— *The Quest of the Holy Grail, translated from the Old French* London and Toronto, 1926.

E. GILSON, " La mystique de la grâce dans la *Queste del saint graal*," *Romania*, LI (1925), 321ff.

FERDINAND LOT, *Etude sur le* Lancelot *en prose*, Paris, 1918.

MYRRHA LOT-BORODINE. See above, Myrrha Borodine.

—— " Le double esprit et l'unité du *Lancelot* en prose," *Mélanges d'histoire offerts à M. Ferdinand Lot par ses élèves*, Paris, 1925, pp. 477-490.

—— *Trois essais sur le roman de* Lancelot du lac *et la* Quête du saint graal, Paris, 1919.

—— et Gertrude Schoepperle, Lancelot du lac *mis en nouveau langage*, New York and Oxford, 1926.

PAUL MÄRTENS, " Zur Lancelotsage," Boehmer's *Romanische Studien*, V (1880), 557ff.

G. H. MAYNADIER, *The Arthur of the English Poets*, Boston and New York, 1907.

LEWIS F. MOTT, *The System of Courtly Love*, Boston, 1896.

GASTON PARIS, " Les cours d'amour du moyen âge," *Journal des savants*, 1888, pp. 664ff., 727ff.

—— " Etudes sur les romans de la Table Ronde : Lancelot du Lac," *Romania*, X (1881), 465ff. ; XII (1883), 459ff.

PAULIN PARIS, *Les romans de la Table Ronde mis en nouveau langage*, Paris, 1868-1877. 5 vols.—Vols. III-V, *Le roman de* Lancelot du Lac.

ALBERT PAUPHILET, *Etudes sur la* Queste del saint graal *attribuée à Gautier Map*, Paris, 1921.

—— (editor), *La queste del saint graal*, Paris, 1923.

—— *La queste du saint graal*, Paris, 1923. A modern French translation of the preceding.

—— Review of Lot, *Etude sur le* Lancelot *en prose*, *Romania*, XLV (1918-19), 514ff.

PIO RAJNA, *Le corti d'amore*, Milan, 1890.

JUSTIN H. SMITH, *The Troubadours at Home*, New York and London, 1899. 2 vols.

H. OSKAR SOMMER (editor), *The Vulgate Version of the Arthurian Romances*, Washington, 1909-1916. 7 vols. (Carnegie Institution of Washington, No. 74).—Vol. I, *L'estoire del saint graal*.—Vols. III-V, *Le livre de Lancelot del Lac*.—Vol. VI, *Les aventures del saint graal ; La mort le roi Artus*.

ULRICH VON ZATZIKHOVEN, *Lanzelet*, ed. K. A. Hahn, Frankfurt-a.-M., 1845.

JESSIE L. WESTON, *The Legend of Sir Lancelot du Lac*, London, 1901 (Grimm Library, No. 12).

NOTES

[1] *Page 3.* Malory, *Morte Darthur*, XXI, ix.

[2] *Page 3.* The passage of the sword bridge by Lancelot (pp. 273f.) is an often repeated subject in medieval ivories. For a famous series of ivory caskets in which it occurs see R. Koechlin, *Les ivoires gothiques français*, 1924, I, 491-497. It also appears on a sculptured capital, assigned to the fourteenth century, in the church of St.-Pierre, Caen ; see E. de Robillard de Beaurepaire, *Caen illustré*, 1896, pp. 177f.

[3] *Page 3.* *Inferno*, V, 127ff. For the scene in the *Lancelot* see p. 213.

[1] *Page 4.* For the continental versions see Bruce, *Evolution of Arthurian Romance*, II, 289-291, 294f., 300-302, 304-306 ; see also above, p. 54. *Morte Arthur* and *Lancelot of the Laik* have been published by the Early English Text Society ; the former, edited by J. D. Bruce, Extra Series, No. 88 ; the latter, by W. W. Skeat, Original Series, No. 6.

[1] *Page 6.* See A. C. L. Brown, *Modern Philology*, XVII, 361ff. ; Bruce, *op. cit.*, I, 207f., 210ff.

[1] *Page 17.* On this episode see L. A. Paton, *Studies in the Fairy Mythology of Arthurian Romance*, 1903, pp. 121ff. On fidelity tests see F. J. Child, *English and Scottish Popular Ballads*, 1882-1898, I, 257ff. ; V, 212 ; T. P. Cross, *Modern Philology*, XVI, 649ff.

[2] *Page 17.* For an analysis of the structure of the poem see A. C. L. Brown, *l.c.*, 365ff.

[1] *Page 18.* See L. A. Paton, *op. cit.*, pp. 170-195.

[1] *Page 24.* See G. L. Kittredge, *Arthur and Gorlagon* ([*Harvard*] *Studies and Notes in Philology and Literature*, VIII), p. 190 ; K. G. T. Webster, *Englische Studien*, XXXVI, 348f.

[1] *Page 27.* *Vita Nuova*, Sonetto X.

[1] *Page 28.* See A. Jeanroy, *Les origines de la poésie lyrique en France au moyen âge*, 1904, p. 10 ; A. Schinz, *Modern Philology*, XXI, 216.

[1] *Page 30.* *Romania*, XII, 518.

[1] *Page 31.* M. Borodine, *La femme et l'amour au XIIe siècle*, p. 281, note 1.

[1] *Page 32.* See F. H. Titchener, *Romanic Review*, XVI, 165ff.

[1] *Page 35.* *Romania*, XII, 513f.

NOTES

¹ *Page* 39. For a summary of the arguments againſt the authorship of Map see Bruce, *Evolution of Arthurian Romance*, I, 368-373 ; F. Lot, *Etude sur le* Lancelot *en prose*, pp. 127ff.

¹ *Page* 40. Lot, *op. cit.*, pp. 7f. ; but this theory forms the main thesis of the entire book.

² *Page* 40. For some of the objeƈtions to the theory see Pauphilet, *Romania*, XLV, 514ff. ; Bruce, *op. cit.*, II, 141ff.

¹ *Page* 42. Bruce, *op. cit.*, I, 410.

² *Page* 42. Lot, *op. cit.*, pp. 74, 107.

¹ *Page* 44. Ban, however, is not an entirely irreproachable charaƈter ; see p. 271 for a sin committed by him and its consequences for Lancelot ; see also p. 320, note 1.

¹ *Page* 46. See pp. 94ff.

¹ *Page* 47. *Op. cit.*, p. 168, note 1.

² *Page* 47. p. 285.

¹ *Page* 48. *Iliad*, XVIII, 165-238.

² *Page* 48. See Lot, *op. cit.*, p. 66. Galehot, however, is sufficiently euhemerized to feel shame for the sin of Lancelot when Maſter Helyes speaks of it (pp. 233ff.). His denial of it is due to the loyalty of his friendship for Lancelot.

¹ *Page* 49. pp. 240, 252, 258.

² *Page* 49. pp. 245f., 318ff.

³ *Page* 49. p. 393.

¹ *Page* 50. pp. 359ff.

² *Page* 50. This has been proved by Pauphilet, *Etudes sur la* Queſte del saint graal, in an argument that extends throughout the book ; but see especially, pp. 27-84.

¹ *Page* 51. pp. 350f.

² *Page* 51. p. 362.

³ *Page* 51. For convenient summaries of the numerous traditions concerning the Grail in the romances see A. Nutt, *The Legends of the Holy Grail (Popular Studies in Mythology, Romance, and Folklore*, No. 14), 1902; A. C. L. Brown, in *Mediæval Studies in Memory of Gertrude Schoepperle Loomis*, 1927, pp. 100-111. The author of the *Queſt* recognises the Grail as the dish used at the Laſt Supper, in which, according to the common tradition, Joseph of Arimathea caught the blood as it flowed from the wounds of the crucified Chriſt. But he has so completely symbolized the Grail that he never describes it in corporeal terms or reveals what definite form he conceives it to have had (see Pauphilet, *op. cit.*, pp. 119, 123). On his symbolism see E. Gilson, *Romania*, LI, 321-347, especially pp. 323, 329, 336. Pauphilet believes that the Grail of the *Queſt* symbolizes God Himself, and hence that the queſt is the search of the soul after God ; see

op. cit., pp. 13-26. Each of these two interpretations explains why the Grail in the *Quest* does not permanently rest at Corbenic, the Grail castle, but manifests itself to mortals at other places, since God's grace and God Himself are everywhere.

On Galahad see Gilson, *l.c.*, pp. 329, 332 ; Pauphilet, *op. cit.*, pp. 135-144.

[1] *Page* 52. p. 361f.

[2] *Page* 52. See Pauphilet, *op. cit.*, pp. 127-130.

[1] *Page* 53. *Epistola* X, 8.

[1] *Page* 54. p. 12.

[2] *Page* 54. Edition Foerster, vv. 4524ff.

[3] *Page* 54. Edited E. T. Griffiths, 1924, vii, 73ff.

[1] *Page* 61. The explanation is given p. 272. See also p. 272, note 1.

[2] *Page* 61. The old French word *berrie* means *desert*. See Lot, *op. cit.*, p. 149, note 1. The geography of the *Lancelot* is for the greater part fanciful, and comparatively few of the places that it mentions, as, for example, Berry and Bourges, can be surely identified with known localities.

[1] *Page* 68. Namely, the lineage of Joseph of Arimathea, who came with his family and other followers from the Holy Land to Britain to preach the Christian faith, bringing the Grail with him. His kindred became kings of Britain and remained guardians of the Grail. For a summary of the *Estoire del saint graal* (*History of the Holy Grail*), where these events are narrated, see Bruce, *op. cit.*, II, 308-312. Britain, namely, the land of Logres, is known as the Adventurous Kingdom, because it is the centre for the adventures and marvels of the Grail.

In the above passage it is implied that Queen Elaine was descended from Joseph, but on p. 67 and in another passage in the *Lancelot* (ed. Sommer, III, 88), where the ancestry of her sister is given, we learn that she was descended from King David. There is evidently a confusion here between Joseph of Arimathea and St. Joseph, the husband of the Virgin Mary, who was of the line of David (cf. Matthew i, 1, 16, 20). The same confusion also accounts for the statement made more than once that Lancelot is descended from David and from Joseph of Arimathea. It is probable that the desire of narrators first to emphasize the resemblance between Galahad and Christ (see p. 272, note 1) by insisting that he, like Christ, was of the line of David, and secondly to connect him, the chosen winner of the Grail, with Joseph of Arimathea, its first guardian, led them to attribute this genealogy to his father, Lancelot, as the most convenient way of accomplishing their purpose. On this question, which is more or less complicated by inconsistencies of statement in the romances, see Bruce, *Romanic Review*, IX, 250-255.

[2] *Page 68.* King Ban thus partakes of the symbolical lay communion, which in the Middle Ages might be administered in cases of sudden death, when the eucharistic wafer could not be procured, as, for instance, before a battle or on the battlefield. The rite in France consisted in laying in the mouth of the dying person three blades of grass, or a single blade broken into three pieces, as a symbol of the Trinity. See G. L. Hamilton, *Romanic Review*, IV, 221ff.

[1] *Page 80.* This is a common expression in Old French to denote that a person or an animal is in extremities. To have scant need of a physician, for example, means to be so near death that a physician can avail naught.

[1] *Page 91.* In stories of the general type to which that of the early years of Lancelot belongs, where the young hero is brought up either in fairyland or by his mother in the solitude of a forest, not infrequently a fairy messenger comes to him, when he approaches the age for knighthood, and stimulates him to demand permission of his guardian to go out into the world in search of adventure. Tyolet, the hero of a French lay, who passes his boyhood alone with his mother in a forest, and later engages in an adventure elsewhere told of Lancelot, meets one day in the woods a large and beautiful stag, that transforms itself before his astonished eyes into a knight, who so charms him by a description of knighthood that he immediately begs his mother to allow him to set out for court. The episode of the stag in the *Lancelot* has no point or meaning as it stands, and is probably a reminiscence of a stag that was a fairy messenger in a similar story (perhaps in *Tyolet* itself). The author here retains it in a scene that is preliminary to the demand for knighthood that Lancelot makes of the Lady of the Lake, but he deprives it of its earlier, or in fact of any, significance. For *Tyolet* see *Romania*, VIII, 42ff.; translated into English by Jessie L. Weston, *Arthurian Romances unrepresented in Malory*, Vol. III. See also J. L. Weston, *Legend of Sir Lancelot*, pp. 30ff.; L. A. Paton, *op. cit.*, pp. 171ff.

[1] *Page 96.* The long discourse on knighthood that follows (not translated in its entirety) is not without parallels in medieval literature. See, e.g., Ch.-V. Langlois, *La vie en France au moyen âge d'après quelques moralistes du temps*, 1908, pp. 15f.

[1] *Page 97.* Derived from *cheval*, horse.

[1] *Page 105.* See p. 90.

[2] *Page 105.* The master of Lionel and Bors.

[1] *Page 208.* The cough given here by the Lady of Malohaut has been immortalized by Dante, *Paradiso*, XVI, 13-15.

NOTES

[1] *Page* 209. The French word used by Guinevere (p. 126), *ami*, means either *lover* or *friend*.

[1] *Page* 213. See p. 3, note 3.

[1] *Page* 252. It is Arthur's frequent custom to refuse to sit at meat until an adventure has presented itself at court.

[1] *Page* 263. Namely, when Lancelot rescued Gawain from the Dolorous Tower ; see p. 241. Cf. P. Paris, *Romans de la Table Ronde*, V, 16, note.

[1] *Page* 267. Gawain, not dreaming that the unknown knight is Lancelot, mistakenly supposes that in his previous explanation he referred to the loan of a horse.

[1] *Page* 271. Namely, Galahad, the son of Lancelot.

[1] *Page* 272. It has been said (p. 61) that Lancelot was christened Galahad, but that his surname was Lancelot. The father of King Ban, after whom it is stated here that Lancelot was named, was Lancelot, a king of Britain. An elder Galahad, mentioned on p. 270, was the son of Joseph of Arimathea and became the eponymous ruler of Gales (Wales). The author by a not unnatural mistake is confusing these two early kings, both of whom were represented in the names of Lancelot, and with both of whom he was connected, with the former by direct descent, and with the latter by his mistakenly derived ancestry from Joseph of Arimathea. See p. 68, note 1. The genealogy of King Ban is given in the *Estoire del saint graal, ed. cit.*, pp. 293f. ; the history of the elder Galahad, *ibid.*, pp. 282f. See also Bruce, *Romanic Review*, IX, 253f.

The name Galahad (Galeed), owing to the interpretation of Genesis xxxi, 47-49, was understood by early commentators as one of the mystical names of Christ. It therefore had associations that made it peculiarly suitable to the destined winner of the Grail, and that would naturally suggest the symbolism that the author of the *Quest of the Holy Grail* adopted, by which Galahad represents Christ (see above, p. 51 ; Gilson, *l.c.*, p. 329 ; Pauphilet, *op. cit.*, pp. 138-141). It followed necessarily that since Lancelot by his carnal sin lost the power to achieve the adventures of the Grail, he was not fit to bear this name, which justly was given to his blameless son (see p. 316). Until Galahad was recognised as the hero of the Grail, Lancelot was accounted the best knight in the world. His place, even to his name, was wholly usurped by Galahad. On the name, Galahad, which has been much discussed, see J. D. Bruce, *Modern Language Notes*, XXXIII, 129ff. ; Pauphilet, *op. cit.*, pp. 119f., 445.

[2] *Page* 272. The story of Symeu is told in the *Estoire*, pp. 263-265, 283f.

[1] *Page* 304. See p. 68, note 1.

¹ *Page* 306. Namely, the Grail castle. It was constructed by Alphasem, a leprous heathen king, who, healed by the sight of the Grail, which had been brought to his domain by Alain, the son of a kinsman of Joseph of Arimathea, was converted to Christianity, and in order to keep the Grail in his land, gave his daughter in marriage to Alain and built Corbenic as a permanent repository for the Grail. The name Corbenic was found mysteriously written in Chaldean over its door, when it was completed, and means " Most Holy Vessel."

² *Page* 306. The account of Gawain's unsuccessful experiences at Corbenic is given in the *Lancelot*, ed. Sommer, IV, 342.

¹ *Page* 307. The leopard is Lancelot ; the lion, Galahad. See pp. 232ff. The Foreign Country (*terre foraine*) is the domain of Alphasem, in which Corbenic is situated ; the King of the Foreign Country is therefore King Pelles.

¹ *Page* 309. See p. 316, note 1.

¹ *Page* 316. In the *History of the Holy Grail* (*Estoire*, p. 290) the dolorous stroke is a blow that Varlan (or Brulan), a Saracen king, gives Lambor, the King of Corbenic, with the sword with the strange girdles. This stroke brings a magical blight upon the land and causes wars of vengeance to arise that devastate the country. The blight, it is foretold, will be brought to an end by Galahad, when he achieves the quest of the Grail. The dolorous stroke assumes various forms in the Grail legend ; see A. C. L. Brown, *Modern Philology*, VII, 203.

The sword with the strange girdles is a magic sword that belonged to King David. It was placed by King Solomon on a ship that he built for his descendant, Galahad, which drifted to the shores of Britain and later bears Galahad with the Grail to Sarras. In spite of its value the wife of Solomon had put girdles of tow and hemp upon it, declaring that even as the Virgin by the birth of Christ made reparation for the sin committed against human kind by Eve, so a virgin would change these base girdles into others that were worthy (*Estoire*, pp. 121-123, 133f.). This virgin is the sister of Perceval, a maiden of unsullied purity, who changes the hempen girdles for cords woven from her own hair mingled with threads of silk and gold adorned with jewels, and then girds the sword on Galahad. (*Queste*, ed. Pauphilet, pp. 202-210, 226f.; translation by Comfort, pp. 164-170, 183f.). The sword has here a symbolic meaning based upon Ephesians vi. 17, "The sword of the Spirit, which is the word of God " (see also Revelations i, 16), and represents the Holy Scriptures. The sword, of which the blade belonged to David, but the hilt and pommel were added by Solomon, in its imperfect state is a symbol of the Old Testament, which remained imperfect in meaning until the coming of the Virgin and of Christ, when it was completed by the New Testament. The wife of Solomon, accordingly, represents the Ancient Law, and the virgin sister of Perceval, the New Law, which clarifies and completes the old. See Pauphilet, *op. cit.*, pp. 152f.

[1] *Page* 320. Hector des Mares, the natural son of King Ban and the daughter of the Sire des Mares. See *Lancelot*, ed. Sommer, V, 117.

[1] *Page* 357. In this chapter there may be detected the influence of the teachings of the great Cistercian, St. Bernard of Clairvaux, according to whom dreams are one of the inferior means by which Divine revelations are made to man. Lancelot by reason of his sin can receive only thus imperfectly the revelations of God's grace. See Gilson, *l.c.*, pp. 337f.

[1] *Page* 359. Namely, in his priestly vestments. See Pauphilet, *op. cit.*, pp. 47f.

[1] *Page* 365. Matthew xxv. 14-30.

[1] *Page* 366. Matthew xxi. 1-20.

[1] *Page* 377. The trance of Lancelot has the characteristics of a mystical ecstasy. See Gilson, *l.c.*, p. 338, note 2.

INDEX

Achilles, 47f.
Adam, 316
Ade, 10f.
Adventurous Kingdom, 68, 234, 405
Aeneas, 321
Agloval, 335
Agrais (the big knight), 129f., 132f., 139
Agravain, 383f.
Aiglin des Vaux, brother of, 148
Alain, 408
Alphasem, 408
Ami, 407
Amour courtois, 27-31, 37, 45, 50, 52-54
Andreas Capellanus, 29f.
Aramont [Hoel], 61-63
Arthur, King, 2, 17, 20, 33, 37, 40f., 46, 48f., 56, 94, 103, 105, 119, 126f., 133, 135-138, 145, 188, 193, 199-201, 206, 215-217, 219-223, 225, 240, 250f., 281, 290, 331, 333, 346, 350, 359, 388 ; in *Lanzelet*, 12-14, 22-24 ; in *Vita Gildae*, 23 ; his marriage, 24, 63, 230, 238 ; clerks of, 38, 230f., 305, 317 ; wars with barons, 63 ; asked by Ban for aid, 63f. ; and the knight of the truncheons, 106, 120f. ; receives the Lady of the Lake and Lancelot at court, 106-110, 112-117 ; knights Lancelot, 118 ; grants Lancelot the

combat at Nohaut, 120-123 ; his war with Galehot, 148-154, 156, 158-163, 170, 173, 176, 184, 187, 189-197, 211, 232 ; his dream, 161 ; entertains the Lady of Malohaut, 164-167 ; his Saxon war, 217-219 ; desires Lancelot to join the Round Table, 219, 223, 240 ; and the False Guinevere, 230, 238-240 ; in Galehot's dream, 231 ; passes sentence upon Guinevere, 239, 384 ; reinstates Guinevere, 240, 384f., 387 ; receives a maiden of Morgain, 242-246 ; his lack of prowess, 252, 258 ; replies to challenges of Meleagant, 253-255, 287f. ; grants request of Kay, 256f. ; forged letters of, 286, 390 ; mounts cart, 286 ; intercedes for Meleagant, 293 ; honours Lancelot, 294f., 305, 317, 330, 339, 389 ; his war against Claudas, 330 ; hears prediction concerning Galahad, 340 ; at the adventure of the sword, 345f. ; at the avowing of the quest of the Grail, 348f. ; laments departure of his knights, 352 ; honours Galahad, 352 ; at the castle of Morgain, 322, 383 ; learns of the guilt of Guinevere, 322, 383f. ; his war with Lancelot, 384-387, 390f. ; entrusts the

411

Guinevere, 230f.; surpassed
by Galahad, 232-234, 271, 346,
354, 399, 407; and the Grail,
233, 271f., 310-312, 318f.,
331, 333, 337, 345, 349, 354-
358, 362f., 367, 369, 371, 373-
375, 377-379, 407, 409; his
combats with Meleagant, 36,
238, 253f., (and followers)
261-264, 276-281, 286, 292-
294; rescues Gawain, 241,
244; in the Vale without
Return, 241; imprisoned by
Morgain, 241f., 247f., 321-
327, 383; incurs the anger of
Guinevere, 36, 247, 281, 284,
331; hated by Morgain, 46,
320; wanders in the forest,
248; reported dead, 249, 283;
meets Gawain on the road to
Gorre, 263, 266f.; rides in a
cart, 34-36, 45f., 265-267,
287, 306; at the castle of the
perilous bed, 267-269; at the
flaming tombs, 270-272, 318;
crosses the Sword Bridge, 270,
272-274, 403; encounters
lions, 274f., 372f.; recognised
by Baudemagus, 277; his
meetings with Guinevere in
Gorre, 281f., 284f.; a prisoner
in Gorre, 283, 286, 288;
attempts suicide, 283; learns
of the death of Galehot, 47,
285; summoned by Melea-
gant at court, 288; escapes
from prison in Gorre, 289f.;
returns to court, 291f.; honoured by Arthur, 292, 295,
305, 320, 392; at the tomb of
Galehot, 295-305; his adventures recorded, 305, 317;
conducted to Corbenic, 305f.;

at Corbenic, 306-314, 331-333,
338f., 371-379; deceived by
Brisane, 313-315, 317, 331;
begets Galahad, 41, 315-317;
the father of Galahad, 327-
329, 339, 350f., 407; resembled by Galahad, 328, 346;
seeks Lionel and Hector, 320;
his war against Claudas, 330;
invested with Gaul, 330, 389;
enters Gannes, 330; at Joyous Isle, 333-338; fights with
Perceval, 334-336; meetings
with Hector, 336, 396; leaves
Corbenic with Galahad, 339;
knights Galahad, 343f., sees
writing above Siege Perilous,
345; refuses to draw sword
from stone, 345; reproved by
a voice, 357, 363-365; his
visits to hermits, 359-369;
his repentance, 42, 357-360,
363, 367f., 383; dons a hair
shirt, 369, 378; at the Marcoise, 369; in the ship of
Solomon, 369-372; parts from
Galahad, 370f.; returns to
court, 380; suspected at
court, 46, 383; surprised with
Guinevere, 384; his war with
Arthur, 384-386, 390f.; re
stores Guinevere to Arthur,
385; banished from Logres,
56, 386, 388f.; his combat
with Gawain, 390f.; retires to
Gannes, 391; his war with
the sons of Mordred, 393f.;
hears of the death of Guinevere
54, 393f.; enters a hermitage,
394-396; his death, 396,
399; burial, 396f., 398f.

Magic rings of, 111, 241f.,
245-247, 275, 284f., 320;

Index